HEALTH EDUCATION
IN
SECONDARY SCHOOLS

HEALTH EDUCATION
IN
SECONDARY SCHOOLS

LESLIE W. IRWIN, Ph.D.
*Professor of Health Education, Boston University,
Boston, Mass.*

and

CYRUS MAYSHARK, H.S.D., M.S. Hyg.
*Associate Professor of Health Education,
Oregon State University,
Corvallis, Ore.*

Illustrated

THE C. V. MOSBY COMPANY
Saint Louis   1964

PREFACE

Teaching, whether skill or art, is difficult and demanding. In few fields of education is this more true than in health science, where it is estimated that the available fund of knowledge doubles every ten years. The health teacher who seeks to transform these new-found medical and health facts into principles and practices of daily living has a challenging, stimulating task and truly must be considered a pioneer in every sense of the word. Too, the training of health educators is increasingly complex since rapid advances in health discoveries have created extreme pressures on the teacher education process. Even as groups and individuals strive to demonstrate the efficacy of certain methods related to existing knowledge, the whole field advances, and sound conclusions are turned into echoes from the past.

Nonetheless, when the past thirty years are viewed in retrospect, there are certain facts that emphasize the timeliness of this text. Historically, the development of the school health program, and school health education in particular, may be viewed in light of the changing demands for professional texts. In its infancy, broad descriptive texts blanketing the entire school health program satisfied the educational needs. As the years passed, the increasing professional needs were met by texts oriented toward each of the main program areas, school health instruction, school health services, and healthful school environment.

In recent years, however, there have been increasing needs for greater textbook specialization. This need was first met by a number of professional texts giving emphasis to the health education needs of students preparing to teach in the elementary grades. The successful reception which these elementary health texts have had serves to emphasize the fact that we now have reached the point at which elementary and secondary health teaching methods and materials are widely different. Consequently, this text has been written to give graduate and undergraduate students who are preparing to teach and/or super-

3

vise on the secondary level and necessary background and abilities in secondary school health education.

In addition, there is a second specific but related reason that makes this text timely. In hundreds of secondary schools across the country the physical education, home economics, driver education, science, athletic, and other programs are directed by men and women who have received excellent training and education in their respective specialties. However, they are often expected to teach one or more health education classes, and it is here that their education is usually limited. Therefore, this text has been written to satisfy the needs of those students, who, because of related major fields, anticipate teaching secondary health education as well.

The text is divided into five parts and three appendices. This segmentation, however, is not rigid, although actual printing suggests a certain finality of form. For example, professional health education students and instructors will readily recognize that methods and materials cannot be arbitrarily divided. We, too, were aware of this, as is implied at several points in the text. Nonetheless, the objectives originally set for this text demanded a distinction between these as well as between other health education curriculum considerations. In the final analysis, the sum total is far more important than the separate parts; we would hope that the organization of this text contributes to the student's comprehension of secondary health education, and we salute the crucial role the instructor will play in the development of this comprehension.

Part I, Orientation in School Health Education, contains background material that will prove invaluable to the experienced graduate student and teacher as well as to the uninitiated teacher-in-training. Included are thorough discussions of current administrative issues in secondary school health education and the relation of health guidance and counseling to health instruction.

Part II, Foundations to Health Teaching, presents important aspects of our philosophy regarding health teaching on the secondary level. Thus, there is a complete discussion of the theory and practice regarding placement, scheduling, and content of health subject matter. A second important consideration is that of safety, its relationship to the health program, and the organization, administration, and responsibility for safety and safety education in secondary schools. Chapter 7, Evaluation in Health Education, is the concluding chapter to Part II and introduces a philosophy of evaluation that permeates the remainder of the text. Placement of this chapter, including the table of specifications, early in the text is a radical departure from traditional positioning. This fact, as well as the material on unit planning in Chapter 9, the eighth grade teaching unit in Appendix A, and the objective examination in Appendix B, is designed to suggest that evaluation should be carefully planned and continuing rather than unplanned and spasmodic.

Part III, Methods in Health Teaching, is concerned with the theoretical (concepts of methodology and unit planning) as well as with the practical (oral presentation, demonstrations and experiments, fields trips, and programed instruction) aspects of secondary health instruction.

Part IV, Teaching Aids in Secondary School Education, discusses the important material aids with emphasis on audiovisual materials. In addition, there is a brief discussion of the secondary health classroom as an aid to instruction.

Part V, The Teacher in Health Education, is a brief but pivotal section of the text. Chapter 19 seeks to tie earlier text material to the specific task of teaching and to stimulate a professional attitude toward secondary health education. The discussion of the student teacher in health education and his relationship with the supervising teacher and college supervisor is included to assist in preparing for this important assignment. Continuing education in health education is emphasized also. The last chapter, School Health in the Emerging Age, is a searching analysis that concerned students and professionals will find provocative and perceptive. It is sincerely hoped that this book satisfies the current need that exists for such a textbook.

We are indebted to those who have permitted excerpts from previously published and unpublished material to be included herein.

Leslie W. Irwin
Cyrus Mayshark

CONTENTS

Part II

FOUNDATIONS TO HEALTH TEACHING

Part III

METHODS OF TEACHING IN HEALTH EDUCATION

Part V

THE TEACHER IN
HEALTH EDUCATION

APPENDIXES

Part I

ORIENTATION IN SECONDARY SCHOOL HEALTH EDUCATION

Chapter 1

INTRODUCTION

A main function of compulsory public school education in a democratic society is to provide each citizen with the fundamental skills believed necessary to maintain and advance the best interests of society without sacrificing the dignity of the individual and his right to self-determination. In the modern educational program these skills include not only the traditional three R's such as reading, writing, and arithmetic, but also much more. The public school student is also taught the principles and values of democracy, the function and purpose of government, the historical facts that provide perspective, and the personal responsibility that he shares with millions of others to assure that his way of life will survive and progress.

Following a brief consideration of personal responsibility, we move to the subject of this text.

PERSONAL RESPONSIBILITY AND HEALTH

Responsibility means different things to different people, and for any one person it may have many different meanings. To the child it means obedience to his parents. To the love-sick teen-ager it means allegiance, however fleeting, to the immediate object of affection. To the eighteen-year-old it means a service commitment to be met. To the newlywed it may mean giving up personal desires in the interests of shared needs and wants. To the recent parent it means the challenge of long-range dreams. At the same time this recent parent has responsibilities to his parents, to his occupation, and to the people he works with as well as to his community, country, and the worldwide brotherhood of man.

Fulfillment of responsibility to oneself and to society is a difficult task for the individual born into the modern era. One hundred years ago a man could forge a successful future by moving into unsettled land. Today, land is at a premium; uncharted country no longer exists. One hundred years ago the choice of a career was comparatively uncomplicated. Artisan skills were highly needed, and they provided occupations in the community. Today, the professional and skilled needs of society number in the thousands, and the correct choice for youth to make is often difficult and frustrating. Wrong choices and unrealized potential are common; frustration and unhappiness often result.

Although life has grown more complicated in most respects, man's outlook healthwise has definitely been improved. In the United States during the first half of the twentieth century average life expectancy at birth increased by slightly more than twenty-three years. This significant increase has been due largely to the direct application of the discoveries of medical science. Striking examples are seen in improved maternal and infant care, in the discovery and widespread use of vaccines and antibiotics, and in improved sanitary conditions.

Advances in health and healthful living have been due more to community effort than to individual acceptance of responsibility. It is unlikely that a similar increase will be reflected in the second half of the twentieth century unless medical science makes many additional discoveries, especially relating to the cause and cure of all types of cancer and heart disease. This appears unlikely at present since medical research teams caution that final answers are still in the distant future.

Thus, it is more important than ever before that the individual accept responsibility for his own health and act accordingly in the interests of others in the community. We know that great strides can be taken to improve total health; yet this can only be done as individuals develop sound health habits and attitudes which, in turn, are based on sound health knowledge. This, however, will not be done in a test tube or in the laboratory, but in the school and in the home. The school and home are where individual responsibility for health is developed, and both must work and plan to meet the challenge.

The school's share in developing the individual's responsibility for his own health poses a strong challenge. Translating newfound medical knowledge into health practices is the challenge which causes us to examine and evaluate the policies, means, and methods of dealing with the health of the school age population. Crystallization of the results of experiences and experimentation with school health, especially since World War II, has made it luminously clear that a new approach is needed if parents, teachers, and the schools are to contribute optimally to the physical, mental, and emotional growth of the nation's youth.

Even in the absence of further medical advances as dramatic as those of the last half century, if we accept our present level of health knowledge, much can be done that is within the logical and accepted province of public school health education. It is estimated that thorough and universal application of the medical knowledge already known would make day-to-day life more enjoyable and would possibly add ten years to life expectancy, a goal not impossible by the year 2000. This means that there must be strong emphasis on education for health. In our democratic society the responsibility for conducting health education will fall largely to public and school health educators. It is the latter, school health educators, who can be most effective since they are dealing with young unformed minds with newly acquired habit patterns.

HEALTH EDUCATION—A RECOGNIZED SCHOOL OBJECTIVE

Evidence of the importance of health and particularly the importance of developing individual responsibility for health is shown by the following objectives of general education as stated by the American Council on Education.

" 1. To improve and maintain his own health and take his share of responsibility for protecting the health of others.

" 2. To communicate through his own language in writing and speaking at the level of expression adequate to the needs of educated people.

" 3. To attain a sound emotional and social adjustment through the enjoyment of a wide range of social relationships and the experience of working cooperatively with others.

" 4. To think through the problems and to gain the basic orientation that will better enable him to make a satisfactory family and marital adjustment.

" 5. To do his part as an active and intelligent citizen in dealing with the interrelated social, economic, and political problems of American life and in solving the problems of postwar international reconstruction.

" 6. To act in the light of an understanding of the natural phenomena in his environment in its implications for human society and human welfare, to use his scientific methods in the solution of his problems, and to employ useful nonverbal methods of thought and communication.

" 7. To find self-expression in literature and to share through literature man's experiences and his motivating ideas and ideals.

" 8. To find a means of self-expression in music and in the various visual arts and crafts and to understand and appreciate art and music as reflections both of individual experience and of social patterns and movements.

" 9. To practice clear and integrated thinking about the meaning and value of life.

"10. To choose a vocation that will make optimum use of his talents and enable him to make an appropriate contribution to the needs of society."*

Further, the American Council on Education has indicated that the first objective, the improvement, maintenance, and protection of health, may be implemented as the pupil acquires the following knowledge and understanding, skills and abilities, and attitudes and appreciations.

A. Knowledge and understanding
   1. Of normal body functions in relation to sound health practice
   2. Of the major health hazards, their prevention and control
   3. Of the interrelation of mental and physical processes in health
   4. Of reliable sources of information on health
   5. Of scientific methods in evaluating health concepts
   6. Of the effect of socioeconomic conditions on health
   7. Of community health problems, such as problems related to sanitation, industrial hygiene, and school hygiene
   8. Of community organization and services for health maintenance and improvement
B. Skills and abilities
   1. Ability to organize time to include planning for food, work, recreation, rest, and sleep
   2. The ability to improve and maintain good nutrition
   3. The ability to attain and maintain good emotional adjustment
   4. The ability to select and engage in recreative activities and healthful exercises suitable to individual needs
   5. The ability to avoid unnecessary exposure to disease and infection

---

*From American Council on Education: A design for general education for members of the Armed Forces, Washington, D. C., 1944, The Council.

      6. The ability to utilize medical and dental services intelligently
      7. The ability to participate in measures for the protection and improvement of community health.
      8. The ability to evaluate popular health beliefs critically
  C. Attitudes and appreciations
      1. Desire to attain optimum health
      2. Personal satisfaction in carrying out sound health practices
      3. Acceptance of responsibility for his own health and for the protection of health of others
      4. Willingness to make personal sacrifices for the health of others
      5. Willingness to comply with health regulations and to work for their improvement

More recently the Educational Policies Commission in an essay states that the elementary curriculum ". . . teaches the essentials of safety and personal health and promotes physical coordination and skill."* With regard to the secondary level, it continues, "The programs of all secondary school students should include English, social studies, science, mathematics and fine arts as well as physical and health education."*

A prominent and progressive school administrator, R. W. Howard, has given an individual opinion regarding the place and importance of health education in our schools today. He states, "Our schools do have a responsibility to teach a living, functioning health program" and that it should be taught "in a planned, sequential manner from kindergarten through grades twelve."† A survey of the educational literature indicates that responsible school officials are accepting this philosophy in increasing numbers.

Before progressing further it may be helpful to consider briefly a few terms that are fundamental to an understanding of the school health program.

TERMINOLOGY IN HEALTH

In a world in which words and phrases may have several meanings, depending upon the culture, intellectual interpretation, and point of view, it is satisfying to learn that there is somewhat consistent agreement concerning the meaning of the term *health*. Since 1948 educators and public health officials the world over have generally accepted the definition of health formulated by the World Health Organization as follows: "Health is a state of complete physical, mental, and social well-being and not merely the absence of disease and infirmity." Other definitions relating to health concepts have not been so widely accepted, and there has been frequent misunderstanding concerning the exact meaning of words and terms used to describe various phases of health programming. Numerous individuals, groups, and organization have at times attempted to define the health terms commonly used. Although these attempts to universally clarify health terminology have been helpful, rapid progress and changing conditions and situations operate to alter the meaning of rigidly defined terms.

---

*From Educational Policies Commission: An essay on quality in public education, Washington, D. C., 1959, National Education Association.
†From Howard, R. W.: Our number one defense line, Journal of Health, Physical Education, and Recreation 32: Sept., 1961.

Public health

After the term *health,* the phrase *public health* perhaps has the broadest meaning for students of etymology. Prior to the contributions of Pasteur, public health referred to the sanitary measures enacted against health hazards over which the individual had little or no control. Thus, in 1799 Paul Revere was appointed the first chairman of the Boston Board of Health with a public mandate to eliminate the foul odors that emanated from the bogs surrounding that city. In the absence of understanding, the people of Revere's day believed disease and "bad air" to be synonymous, and the public health officer attacked the former by attempting to eliminate the latter. Public health in the early days was largely a sanitary science.

The bacteriological and immunological discoveries of the late nineteenth century gave to public health a new meaning. These advances meant that the individual was no longer an almost completely helpless victim of his environment but was better able to protect himself and others. Consequently, the concept of prevention of disease became an objective of public health. In this newer concept public health came to be regarded as a combination of sanitary science and medical science.

Through the early years of the twentieth century public health continued to expand in its relationship to other fields. The breadth of its responsibility is reflected in the following definition by C. E.-A. Winslow, former Professor of Public Health at Yale University.

"Public health is the science and art of preventing disease, prolonging life, and promoting physical and mental health and efficiency through organized community efforts for the sanitation of the environment, the control of community infections, the education of the individual in principles of personal hygiene, the organization of medical and nursing service for the early diagnosis and preventive treatment of disease, and the development of the social machinery which will ensure to every individual in the community a standard of living adequate for the maintenance of health."*

Winslow's definition continues to be satisfactory today as shown by the following more recent definition.

". . . health work carried on through organized community effort is public health work, whether done by a voluntary or a governmental agency. In this sense the word public refers to the people of the community, who decide that concerted action is needed to accomplish its health goals."†

Health education

An accepted and long-standing definition of health education is credited to Wood. He states that health education is "the sum of experiences which favorably influence habits, attitudes, and knowledge relating to individual, community, and racial health."‡

---

*From Winslow, C. E.-A.: The untilled fields of public health, Science **51:** Jan., 1920.
†From Leavell, H. R., and Clark, E. G.: Preventive medicine for the doctor in his community, New York, 1958, McGraw-Hill Book Co., Inc.
‡From Wood, J. D.: Fourth Yearbook of the Department of Superintendent, Washington, D. C., 1926, National Education Association.

School health

In recent years two groups have been most influential in helping to clarify the use of terminology in the area of school health. These are the Joint Committee on Terminology in School Health Education of the American Association for Health, Physical Education, and Recreation and the American School Health Association* and the National Committee on School Health Policies of the National Conference for Cooperation in Health Education.† These two committees concur in their definitions, and many of the health terms used in this volume will follow the material found therein so far as possible in view of changing emphasis, practices, programs, and needs.

School health program. The school health program refers to all aspects of the program that affect the health of the school population. It involves all health activities which are planned, organized, and conducted by the school and under the jurisdiction of the school. It includes all school activities that contribute to understanding, maintenance, and improvement of the health of the school population. Ordinarily, a major part of the health program is carried on within the confines of the school, although highly important parts of the work may be on a community-wide basis and may involve numerous community organizations and agencies. The modern school health program is usually considered to embody three main aspects: health services, health education or health instruction, and healthful school living. While no one of these is mutually exclusive, for in a well-integrated program there must be some overlapping, almost complete agreement about the definition of each has developed in recent years.

School health services. Health services as applied to the school program embodies all efforts of the school to conserve, protect, and improve the health of the school population through activities and procedures such as medical and dental examinations, follow-up of health examinations, encouragement and assistance in plans for the correction of defects, observation of students, control of communicable diseases, health counseling, providing emergency care for the sick and injured, provisions for the care and education of the handicapped and exceptional student, and appraisal of health status.

The term *health appraisal* contains elements of possible overlap between other phases of the school health program. It has been adopted in late years to indicate that phase of the school health service program which attempts to determine the total health status of the student through the use of such means as health histories, observations, screenings, and medical, dental, and psychological examinations. The information secured through the total appraisal of the student helps teachers, nurses, physicians, and other interested persons to recognize and understand the needs of the individual. Also the various appraisal procedures are frequently used as important learning experiences for students or as a basis for individual health counseling.

---

*Report of the Joint Committee on Terminology in School Health Education, Journal of Health, Physical Education, and Recreation **33**: Nov., 1962.

†National Committee of School Health Policies: Suggested school health policies, ed. 3, National Education Association-American Medical Association, 1956.

A second point, in addition to appraisal, in which there may be some overlapping in the three phases of the school health program is in health counseling. School health counseling is the process by which various members of the school personnel may help students with their personal health problems and assist them in developing plans of action which will lead to solutions. Teachers, physicians, guidance personnel, nurses, administrators, and other persons may at various times, depending upon needs, assist in school health counseling. In some cases the counseling may take the form of interpretation and determination of the extent, nature, and significance of health problems of students. In many cases it is frequently necessary for health counseling to involve the student's parents in order to satisfactorily solve personal health problems. A well-integrated school health program will provide both health appraisal and counseling for all students that are meaningful, current, and complete.

School health education. The term *school health education* has taken on new meaning in recent years. At one time health education was used to designate the total school health program. Within the context of Wood's definition cited earlier, school health education is now commonly used to designate that part of the school health program which provides teaching and learning experiences and activities for the purpose of favorably influencing knowledge, habits, attitudes, practices, appreciations, and conduct pertaining to individual and group health. The term *school health instruction* is frequently used alternatively.

In joining *health* with *education* we have created an educational field for the purpose of improving effective and enjoyable living. Education is the process, and health indicates the content; the educational process determines how learning takes place and the scientific information that is rapidly accumulating is the health content.

Healthful school living. *Healthful school living* is a term used to designate the plans, procedures, and activities involved in the provision of conditions within the school which are most conducive to optimum physical, mental, and emotional health and safety of the students. It includes such factors as total school organization basically designed to maintain optimum health, satisfactory relationship between teachers, students, and administrators, and ample periods of rest, relaxation, and recreation. It is also concerned with an ample and safe water supply, the safe disposal of sewage and other wastes, adequate and properly equipped toilets and washing facilities and drinking fountains, elimination of fire and safety hazards, and proper lighting, heating, and ventilation.

The terms *healthful school living* and *healthful school environment* are used more or less synonymously by many educators and in much of the literature dealing with school health. It is usually thought that healthful school living embodies all factors making up a healthy school environment. In many cases however the term *school environment* is used in a broader sense to indicate not only the school plant and facilities but also the surrounding area in the community. An example of this is that of considering traffic conditions, particularly in the vicinity of the school, as a part of the school environment.

GROWTH AND DEVELOPMENT OF THE SCHOOL HEALTH PROGRAM

In order to understand the present status of school health in the United States as well as to be prepared to take advantage of past experience in improving programs for students, it may be helpful to consider the stages of growth and development of school health programs as they exist today.

School health programs in the nineteenth century. Early concern for the student's health was centered in school construction and sanitation. William A. Alcott's publication entitled *Construction of School Houses* in 1829 and Horace Mann's discussion of school hygiene in his *First Annual Report* in 1837 are examples of this early concern for problems in the area of healthful school living.

In 1842 Horace Mann also advocated the teaching of health principles, and during the middle years of the nineteenth century the pressure to teach basic physiology in the public schools under the course title of Hygiene was promoted by physicians. A trend toward health teaching rather than rote memorization of physiological terminology began after 1880. This came about largely because of pressure from groups such as the Women's Christian Temperance Union acting to influence state legislatures and state level education departments. By 1890 nearly all states required instruction concerning the effects of alcohol and narcotics, and forty states required that it be part of a larger area of subject matter broadly described as physiology and hygiene.

The early health service phase of school health was a development of the late nineteenth century and grew out of concern for the increasing prevalence of disease as well as a dawning of knowledge about how disease was transmitted. In 1872, the Elmira (New York) School Department employed a "sanitary superintendent," and in 1894, after a series of epidemics, Dr. Samuel Durgin established a system of medical inspection in the schools of Boston, Massachusetts. Characteristic of this latter program was a daily examination of students in the schools by physicians and the subsequent exclusion from school and the quarantine of all students found to be infected. Similar programs followed in Chicago in 1895, in New York in 1897, and in Philadelphia in 1898.

School health programs in the first half of the twentieth century. Experience with school medical inspections following 1900 gradually showed that although helpful to some extent in controlling communicable diseases they were wholly inadequate as a school health program. Thus there began a slow but gradual development of more complete school health service programs. An important contribution was the nation's first school nurse program initiated in New York City in 1902 with twenty-five nurses following the earlier influence and leadership of Miss Lillian Wald. In 1903 the first school dentist was appointed in Reading, Pennsylvania, and in 1914, ten dental hygienists were employed in the schools of Bridgeport, Connecticut. In 1910, following two trial years, New York City installed the first formal school lunch program. Initial cost for a balanced nutritious lunch was 3 cents.

The physiology and hygiene courses developed prior to 1900 were almost completely discontinued because of a lack of agreement concerning needs, results, and methods of teaching. Furthermore, it was never fully established and agreed upon among educators that responsibility for the health of the school population was a function of the schools.

Although the period between 1900 and World War I was not particularly fruitful from the viewpoint of health, rapidly developing public health work in the United States gave considerable impetus to the formation of various groups and organizations interested in the study, development, and promotion of child health. These were to have a later influence on school health programs.

Great emphasis was placed on the health of the school child following World War I. Revelation of the adverse physical, mental, and emotional conditions of a substantial percentage of the draftees in World War I was a main factor in awakening a realization on the part of educators and the American public of an urgent need for better school health programs. Educators in particular became highly conscious of the need for programs designed to improve and maintain the health of the school population. The emphasis upon health was so strong following World War I that national education groups placed the students' health as one of the major objectives of education.

However, even though health was listed as one of the most important objectives of education, the development of acceptable school health programs was comparatively slow. One of the reasons for this somewhat slow development immediately following World War I was that major emphasis was placed on physical education programs in attempting to improve and maintain student health. Physical education programs came into wide popularity and developed very rapidly. However, over the years the physical education phase of the work was emphasized almost to the exclusion of what is now recognized as acceptable and desirable school health programs. Unfortunately, a rather general impression grew that physical education was the same as health education and that a physical education program was entirely adequate. This was to be expected as a majority of the teacher education institutions preparing physical education teachers did not prepare them to deal properly with a modern school health program. Furthermore, physical education teachers on the whole did not have sufficient time in the school program to properly handle and develop both physical education and health education. In most schools, teaching physical education was a full-time position, and serious difficulties developed when the additional work of conducting a satisfactory health program was also required.

Another reason for the comparatively slow development of school health following World War I was the growing recognition of the need for specialists not ordinarily a part of the school personnel. Physicians, nurses, dentists, dental hygienists, nutritionists, health educators, and psychologists were among those considered necessary in certain phases of the developing school health program. Although most schools do not as yet have the services of all these specialists, nevertheless some of them are considered indispensable, particularly to the school health service program.

The shortage of medical and health education specialists was most acute in rural areas. Consequently, children in rural areas were most neglected so far as school health programs were concerned.

School health program today. The results of medical and psychological examinations of millions of people during World War II revealed a high percentage of youth unfit for military service. Approximately 40% of those examined for military service were rejected for medical reasons or for mental and emotional disorders. Because the physical, mental, and emotional status of youth of military age in World War II had not seemingly improved over the status of military personnel in World War I, it was reasoned that little progress was made during the interim between wars, despite the greater emphasis placed on school health and physical education. Consequently, the schools were frequently criticized by some people for what was considered a failure of school health programs. However, such criticisms were unjustifiable because even at the dawn of World War II the great majority of schools in the United States did not have more than the bare minimum requirements of what is now considered a modern school health program. If any criticism is justifiable, perhaps it should be that in a majority of the schools in the United States there was almost a complete lack of what is now considered desirable and necessary for the proper improvement and maintenance of the health of children and youth.

Although the verbal emphasis on the importance of school health following World War I was great, it has been even greater during and since the end of World War II. In addition to continued interest and emphasis on the part of educators, there is far greater interest than ever before on the part of local, state, and national medical and public health groups as well as of public and private welfare agencies and organizations. The trend in making adequate provisions for the school health services and protection programs has moved in the direction of close cooperative planning between school and community health departments and organizations.

It is now generally recognized that physical education, the same as other areas in the school program, has certain contributions to make to student health. It is also recognized that a physical education program should not be considered a health program. Neither should a physical education program be considered a substitute for a health program.

Staffing and financing health programs continue to be problems in the present day. A few schools have been fortunate enough to have adequate funds to employ the services of sufficient medical and health education specialists to have excellent health programs. Some schools have recognized the need for the help of many health specialists, and sometimes they have had sufficient funds to employ them only to find that they were not available. Other schools have recognized the need for health specialists but have not had funds to employ them even if they were available. Some schools, of course, neither have the funds nor recognize the need for medical and health education specialists.

There has been comparatively rapid progress in school health service and protection programs since World War II and very marked progress in health education programs in elementary schools and junior and senior high schools particularly since 1950. School administrators in increasing numbers are recognizing the obligation of the schools to provide healthful and safe conditions for work and play, to maintain reasonable standards of appraisal of the status of students, and to provide learning experiences which will prepare students to live healthfully throughout their lives.

In Chapter 2 some of the administrative issues which influence school health programs are considered.

QUESTIONS FOR DISCUSSION

1. What changes have occurred in the major causes of death between 1900 and 1964? Has there been a corresponding change in medical research, public health practice and school health education?
2. Why do you think the American Council on Education listed health as its first objective?
3. In this age of science why should school administrators support a health education program?
4. Define in your own words the following terms:
   (a) Public health
   (b) Health education
   (c) School health program
   (d) School health services
   (e) School health education
   (f) Healthful school living
5. The terms *school health program* and *school health education* are sometimes confused. Are you clear as to the distinction?
6. What have been some factors that have done the following:
   (a) Aided the development of the school health program?
   (b) Slowed the development of the school health program?

SUGGESTED CLASS ACTIVITIES

1. Arrange for a panel discussion on the difficulty of extending present life expectancy.
2. Develop a gross chart of the school health program.
3. Have three groups of students do research and report more completely on the historical development of the school health program.

REFERENCES

1. Anderson, C. L.: School health practice, ed. 2, St. Louis, 1960, The C. V. Mosby Co.
2. Bernstein, Jean, and Behringer, Harriette: We needed a school health program and we got it, Journal of School Health 29: Nov., 1959.
3. Beyrer, Mary K.: The significance of current trends in school and college health programs, American Journal of Public Health 50: Dec., 1960.
4. Guthrie, E. H.: Whether and whither, Journal of Health, Physical Education, and Recreation 31: Nov., 1960.
5. Johns, E. B.: Words into action, Journal of Health, Physical Education, and Recreation 32: March, 1961.
6. Langton, C. V., Allen, R. L., and Wexler, Philip: School health: organization and services, New York, 1961, The Ronald Press Co.
7. Lifson, Sol: Why support school health, Journal of Health, Physical Education, and Recreation 33: Jan., 1962.
8. Lowry, Antoinette: The turbulent years, Journal of Health, Physical Education, and Recreation 32: Feb., 1961.
9. McCaskill, J. L.: Evolution of federal educational policy from 1785 through World War II, Journal of National Education Association 41: Nov., 1952.
10. Nichols, H. L.: Problems in developing an adequate health-instruction program, Journal of School Health 28: Sept., 1958.
11. Nyswander, Dorothy B.: Solving school health problems, New York, 1942, The Commonwealth Fund.
12. Oberteuffer, Delbert: Philosophy and principles of the school health program, Journal of School Health 23: April, 1953.
13. Sigerist, H. E.: Landmarks in the history of hygiene, London, 1956, Oxford University Press.

14. Sliepcevich, Elena M.: Echoes from the past, Journal of School Health **30:** May, 1960.
15. Wilson, C. C.: Trends in school health, Journal of School Health **24:** Feb., 1954.
16. Wilson, C. C.: School health programs, Journal of Health, Physical Education, and Recreation **31:** Feb., 1960.
17. Vaselak, K. E.: Historical steps in the development of the modern school health program, Journal of School Health **29:** Sept., 1959.

Chapter 2

ADMINISTRATION OF THE
SCHOOL HEALTH PROGRAM

There is practically unanimous agreement among school and public health officials that the health of the school population is of paramount importance and that there should be an effective school health program. Yet, there is wide difference of opinion, as well as much misunderstanding, concerning the administration and conduct of the modern school health program.

PUBLIC SCHOOL EDUCATION

One of the original aims of public school education in the United States was to provide equal educational opportunity for all students. This continues to be one of the main and basic principles in American education. Although people often differ in opinion regarding the management, direction, and conduct of the educational program within the schools, they are in practically unanimous agreement that every student should have the best education possible in the tax-supported schools.

In order to determine the ultimate responsibility for the health program in the schools, it is necessary to call attention to the development of public school education in the United States. The Tenth Amendment to the Constitution of the United States clarifies the power of the federal and state governments concerning public education for the people. This amendment clearly places upon each state the responsibility for the education of its people, to the extent, at least, that education through the public schools is not the direct responsibility of the Federal Government.

During the growth of the public schools the extent of responsibility assumed for public education has varied greatly from one state to another. In most states the balance of power in establishing, conducting, and operating the public tax-supported schools has remained largely in the hands of the local communities. The local communities have the power to establish any kind of education desired by its citizens within the limits of state laws and regulations pertaining to public school education and to available funds. It is true that many states have controlled education in the local communities to a certain extent through state laws and the dispensation of financial aid through official agencies such as state departments of public instruction. Yet, in the main, it remains the power of the local community in most states to almost completely control the educational programs in the public schools.

RESPONSIBILITY FOR SCHOOL HEALTH PROGRAMS

Those responsible for public school education must necessarily be responsible for the school health program as it is considered a part of the total educational program. If local communities are directly responsible for their public schools, limited only by existing state laws and regulations, then naturally they are directly responsible for all health activities conducted within the jurisdiction of the schools. Boards of education or other duly elected or appointed representatives are usually vested with the power to represent the citizens within the community in the direct operation and control of the public schools. So far as existing functioning programs of health in the schools are concerned, then, boards of education are directly responsible for school health activities the same as for other phases of the educational program.

The authority of school boards to deal with the health program in the schools is to some extent limited by the power of state and community health authorities. That is, the authority of school boards is limited in school health to the extent of the power of local and state health authorities to protect and conserve the health of the citizens within the community of which the school children are a part. Frequently, the power of local and state health authorities is limited largely to the protection of the public and individual health in times of emergency or in situations or circumstances in which there is an urgent need for lawfully controlled health measures. Although the actual power of local and state health groups is frequently limited largely to the protective phases of health, nevertheless, these groups are frequently active in health education movements designed to improve the general health status of both the school population and adults.

There has been a growing feeling among certain groups in late years that health specialists, particularly medical specialists, should assume full and complete control of certain phases of the school health program. This feeling has come about partly because of the need for health specialists in carrying out certain phases of the school health program. In the area of health service, particularly, it is necessary to use many health specialists; physicians, nurses, dentists, dental hygienists, nutritionists, health educators, and others are considered necessary to the proper conduct of the most acceptable and desirable types of health service programs. It is the feeling of some medical specialists, because state and community health groups are responsible to a certain extent for the health of the school population at all times, that the school health program should be considered only one part of the community-wide health program. Also, some medical groups feel that members of the school personnel are not qualified to effectively organize and administer the work of health specialists.

Although there frequently exists divided opinion relative to the question of the ultimate responsibility for school health services and certain parts of the healthful school environment program, there is almost unanimous agreement among all groups that the schools should continue to assume full responsibility for organized health teaching programs.

The controversy surrounding the administrative control of school health programs began many years ago when the main function of community boards of health was to assume control of and accept at least partial responsibility for communicable disease control in the school. The growth of modern school health programs has heightened the controversy as to the extent of responsibility of both boards of education and official community health agencies. Many of the differences of opinion have arisen largely because of the varying backgrounds of training and experience of school and health authorities. Diversity of needs in different communities and methods used in trying to care for the needs have added to the complexities of the problem and to misunderstandings between health and school authorities.

SCHOOL HEALTH PROGRAM UNDER THE LOCAL HEALTH DEPARTMENT

Many of the reasons frequently given to justify the administration of school health programs by community health departments are the following:

1. Official community health organizations have the power and legal status and are organized and prepared to deal with the control of communicable diseases. The control of communicable diseases often involves the entire community of which the schools are a part.
2. Children are a community problem from the viewpoint of health a large part of the time as they attend school only 4 to 6 hours a day through 6 to 10 months of the year.
3. Duplication of services rendered by health specialists employed by the schools and those employed by a community health department can be eliminated.
4. Mistakes made in the administration and conduct of health programs because of a lack of specialized training needed in the health field can be avoided and thereby can decrease the cost and increase the efficiency of the total school and community child and youth health program.
5. The official local health organization ordinarily has a more comprehensive knowledge of community conditions which are likely to affect the health of all, including the school population.
6. Health and medical specialists should be considered authorities in selecting subject matter employed in instructing the school population in health and healthful living in order to avoid misunderstandings and misinterpretations of technical and specific health knowledge.

Although the arguments in favor of the administration of the school health program under an official community health organization rather than under a board of education are convincing, careful consideration of the arguments shows that there are some justifiable criticisms of such a plan, at least at the present time. Experience shows that the assuming of full and complete control of any regular school activity on the part of organizations or agencies outside the jurisdiction of the schools is a highly questionable procedure for a number of reasons. First, with the present legal arrangements for the direct control of the schools in local communities in most states, boards of education are directly and legally responsible to the community for all phases of education conducted in the schools, including health education. If health departments attempted to assume full and complete control of the school health program without being under the control of the school board, there would be divided responsibility for the educational program within the schools. In the absence of state legislation which might legalize such an arrangement, it becomes questionable. Second, divided responsibility leads to misunderstandings and inefficiency in the conduct of the total school program. Third, personnel of health departments usually lack experience, training, and understanding of education routine and methods which are highly essential to the most efficient and effective operation of an educational program for the millions of children and youth in the schools.

The argument concerning the duplication of services of health specialists such as physicians, nurses, and dentists is valid for those schools and communities in which health specialists are in sufficient number to bring about a duplication of work. However, this argument does not apply to a vast majority of the schools and communities in the United States, for there are not enough health specialists available to handle even a bare minimum of activities that should be included in an acceptable and desirable school health program. As a matter of fact, large numbers of schools throughout the country do not have sufficient services of school or community nurses, and only a very small percentage have the services of physicians to the extent of providing what is considered a modern and acceptable health service program. Therefore, at this time, at least, and likely for many years to come, the problem of duplication of school health services on the part of school and community health specialists in a majority of the communities in the United States does not necessarily constitute a problem which would justify dividing the responsibility for the administration and conduct of school health programs. Furthermore, in those communities fortunate enough to have sufficient school and community health specialists to cause some duplication of health services, it is likely that the most advisable procedure would be to work out some kind of joint or cooperative plan to eliminate the overlapping without dividing the responsibility for the conduct of the schools.

The argument that members of community health departments should have full and complete control of school health because they are better prepared to organize and administer the program in view of their specialized training is becoming less valid with passing time. With the growing and widespread knowledge concerning health and healthful living, school administrators and health specialists employed by the schools, as well as other members of the school personnel, are becoming better prepared to administer school health programs and thereby better able to properly coordinate all activities in the educational program without dividing the responsibility which might serve to lessen the efficiency of the total educational program. Furthermore, it is both possible and desirable, particularly in the larger schools, to employ medical specialists responsible to school administrators and to the board of education to assume responsibility for the administration of the school health service program. In such cases the school medical specialists and other members of the school personnel can work on a cooperative basis with the community health department without dividing the responsibility for the operation of the schools.

The claim that local health departments have a wider knowledge of community conditions which might affect health is convincing when considered from the viewpoint of protection. So far as the type of health program that should be conducted in the schools is concerned, however, it is questionable whether health departments are as well aware of conditions which affect the positive health of students as teachers and some other members of the school personnel. For example, a classroom teacher becomes thoroughly familiar with all homeroom students. The classroom teacher becomes so familiar with them within a very short time after the beginning of school that he is at once able to tell which factors within the life of a student are conducive to his health. It may be that a student's health is adversely affected through a failure to practice the proper health measures pertaining to foods, rest, sleep, and the like. It may be necessary for the teacher to contact the home in trying to establish the best health routine for the student. Or, the student's health may be affected because of an imbalance of school work and work outside school. In such cases the classroom teacher may need to help make the proper adjustments through the assistance of a well-functioning health appraisal and counseling program. After consideration of the many factors involved in an educational and positive health program for students, it is evident that members of the school personnel may be far more familiar with conditions within the community and homes of the students than the health department simply because of the nature of certain factors affecting the student's health. It is very true that health departments are in a position to understand general health conditions within the community far better than other persons. Because they are not in a position to know about most of the more intimate factors concerned with the maintenance of health, such as is learned, for example, by classroom teachers in the course of their daily living with the student, it is questionable whether the direct responsibility for the total educational program of the school should be divided on this basis.

The idea that medical specialists should be considered authorities on health subject matter used in teaching students hygiene and healthful living in order to avoid misunderstanding and misinterpretation of technical and specific knowledge can be accepted only in part. There is no question but that medical specialists are authorities on technical and specific health matters. However, they usually cannot be considered authorities on subject matter used in teaching students. Persons in the medical field who continue to insist upon authority of this kind which is, in the absence of experience and specialized preparation in teaching, beyond their capacity and training to assume successfully are certain to create discord and a resentful attitude among teachers who are specifically and professionally trained in methods, techniques, and procedures in teaching. Furthermore, there is not the need for such high specialization to select authoritative and technically correct health content materials for students as is often implied by those who insist upon this point. The level of maturity of students is such that highly technical matters in the field of health and hygiene are beyond their capacity and therefore undesirable for introduction, particularly at the elementary and lower secondary grade levels. Also, ample health study materials written and prepared on a coauthorship basis by specialists in both the field of medicine and the field of professional education are available at present from which to select. If medical experts in local health departments attempted to determine the health content material a seventh grade teacher, for example, should offer as study materials for her students, the process would likely resolve itself into the selection of textbooks and reading materials prepared by authors who are both medical and professional education experts. In many instances it would be a case wherein a community physician attempting to tell a seventh grade teacher what to use would be far less capable of judging the health content material of the study materials or books. Therefore, it is relatively safe to say that considering the present general level of knowledge of teachers and the public the matter of the selection and gradation of health study materials should be left very largely to the teachers and school administrators. Then, if they feel the need of consultation and assistance in the matter of selecting health content materials for the students, they are free to seek assistance from among those health authorities of their choice and in whom they have confidence rather than to be compelled to abide by arbitrary decisions of individuals in whom both the teachers and the students may lack confidence. In many schools throughout the country there are health specialists such as nurses, health educators, and others who are fully capable of assisting teachers in selecting health study materials if they feel the need of assistance.

The argument that medical specialists should be considered authorities in selecting subject matter employed in teaching students in health and healthful living is incompatible with the generally accepted fact that, even though community health departments do assume full and complete control of the health service program within the school, they should *not* assume control of the health teaching program, which must be left to those persons specifically educated and trained to teach.

SCHOOL HEALTH UNDER THE BOARD OF EDUCATION

The health program in most schools began as a function of the school under the jurisdiction of the board of education. Many educators and health specialists feel that all phases of the school health program should continue as a direct responsibility of the board of education. Some of the reasons usually given to justify this are as follows.

1. The board of education in the absence of local or state legislation is dutifully and legally obligated to the citizens within the community to assume full control of and responsibility for all phases of the educational program, including the health program conducted in the public schools.
2. School administrators and teachers, by virtue of their training in pro-

fessional education methods, are better prepared to coordinate, organize, and conduct the total school program for students, which requires a unique kind of preparation and experience.

3. The school plant, facilities, and equipment belong to the school. Responsibility for the sanitation and hygienic condition of school facilities should be accepted by the school authorities.

4. The organization of the total school day for the optimum health of the students can be done best by the school personnel.

5. The division of responsibility for the educational program which would exist if health departments assumed full and complete control of the school health program places teachers in a position of being responsible to two community authorities. It is not considered administratively sound to have two separate and distinct groups attempting to direct the work of teachers. Any friction that might develop between the board of education and the community health department would place the teachers in a difficult position.

6. Teachers are far more likely to cooperate with the board of education and school administrators than with organizations outside the schools.

7. In many communities in the United States the schools are less likely than health departments to be subject to political interference, particularly in matters surrounding the determination and allotment of financial support.

8. Teachers are better able to handle organized health teaching programs at all grade levels throughout the school. Medical experts and health department specialists are usually neither qualified nor prepared to assume responsibility for organized health teaching in the schools.

9. When the health program is under a board of education, it can be considered with and take its place alongside other phases of the school program in curriculum revision projects which are a common and constant procedure in the modern educational program.

Under certain circumstances a majority of the arguments in favor of the administration of the health program under a board of education can be surmounted. In regard to the obligation of the local school board to assume full and complete control and responsibility for the school health program, it may be said that local and state legislation can relieve the schools of this obligation. Also, the schools can delegate authority to health departments for the administration and conduct of the program.

In answer to the argument that school administrators and teachers, by virtue of their education and experience, are better prepared to coordinate, organize, and conduct the total school program including health, it may be said that health departments can overcome this argument by requiring members of their personnel who are to work directly with schools to get sufficient training in educational methods to enable them to function more efficiently and effectively in the public school program. The argument pertaining to the division of responsibility is the most difficult to surmount because all teachers in the school program should have a part in the health program. If only the health specialists in the schools were involved, it would not be so difficult, for they could be employed by a health department, or perhaps they could be employed jointly by a board of education and a health department, which is a common practice at present in some communities.

With respect to the health teaching program, it seems reasonably certain that this phase of the health program will remain in the hands of the school administrators and the teachers, regardless of who may finally assume the total and complete responsibility for other phases of school health. Furthermore, it is not likely that health departments will ever have final authority in the determination of subject matter and study materials to be used in educating children in health and healthful living.

In organizing the total school day on a basis conducive to the best health of the students, it may be done better finally as a joint responsibility of the school and health department. That is, when health authorities have progressed to the point of securing sufficient preparation in professional education methods to properly understand the school educational program in all of its ramifications, they can be helpful to the school personnel in arriving at the best organization of the school day.

In attempting to finally determine whether a board of education or a health department should administer the school health program on the basis of the arguments in favor of a board of education taking the responsibility, it must be admitted that, largely because of the background of growth and development of the present educational system, it seems that full and complete responsibility should be retained in the hands of the school. If health departments attempt to take the full responsibility for the health program, they are taking away from the schools certain prerogatives and rights which have grown and developed with the public school education system. However, as the modern school health program broadens, it becomes increasingly evident that the schools must have the aid and assistance of community health departments. It is quite possible that in the distant future the most logical and acceptable procedure will be for health departments to take full responsibility for school health programs. The present, however, does not seem to be the opportune time for a wholesale change in responsibility in this area. There are unquestionably many schools and communities which can function best, because of circumstances peculiar to the individual community, with the health department administering the school health program.

SCHOOL HEALTH AS A JOINT RESPONSIBILITY OF THE SCHOOLS AND THE COMMUNITY HEALTH DEPARTMENT

Present trends indicate growing cooperative efforts between schools and local health departments toward joint administration of the school health program. In some communities such plans have been in operation for many years. The arguments ordinarily advanced in favor of the joint responsibility plan are as follows.

1. Specialized health personnel can be employed jointly by the board of education and the health department.

2. Communicable diseases can be controlled better through a joint administrative responsibility.
3. Sanitation and hygienic conditions within the school plant and facilities can be more readily assured on a joint basis.
4. Jointly employed health specialists can help to secure better cooperation of all teachers when they are recognized members of the school personnel.
5. Jointly employed health specialists are in a better position to participate in curriculum revision within the school which may have a bearing upon the health program. Also, the health specialist is in a position to take some part in the total health teaching program.

These benefits and others are most likely to occur when the school superintendent and the health officer share supervisory responsibility and the functional head of the program is the school health program director or health coordinator. Under such an administrative structure the health coordinator is able to integrate educational and public health interests best if he himself has both public school and public health training. In addition, he should also have had two or more years experience either as a health teacher or with a public or private health agency whose program is in the area of student health.

The administrative lines shown in Fig. 1 suggest the relationships most functional when the school health program is the joint responsibility of the public school district and the local health unit.

On first consideration it may seem that the joint responsibility plan is the solution to the problem of administering the school health program. As a matter of fact, it has many shortcomings. Yet, it is quite possible that this plan will emerge in the future as the one most readily accepted during the period of transition and development of more effective ways and means of capitalizing upon present knowledge in providing for and assuring the optimum health, growth, and development of the school population. The fact that neither health authorities nor educators are willing to agree unanimously on the responsibility for the administration of the school health program makes it seem more than ever likely that the joint responsibility plan will be accepted as a compromise for many years to come. The joint responsibility plan may be best in most communities, for it should tend to make both educators and health specialists more tolerant of the positions of each, as well as more likely to cooperate to the greatest extent for the best interests and welfare of the school population.

Even though the joint responsibility plan seems to be gaining adherents at present, it should be pointed out that the most sensible and logical approach to the problem of deciding upon the responsibility for the administration of the school health program is in first considering the needs in the individual community. The circumstances peculiar to the individual community should be the determining factors in assigning final responsibility regardless of the general trends throughout the country.

Another point that should be strongly emphasized in the joint responsibility for school health is that there must be full cooperation and participa-

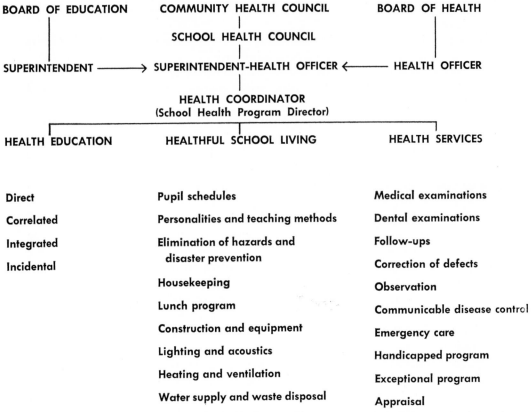

Fig. 1. The school health program as a joint responsibility of the schools and the local health department and administered by a health coordinator or school health program director.

tion on the part of both the school personnel and health department specialists. Domination by one group and acquiesence by the other does not represent true joint responsibility. Neither is it conducive to close cooperation and smooth functioning of the plan. An administrative arrangement on a joint basis between the educators and health authorities within the community in which one group or the other dominates or attempts to dominate the arrangement is likely doomed to failure. It may function partially for a time, but sooner or later there is likely to be friction of a nature to cause withdrawal of one group or another from the plan and thereby deprive the students for many years to come of a desirable health program. Experience has shown that public health groups are more likely to attempt to dominate the arrangements in the joint responsibility plan, although this is not always true. Apparently the tendency on the part of health specialists to dominate in the school health program is frequently based upon the fact that they often fail to properly appreciate and understand the emphasis placed upon democracy in the modern educational process. Modern educational methods strongly emphasize the need to organize and conduct the school program on a democratic basis in the process of educating youth for democracy. Health authorities, on the other hand, may not be cognizant of the usual democratic approach in the schools. A part of the lack of understanding may stem from the fact that it has often been necessary for health authorities to be more or less arbitrary in their approach and manner of dealing with the public in order to safeguard the welfare of all. In the school heatlh program, however, an arbitrary or dictatorial attitude on the part of either educators or health specialists is likely to both jeopardize close cooperation and lead to friction, with the ultimate result of hindering and handicapping the health of students. Both educators and health specialists should keep in mind that there are times when each must accept and act upon the advice of the other.

ADMINISTRATION OF THE HEALTH PROGRAM WITHIN THE SCHOOL

Previous discussion indicates that there are many differences of opinion concerning the ways the school health program should be organized and administered. There may be frequent conflict among the teachers, health specialists, and school departments regarding the conduct of various phases of the school health program. Perhaps most of the arguments surrounding the conduct of the school health program concern the person or department to head or direct the program. Next in order are questions relative to whether health service should be organized separately from other phases of the health program and whether there should be a health director or coordinator. Plans for the best type of administration for health within the schools have not fully crystallized. It is likely to be many years before the most advantageous plans emerge to the point at which it can be said with any degree of certainty which plan is best to use in the average school situation. As a matter of fact, plans for administration and organization of school health programs may never crystallize to the point at which it will not be necessary to make adaptations on the basis of existing conditions within the individual school and community. At the present time there are numerous plans of administration for health in operation in the schools throughout the country. The type of health administration to use naturally depends upon many factors such as the size and location of the school, financial conditions, local and state laws pertaining to health which may affect the school program, specific needs of the students within the particular school, availability of health specialists, and perhaps most important of all the attitude, interest, and leadership of boards of education, school administrators, and health officials within the community.

In the larger city school systems it is often the custom to have a school health division which is primarily responsible for the health service program as well as for a large share of the healthful school living program. Ordinarily, in the large city system the organized health teaching program is not a part of the school health division. More often it is organized entirely separately and as a part of the total school instruction program. Or it may be a part of the physical education program, particularly at the secondary school level. However, it is no longer considered most desirable for the health teaching program to be a part of the physical education program.

In the medium-sized or average-sized schools, various kinds of organizations are evident. In some cases the health program remains as a part of the physical education program. In other cases there may be a separate health division under the guidance of a director of health or a health coordinator, or there may not be any clear-cut lines of control.

In the smaller schools, and a majority of the schools in the United States are small schools located in small communities, there is little need for highly organized health programs, for they usually lack the personnel to conduct even a bare minimum of the health education essentials. In many of these the physical education teachers remain responsible, for they are usually the only teachers in the school who have any kind of special preparation bearing directly on health. In some cases the principal of the small school assumes almost sole responsibility for organizing and conducting the health program, especially in matters of health service and healthful school living. Also, some small schools are most fortunate in having the full-time or part-time services of a school nurse in conducting some health work. There is a great need in the smaller schools for improved health work. The immediate efforts of those persons in the health field should be given to developing ways, means, and plans whereby the students in the smaller schools can be provided with better and more acceptable school health programs.

FUNDAMENTAL POLICIES AND PROCEDURES

If the school health program is to be organized and administered in the best interest of the school population, those responsible for the schools must have a clear concept of the relationship of health to the total educational program. Perhaps the first step in considering a school health program is to determine the aims and objectives and then proceed to the next step of setting up ways and means to accomplish them. In this the school administrators must accept the main responsibility in assuring that the aims and objectives are accomplished to the best ability of the school personnel. Connected with aims and objectives is the problem of determining the scope of the health program. Other fundamentals to be considered in the general administration of the school health program are the following:

1. Possible need of centralized control to assure the efficient functioning of the total program
2. Adequate budgeting of finances to provide necessary salaries, supplies, and equipment
3. Proper coordination of the various divisions, departments, and areas involved in the health program
4. Selection of teachers and health specialists best qualified for the particular school and community
5. Allotment of sufficient time in the school curriculum for the health program to function effectively
6. Definite assignment of duties and responsibilities to teachers, health specialists, and administrative assistants
7. Organization of a health teaching program on a school-wide basis

8. Consideration of legal provisions and state and local laws and requirements pertaining to and affecting the school health program

9. Provisions for assuring the maintenance of the school plant and facilities in a sanitary and hygienic manner

10. Special measures necessary to recognize and provide for the individual physical differences of students

11. Methods and plans for safeguarding the health of teachers as well as of the students

12. Evaluation of the total school health program

Experience in the schools has shown very clearly that the success of a school health program is basically dependent upon the attitude of school administrators. When school administrators are in favor of and enthusiastic about the health program it is likely to be successful.

QUESTIONS FOR DISCUSSION

1. What is the respective responsibility of federal, state, and local governments for determining policies and practices of the health program in the public schools? What do the education statutes in your state say regarding this?

2. School officials are incompetent to administer the school health program. Do you agree? Why? If *not*, why not?

3. Local health department officials should be allowed no administrative responsibility for programs conducted within schools. Do you agree? Why? If not, explain.

4. Is the health education phase of the school health program undeniably subject to school personnel control and thus not to be involved in the problems of administrative control that occasionally plague health services and healthful school living?

5. Should medical personnel (doctors, nurses, dentists, etc.) be included as active members on the working committee when a school district organizes to revise the health education curriculum?

6. All the controversy notwithstanding, why is it essential that school and local health department personnel cooperate closely in the conduct of the school health program?

7. What is the role of the school administrator in organizing and conducting the school health program?

SUGGESTED CLASS ACTIVITIES

1. Have two class members affirm and two negate each of the following statements.
   (a) School health programs should be administered by school boards.
   (b) School health programs should be administered by local health department officials.
   (c) The size of the school district is the crucial factor in determining who should administer the school health program.

2. Have your local public health officer and a representative school official present their views regarding administrative control.

3. Study the relationship of the school and community health organization in a community with which you are familiar. Report the administrative structure to the class and compare your findings with those of others in the class. Prepare a summary paper of 2500 words.

4. On the basis of personal study and observation, report to the class on cooperative activities engaged in by medical and educational personnel in the interests of various phases of the school health program.

5. Prepare some criteria for evaluating school health programs subject to the following administrative controls:
   (a) Complete school department authority
   (b) Complete health department authority
   (c) Joint and cooperative control between school department and health department

REFERENCES

1. Brown, C. A.: Present-day concept of the school health program, Journal of the American Medical Women's Association **6**: March, 1951.
2. Bucher, C. A.: Administration of school health and physical education programs, ed. 2, St. Louis, 1958, The C. V. Mosby Co.
3. Dailard, Ralph, and Byrne, C. T.: General administration and school health services, Teachers College Record **59**: Jan., 1958.
4. Grout, Ruth E.: Health teaching in schools, ed. 3, Philadelphia, 1958, W. B. Saunders Co.
5. Haag, Jessie H.: Work conference for public school health coordinators, Journal of School Health **31**: Sept., 1961.
6. Handbook for health coordinators, State Department of Education, Tallahassee, Florida, 1958.
7. Hill, A. E.: Correlation between school health and public health, Journal of School Health **28**: May, 1958.
8. Irwin, Leslie W.: Analysis and consideration of the controversy regarding the responsibility for school health education, Education **70**: Oct., 1949.
9. Joint Committee on Health Problems in Education of the National Education Association—the American Medical Association: Health education, ed. 5, Washington, D. C., 1961, National Education Association.
10. National Committee on School Health Policies of the National Conference for Cooperation in Health Education: Suggested school health policies, ed. 3, Washington, D. C., 1956, National Education Association.
11. National Conference for Cooperation in Health Education: The school administrator, physician, and nurse in the school health program, New York, 1947, Metropolitan Life Insurance Co.
12. Neilson, Elizabeth A., and Irwin, Leslie W.: Analytical study of school health service practices in the United States, Research Quarterly **29**: Dec., 1958.
13. Patty, W. W.: The school health coordinator, Journal of School Health **25**: May, 1955.
14. Turner, C. E., Sellery, C. M., and Smith, S. L.: School health and health education, ed. 4, St. Louis, 1961, The C. V. Mosby Co.
15. Wesley, W. A.: Should health services be under administration of board of education or board of health? Bulletin of the National Association of Secondary School Principals **44**: May, 1960.
16. Williams, J. F., Brownell, C. L., and Vernier, E. L.: The administration of health education and physical education, ed. 5, Philadelphia, 1958, W. B. Saunders Co.
17. Wisconsin Cooperative School Health Program: Administrator's outline for study of the school health program, Madison, 1946, Department of Public Instruction.
18. Wishik, S. M.: Administrative jurisdiction of school health service, American Journal of Public Health **41**: July, 1951.
19. Working together for school health, Health Bulletin for Teachers, Metropolitan Life Insurance Co. **21**: April, 1950.

Chapter 3

HEALTH EDUCATION THROUGH GUIDANCE

The wise and competent guidance of secondary school students in all aspects of their lives is a tremendous responsibility. When a teacher or counselor assumes any significant part of this responsibility, he is likely to become an important influence in the life of one or more people. All of us, of course, affect others through our normal daily contacts, but the high school counselor, whether guidance specialist, academic teacher, nurse, health education teacher, physician, or physical education instructor, has many opportunities to practice purposeful guidance. All members of the school personnel should take a critical look at the goals young people have in mind as well as search their own attitudes for possible blocks to working successfully with adolescents. The health problems that confront youth once were problems for the adult to whom they now look to for guidance. Wise advice demands understanding and compassion; hopefully, but not necessarily, these are in the makeup of all teachers, especially in those who presume to guide.

MEANING OF HEALTH GUIDANCE

The term *guidance* as used in secondary schools was originally used primarily to refer to efforts made to help youth select professions and occupations compatible with their abilities and interests. This is shown by the definition given in the 1934 edition of *Webster's New International Dictionary* which defines educational guidance as "advice given to pupils to enable them to choose appropriate educational or vocational work." In recent years the field of guidance has expanded to include other guidance services designed to help the schools more fully achieve their total educational objectives. Since the place and importance of health is so well recognized as an educational objective, as shown in Chapter 1, there is little doubt that health guidance should be an integral part of the total school program.

RELATIONSHIP BETWEEN HEALTH GUIDANCE AND HEALTH TEACHING

The title of this chapter implies that there is a relationship between health guidance and health teaching. Certainly this is true. Although each area is different, they tend to complement each other. Also, in a broad sense guidance is teaching.

Health teaching has been described earlier as the presentation of experiences and activities for the purpose of favorably influencing knowledge, habits, attitudes, practices, appreciations, and conduct pertaining to individual and group health. To facilitate comparison with health guidance, health teaching may also be described as occurring not only on an individual basis, but also as a group situation in three parts as follows.

1. It is usually a health, biology, or physical education class.
2. It seeks to develop favorable health habits, attitudes, and knowledge through group activities.
3. It strives through group study and activities for satisfactory fulfillment of long range life goals.

How then does health teaching differ from health guidance, if at all? Health guidance is usually concerned with the following:

1. Individual health problems through a face-to-face student-counselor relationship
2. Implementation of favorable health habits, attitudes, and knowledge
3. Realization of immediate health goals

As an example, a school physician who confers with a tenth grade girl about a serious acne problem is practicing *health guidance*. So also is the health education teacher in counseling a slowly maturing ninth grade boy who feels defeated by his inability to perform well in physical activities.

Fig. 2 shows both the relationships and differences between health teaching and health guidance along a broad continuum.

Guidance may occur during a short 5 minute discussion with a student after a 50-minute class that has touched on some personal health problem.

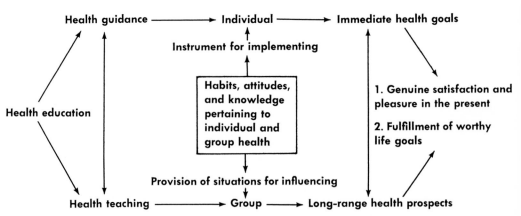

Fig. 2. Flow chart showing the relationships and differences between health teaching and health guidance.

Thus, Fig. 2 indicates the possible flow from teaching to guidance and back again. Still further, even as achievement of immediate health goals provides genuine satisfaction and pleasure in the present, the student enhances his long-range health prospects and eases the road to fulfillment of worthy life goals.

WHAT ARE THE NEEDS FOR HEALTH GUIDANCE?

There is little doubt that when consideration is given to the present web of environmental forces in which the youth of our country are placed health guidance as a function of our schools is of utmost importance. Without health guidance the adolescent will often become indifferent to the challenge of doing his physical and mental best in all situations and will reflect an attitude similar to that captured in a popular caricature that shows a simpleminded smiling boy with a pointed head saying to all the world, "Me worry?" His expression conveys to the observer, "Of course not!" The environmental factors which follow indicate the increasing need for health guidance if the indifference of youth to their personal health problems is to be avoided.

More than half of all our hospital beds in the United States are occupied by mentally ill persons. Recently, encouraging statistics seem to indicate that this hospitalized population is gradually being reduced, and, in fact, it is. However, while the number of days in a hospital per mental patient has been reduced through the practice of several new methods, the over-all incidence of mentally ill persons has actually increased. There has been a decided shift from the less numerous, long-term psychotic types of illnesses to the much more numerous neurotic illnesses with a shorter hospitalization period. Patients in the neurotic group are usually ambulatory and are often able to be at home, but they may not have solved their problems to the degree that they are considered cured. The stress and tension created by our dynamic and scientific society as well as by perpetually unsettled world conditions seem to contribute to the growing number of mental and emotionally ill persons.

Other conditions that show a need for more and better guidance are the growing incidence of teen-age marriages, the increasing divorce rate that now stands at about 19.6% of all marriages, the countless broken homes not actually terminated in divorce, the tragic instances of abortion, and the continuing high prevalence of venereal disease. Many of these categories do not include people who are considered neurotically or psychotically ill; yet they constitute real mental and emotional problems in our society. Satisfactory and timely guidance generally and the aspects of these problems that pertain directly to health specifically may prevent, correct, or ease the problem for the individual or individuals involved.

Although most students follow the normal course of human growth and development, a small percentage of the school population can be expected to deviate from the normal pattern. In this category are students with a variety of physical anomalies such as epilepsy, residual poliomyelitis, and speech defects. Health guidance can contribute to the lives of these atypical students by helping them to a better understanding of themselves, their physical problems, and the world they must face.

The high fatal accident rate among teen-agers, particularly on our highways, in the home, and in recreational pursuits, in addition to the large number of injuries, especially those that are permanently disabling, gives rise to the belief that more adult guidance is needed in the area of safety and accident prevention.

Wide differences in practices and knowledge of nutrition, dental care, family living, and personal health promotion indicate the need for proper guidance in meeting the present and future needs of youth.

Health guidance is needed to offset the pressures of commercial advertising which bear most directly on youth. Much of the advertising is misleading, and the products may be harmful; yet youth are implored to smoke this cigarette, drink this beverage, use this skin preparation, and adopt this surefire diet.

Often when attempts are made to counsel teen-agers, many will answer "But I don't care," thus reflecting the view of our simple, worryless boy depicted earlier. Others will seek advice from parents, church, and recreational leaders and teachers. The school and of course the private physician are the logical and most authoritative sources the youngster and hopefully his parents will turn to for counsel. Guidance can only have value if it is scientifically accurate on the basis of present knowledge. Thus, it behooves school administrators to ensure that health guidance given by faculty members is accurate. Equally as important, it is the responsibility of each prospective teacher to prepare himself adequately to serve well as a health guidance counselor. For example, the adolescent tends to practice poor dietary habits, especially with regard to skipping breakfast, with the idea that this is an excellent way to reduce. The questionable dietary habits of many adults and the popularity of food fad pills, supplements, and diets compound the problem. Also, by way of example, poor habits related to dental care and the reluctance of many communities to accept fluoridation point to a need for health guidance to prevent students from following faulty adult examples.

WHAT ARE THE AIMS OF HEALTH GUIDANCE?

It has been said that the adolescent is extremely difficult to understand much of the time and almost impossible to understand all of the time. His behavior can fluctuate rapidly over a wide continuum. At one moment he may seek and desperately need the advice of trusted adults. Almost instantaneously he may change to a superior sophisticate who is completely independent and needs no help or advice. More often than not this latter role is a facade which screens confusion, uncertainty, incomplete understanding, and lack of confidence in himself. Since the often reluctant but still dependent secondary school student may seek health guidance if provision is made for it in the school program, health guidance should be designed to do the following:

1. Help students develop a more complete understanding of themselves
2. Direct students in accurate evaluation of their health problems.
3. Motivate students to correct their health problems to the extent that personal means and community resources provide
4. Assist students in the development of sound health habits and practices

5. Assist students in developing a clearer understanding of the available health services in the school and community

INITIATING HEALTH GUIDANCE

Health guidance does not occur without planning. There is no special time during the school day, such as during lunch or study hall periods, when health guidance occurs. In the secondary school program in which each student comes in contact with several teachers daily and, conversely, in which teachers, in addition to homeroom responsibilities, have contact with large numbers of students daily, it is easy for situations which indicate the need for health guidance to be ignored. Ideally, some one faculty member should be designated to direct the health guidance program and should be given time to devote to these duties. Some schools have adopted this procedure with success since it serves to alert all faculty members to the needs and prompt referral of youth with health problems.

Whether or not the school is fortunate in having one interested teacher allotted time to direct health guidance services, all teachers should be aware of the following five ways in which health guidance may be initiated and conducted.

1. Teacher observations
2. Surveys of student health needs
3. Health appraisal
4. School records
5. Conferences with parents

The most important of these, particularly from the viewpoint of individual teacher responsibility for student health, is observation.

Teacher observation

In addition to his academic responsibilities, each teacher should keep in mind that students may not achieve their academic optimum if they possess even a relatively minor physical or mental deficiency. The teacher's daily observation of his class or classes for indications of departures from good health is a key factor in guaranteeing optimum learning.

The good teacher will develop his observation techniques so that he does a thorough, conscientious job and yet does not lose too much time from normal class routine. Three methods will be of value. First, he should develop the practice of quickly scanning the faces of the students in his homeroom for any deviations from their usual appearance. Second, he should be alert to the symptoms of specific illnesses that periodically spread through all schools and look for these, as they may occur, in the appearance of each student. In doing so, he can detect some cases before they become most communicable. In this way he can help reduce the spread of disease. (A very brief description of the major diseases of concern appears in Table 1. A chart similar to this should be made available to all teachers.) Third, he can concentrate his observations for a few minutes each day on a particular student. Thus, he can better understand the individual student's mannerisms and personality. Consequently, when a deviation occurs at a later date, he will be quick to recognize it. Results of short

Table 1. Recommendations concerning communicable diseases and contagious skin, hair, eye, and foot conditions*

Condition or disease	Description	Exclusion
Athlete's foot	Scaling; itching between toes; blisters on feet	No—only from showers
Chickenpox	Rashlike water blisters	Yes
German measles (three-day measles)	Blotchy rash	Yes
Impetigo	Blisterlike sores; scabs found usually where student can pick easily	Yes
Lice and larvae (nits) on head	Larvae looks like dandruff but cannot be rubbed off hair	Yes
Measles (red or 14-day measles)	Fever; blotchy, dusky red rash	Yes
Mumps	Sudden swelling and pain at jaw or jaws in front of ears	Yes
Pink eye (conjunctivitis)	Eyelashes mattered and stuck together; white of eye vivid pink	Immediately
Ringworm of scalp and body	Ringlike patches; moist, pink, and scaly with clear space in center	Yes: scalp—7 days medical care; body—from gymnasium and showers
Scabies	Tiny bitelike red marks; usually found between fingers and in folds of skin	Immediately
Scarlet fever or streptococcic infection of throat	Fever; sudden severe sore throat; vomiting; fire-red rash	Yes; *must* have medical care to help prevent rheumatic fever; 14 days or after 48 hours of antibodies and clinically well enough
Whooping cough (pertussis)	Feverish cold; persistent cough becomes spasmodic	Yes

*Courtesy Benton County Health Department, Oregon.

observation periods of each student should be summarized briefly and placed in the student's folder.

Whether the teacher practices any one or all of the three methods just discussed, the essential features of health observation are (1) the teacher's constant alertness to matters of health and (2) the teacher's awareness of the characteristics of normal health and the signs and symptoms of deviant health conditions most likely to occur among secondary school students.

It is important to point out that the responsibility for continually observing students for evidences of departure from optimum health and the making of suitable referrals does not carry with it the further responsibility of diagnosing specific illnessess. Diagnosis is a matter which rests with medical, psychological, speech, and other specialists. However, the more detailed and accurate the teacher's noting of pertinent symptoms, the more valuable will be the information he can provide to those persons responsible for diagnosis. For example, the teacher may give details about a particular student's increased irritability, reduced vitality, or tendency to withdraw from activities which might not be apparent in an interview or medical examination but which might be important factors in general health appraisal.

Acute illnesses, such as the onset of influenza and appendicitis, usually attract attention quickly and offer relatively little difficulty in the way of diagnosis to qualified specialists. On the other hand, the less abrupt departures from health, such as growth failure due to certain diseases of malnutrition and some behavior disorders due to problems in the emotional life of the student, tend to offer greater difficulties for early observation and diagnosis and point up the need for all teachers to develop satisfactory techniques of observation.

Although there are numerous factors in addition to freedom from disease which influence the quality of student health, for practical purposes it is desirable to pay particularly close attention to the following four considerations which are basic to good health throughout life: (1) proper diet, (2) judicious exercise, (3) adequate rest and sleep, and (4) a reasonably undisturbed state. It is important to stress that these bases of health are interdependent. For example, if a student does not get sufficient physical activity, he is not likely to eat well or to rest well, and his emotional adjustments may be affected. If rest and sleep are inadequate, his appetite is likely to be affected, and his emotional reactions are almost certain to be negatively affected. If the student's diet does not include adequate amounts of the various essential foods, the effects will soon be apparent in terms of reduction in physical vigor, disturbed appetite, and altered emotional responses. And, finally, if severe emotional problems exist in the life of the student, his appetite, activity level, and sleeping habits are likely to be affected.

A defect in diet, physical activity, rest, or emotional stability is probably the most frequent opening wedge that is driven into the health of students. On the other hand, close attention to these things is probably the best and most available assurance that a healthy state will be maintained and that satisfactory recovery will be made in the event of accidents or invasion of the body by disease entities.

The teacher must be well informed regarding certain principles of human growth in order to make intelligent observations. Although the growth of all normal students follows a general pattern, it is essential to realize that growth is a highly individual matter and that it does not progress at a constant rate. The important thing is not that a student grow as others are growing, but that he grow properly in his own way and that he not stop growing until his growth potential is attained. What a student's own way of growth is depends upon such factors as his heredity and his particular body build or structure. Therefore, some students of a given age will be slender and some stocky. For them such a condition is healthy. Other students have been the victims in prehigh school years of parents and even teachers who insisted upon huskiness as a criterion of health, and sometimes these well-meaning but misinformed "advisers" have created difficult problems of an emotional kind by attempting to force heavy eating upon individuals who are naturally slight of build and normally light eaters.

The teacher should have clear knowledge of the growth characteristics of the age level with which he works; however, the focus of the teacher's attention must remain upon the individual. Only in this way can he hope to note the various symptoms associated with abnormalities including growth failure.

Aids to observation

Many school systems now provide health record cards for each student. These should be started in grade 1 and should follow the student through grade 12. Teachers use them to note pertinent observations which lend insight into the status of health during the school years. Whether an official card or one devised by the teacher is used, care should be taken to include only information which actually contributes to a knowledge of the student's history. For example, if indications of some visual difficulty are observed, this and the subsequent action taken should be noted. If appropriate treatment is given and improvement is noted, these facts too should be recorded.

The health record card should also contain notes regarding behavior of an exceptional kind as well as evidence of good health to be used as a basis for future comparison. Experience has shown that a health record kept conscientiously over a period of years can be very useful in an analysis of present student health status.

In recent years means have been devised for taking into account the individual nature of growth. Various grids such as the Wetzel* and Meredith Physical Growth Record† are now availabe to many teachers which in simple style on the basis of age, height, and weight reveal whether a student's growth is progressing properly in terms of his own body build and how his size compares with that of other students of his age. It is best that these grids, which are cumulative, be started in the elementary grades and follow the student throughout high school if the maximum benefit is to accrue.

Signs, symptoms, and warning signals

The following discussion of signs and symptoms is presented merely as a guide. In some instances, as in the case of vision and hearing, simple testing procedures are suggested which may be useful in very rough screening. When *acute* signs and symptoms are observed, arrangements should be made to get the student home, and the parents should be urged to consult a physician immediately. All schools should have established procedures to follow in cases of student injury or illness.

Facial appearance. The facial appearance of the student frequently gives an indication of present health status.

The teacher should be alert to such symptoms as unusual redness or pallor of the face, inflammation of the eyeballs, and nasal discharge. Such signs, individually or in combination, can be brought on by various diseases,

*Available from the N.E.A. Service, Inc., 1200 W. Third St., Cleveland, Ohio.
†Available from the American Medical Association, 535 N. Dearborn Street, Chicago, Ill., or from the National Education Association, 1201 Sixteenth Street, N. W., Washington, D. C.

but in any event they are common signs of trouble and should receive attention.

Respiratory system. Respiratory diseases are the principal cause of absenteeism among students, and although they are not usually severe, in some cases they are quite serious. Colds and other respiratory disturbances are thought to be most contagious in their early stages, that is, within the first two or three days. If students stay at home when persistent coughing, sneezing, and nasal discharge are observed, infection of large numbers of other students and perhaps the teacher may be avoided. Since many more serious diseases, such as sinusitis, mumps, diphtheria, and poliomyelitis, may resemble a simple cold in their early stages, the student should be watched closely for evidence of mounting fever, muscular pain, nausea, and other symptoms. Although there are not at present effective means of curing colds, high school students are not yet too old to be counseled in the importance of wearing proper clothing, eating wisely, and getting enough rest in order to keep the frequency and severity of colds to a minimum.

Teachers can easily check mouth breathers to determine whether they are unable to breathe through the nose freely. Inability to breathe easily through the nose is indicative of some form of nasal blockage which should receive medical consideration.

Special note and suitable referral should be made of those individuals who are subject to repeated colds. Frequent colds may be indicative of a dietary deficiency, some chronic infection, poor dressing habits, or other factors related to lowered resistance. They may also be related to emotional disturbances.

Eyes. Certain behavior patterns should give rise to suspicion that the eyes are not functioning properly. For example, a student may hold reading material within a few inches of his face, he may squint and make faces as he strains to read what is on the blackboard, his eyes may be very sensitive to light, he may wipe or rub his eyes frequently, or he may close one eye when trying to see. Upon being questioned he may complain of blurred vision, headache, and dizziness when reading or doing close work or of not being able to see distant objects when participating in competitive activities. In appearance his eyes may be watery and inflamed, and the lids may be swollen and encrusted.

Glasses do not always assure correction of visual defects. When students with glasses show signs of visual difficulty, it is well to bear in mind the possibilities that diagnosis may not have been correct, that the glasses do not provide the necessary compensation, or that new difficulties have developed since the previous diagnosis.

Many schools now attempt to provide regular vision testing programs in which all students are screened for visual defects at regular intervals. However, in some cases it may be necessary for a teacher to administer a simple test, such as the Snellen test, to one or more students.

The teacher has an important role to play in encouraging students to wear their glasses. The desire to be socially acceptable and attractive may influence wrongly some adolescents to forsake regular use of their glasses. Skillful teaching and guidance can help to make glasses socially acceptable among students.

Ears. Partial hearing loss can frequently be identified by certain typical behaviorisms of students. They may strain forward with an intent look when instructions are being given, turn one ear toward the speaker, or cup a hand behind the ear. If a student cannot hear his own voice well, his speech may become flat and poorly modulated. It sometimes happens that students who appear dull or disinterested in class activities are merely unable to hear clearly what is taking place.

Screening tests should be conducted periodically in order to locate individuals with subnormal hearing. Hearing test programs are becoming standard practice throughout the country. In localities in which programs of this kind are routine, large numbers of cases have been treated which had not previously been suspected. Even though screening is done, the teachers should remain alert to behavior which suggests the possibility of a hearing difficulty since infection, injury, and wax accumulation can reduce acuity of hearing rapidly, with the result that symptoms may appear suddenly.

There are simple tests which may be used by the teacher to check for gross hearing failure. For example, the watch test may be given. In this test, a watch, preferably with a loud tick, is held at various distances from the student's ear. The watch is shifted to the right and left and above the student's head, and in each position the student is asked to indicate whether he hears ticking. Caution should be taken so that the student is not aided by peripheral vision. Occasionally the watch should be placed at a distance at which it cannot possibly be heard in order to be sure that the student is not guessing. A stopwatch may be used and is snapped on and off occasionally to determine whether the student really hears. Of course, badly blocked or damaged ears will not hear the tick even though the watch is very near.

Neck. Lumps in the neck may be due to mumps which cause a swelling of the salivary glands or to swelling of the lymph nodes just below the ear and behind the jaw. Lumps of either kind should receive the attention of a physician. Swelling of the lymph nodes indicates the presence of infection, perhaps in the gland itself or in some region of the head, the ear, scalp, or throat.

Teeth. Dental screening in schools often reveals that approximately 80% or more of the students are in need of treatment. Although a satisfactory evaluation of dental health requires trained personnel, there are certain gross symptoms which the teacher should recognize. Some of these are (1) very bad cases in which it is possible to see the dark yellow spots of decay at the base and sides of the front teeth, (2) a foul smell of infection that may be perceptible on the student's breath, (3) gums that may be inflamed and sore, (4) upper and lower sets of teeth which may not fit properly together when the mouth is closed, and (5) very obvious symptoms of toothache. Periodic dental screening should be done by qualified persons, but the teacher must remain alert to gross difficulties.

The teacher's role in dental health teaching is to cultivate the student's interest in his own total health, including his teeth, his realization of personal responsibility for his own health, and his knowledge of those practices which promote good health.

Students should be made aware of the contribution of proper diet to the proper development of their teeth. They should also understand that certain foods, principally sugars, may have the effect of damaging the teeth, especially if they are eaten in such quantity that they crowd essential foods from the diet.

Orthodontia ordinarily should be started by grade 5 to 7 at the latest for optimum results. However, if an eighth or ninth grade student has a severe orthodontial problem and has received no treatment, need for wise and expedient health guidance is indicated. Malocclusion, extreme crowding of the teeth in the jaw, and other conditions that are both physical and esthetic problems should be referred and followed up.

The high school teacher can also play an important role in continuing to stress desirable attitudes toward periodic dental examinations.

Hair and scalp. Pediculi or lice usually first appear on the bodies of students who live in areas in which the living conditions are unhygienic and may spread rapidly to any nearby persons. Recently developed insecticides simplify the handling of this problem; however, the teacher should be able to recognize the pests and become suspicious when the small eggs or nits are discovered clinging to the hair. Frequent itching and scratching of the scalp should be investigated for disease or infestation.

Posture. Poor posture may take several forms such as the head carried too far forward, round shoulders, one shoulder held higher than the other, sway back or forward curvature of the spine, pronated ankles, and flatfeet. The poor posture of some students is due to actual deformation of the skeleton, and treatment is necessarily a medical matter. Most cases of poor posture are functional and are due to difficulties other than skeletal abnormality.

It should be recognized that, although poor posture may be due to bad habits of sitting, standing, and moving or to the influence of unfortunate fads and styles, it is frequently a symptom of some underlying difficulty. Therefore, it is unwise to require students to begin taking exercises or other corrective measures until the cause is known. For example, it would be unwise to initiate an exercise program for a round-shouldered student if his stance is due to weakness from disease or malnutrition. Similarly, it would be unwise to suggest corrective activities to a student whose head-forward stance represents an attempted compensation for poor vision which actually can only be corrected by glasses. It is known, too, that prolonged emotional upset can be a cause of poor posture, and that improvement must begin with relieving the disturbing situation.

Once the underlying causes for poor posture have been removed, the task is to convince the student that good posture is advantageous and to guide his self-analysis so that improvement can take place. Whatever its cause, poor posture may become a habit which is broken only with conscious effort. Therefore, it is plain that the individual must want good posture if improvement is to take place.

The teacher's guidance can also be of great importance in the matter of selecting proper footwear, especially as comfort is often denied for the sake of style. Students should be taught to have their feet properly measured and fitted, and they should be taught the hazard to their feet of wearing shoes that are in poor repair. For example, as a heel becomes worn on the inside, additional body weight is thrown upon the inside of the foot, and there is an increased tendency toward pronation or forcing the ankle inward and downward. Continual use of tennis shoes or sneakers should be discouraged.

Speech difficulties. Speech defects should be mentioned because of their frequency, often in combination with hearing loss. The full implications of speech defects cannot be appreciated until they are considered in the light of (1) their obvious interference with the most essential of our communication media, (2) the impact that they tend to have upon the emotions of the individual who possesses them, both because of the defective communication and because of the typical parental and other social reactions to them, and (3) the role that emotional upset commonly plays in the formation of speech defects.

Speech difficulties should be approached with caution because inept handling may complicate and aggravate rather than improve. One well-known specialist on speech has pointed out that most speech problems have their beginning, not in the mouths of the students, but in the mouths of their parents. This statement suggests that emotional problems are intimately involved in the speech situation, and it is likely that therapy in specific cases involves more than practicing saying words or being reminded not to stutter. As a matter of fact, the teacher who has not had specialized training in the area of speech correction should realize that this difficulty, like a physical or mental disorder, is best left to a specialist.

Mental and emotional health. It is not possible to specify a list of behavior traits which always signal poor mental and emotional health because virtually all such traits are observed in most everyone at one time or another. For example, daydreaming is commonly indicated as a symptom of withdrawn behavior; yet we know that all normal people, adults included, daydream, and we know that various factors such as boredom and emotional stress commonly lead to increased daydreaming. Consequently, when evaluating behavior for evidence of poor mental health, it is necessary to think in terms of *persisting* and *extreme* traits. Thus, habitual daydreaming may suggest a tendency to withdraw from reality. Similarly, habitual defiance of adult authority, cruelty, or extreme excitability would suggest a need for careful investigation by specialists so that the cause might be discovered. Although isolated episodes of unusual or extreme behavior might deserve noting, they would not in themselves necessarily be symptoms of behavior disorders.

The following list includes some behaviorisms which are sometimes associated with disturbance at the psychological level. *Individual students must, of course, be reckoned with in terms of persistence and severity of symptoms.*

1. Withdrawnness, shyness, seclusiveness, and timidity
2. Daydreaming
3. Fearfulness and strong anxiety
4. Tenseness, excitability, and lack of emotional control
5. Extreme desire to please

6. Lack of self-confidence—an "I can't" attitude
7. Inability to assume responsibility for own errors
8. Unhappiness and feelings of depression
9. Suspiciousness
10. Avoidance of need to adjust to others
11. Inability to adjust to the group, especially in physical activities
12. Nail-biting, habit tics, and finger-sucking or lip-sucking
13. Failure to make progress which is in keeping with physical and mental capacity
14. Hostile and aggressive behavior
15. Destructiveness
16. Cruelty
17. Temper displays, often and uncontrolled
18. Irresponsibility
19. Showing off and other attention-getting activities
20. Lying, cheating, and stealing
21. Lack of self-control

Because so many of the mental and emotional problems among adults had their beginning in childhood, it is extremely important that secondary school teachers be ever alert to the deviations among their students that may be insidious indicators of mental or emotional ill health which will continue into adulthood if unchecked.

Surveys of student health needs

Health guidance may also be initiated by the teacher through the use of a well-designed survey which seeks to identify the health needs of students. There are several survey forms available commercially. However, the teacher may wish to construct his own, a task that can be as simple or as complicated as the occasion and purpose demands.

A recent survey of high school students used a variety of methods to identify health needs. With considerable consistency between the survey tools used, student needs were identified in the areas of sleep, rest, and relaxation, prevention and control of chronic and degenerative diseases, safety education, consumer health, personal health, and nutrition. On the basis of her findings, the author believes the following implications to be evident for health and counseling services, as well as for administrative and teaching staffs.

"1. There is a need for a definite block of time allotted for health education at the high school level.

"2. There is an apparent need for more intensive health counseling and follow-up programs to assist students to interpret their health problems more realistically and to encourage the correction of remediable defects.

"3. The need for a more intensive counseling and guidance program is indicated for twelfth grade as well as for tenth grade students.

"4. There is evidence of the need for health and counseling services personnel and teaching staff to work together jointly in an effort to assist students to interpret their problems realistically, to resolve those which are present, and to learn how to prevent others from developing.

"5. Since the school has a supportive but very important role in health education, health and counseling services personnel, teachers, and others must work with parents and family physician and dentist to help resolve student problems."*

On the basis of this and other similar studies it is clear that surveys of student health needs will contribute significantly to both the health teaching and health guidance programs.

Health appraisal

In this area the secondary school teacher is less likely to be of direct influence in identifying those in need of health guidance to the extent that he is in observation and survey of health needs.

As indicated in Chapter 1, health appraisal refers to the cumulative results of several procedures designed to determine the student's health status. These include health histories, medical and dental examinations, psychological examinations, and screening examinations to detect deviation in such areas as hearing and vision. Successful conduct of this aspect of the school health service program requires the cooperation and contribution of parents, teachers, physicians, dentists, health educators, nurses, psychologists, and other persons who may have contact with the students. The responsibility of each of these people to the health guidance program is discussed at the end of this chapter. A more complete discussion of health appraisal is outside the context of this book except to summarize the aims and objectives of health appraisal as related to guidance. These are the following:

1. To locate students in need of medical and dental attention
2. To determine those students with personal health problems such as diet, nutrition, and marginal illness
3. To find those students who are maladjusted and in need of special care at school or who have problems serious enough to be referred to a psychiatrist or to a guidance clinic
4. To assure that all students maintain normal growth and development
5. To locate students with nonremediable defects who may require modified programs of education (also known as special education) and those in need of special rehabilitation programs
6. To screen students who need a more thorough examination than is usually provided at school, including the services of a medical specialist and x-ray and extended laboratory examinations
7. To determine those students who may be cared for best apart from the regular school situation

School records

Through a study of school records which reveal to some extent the backgrounds of students, it is possible to identify numerous health problems which may require guidance. Included here are the cumulative records, health and

---

*From Rich, Ruth: Health education needs of high school students in a large diversified metropolitan area, Research Quarterly **31**: Dec., 1960.

medical records, school absence reports, individual teacher summaries garnered through observations, and transcripts of all interviews with students and their parents. These records should be readily available to the school physician, nurse, and health educator, and other school personnel should be permitted to scan them in conference with a responsible member of the school health program.

Conferences with parents

Conferences with parents can be a rewarding way of gathering facts for use in the health guidance program. Support for this has been demonstrated by a new approach to the handling of psychiatric patients.* This technique confirms the belief that it is necessary to look beyond the student into the home if the more complex health problems are to be solved through guidance. In many schools the school physician, nurse, or health educator is on a friendly basis with most parents; consequently, conferences of an informal nature often iron out difficulties. Most often, however, it will be necessary to arrange a special conference with one or both parents. Home visits are advisable to discover the social environment that may be influencing the student. When the information derived from parent conferences and visitation is placed in the student's cumulative school folder, along with other data from sources discussed earlier, the health objectives of both health guidance and health teaching will be more likely to be attained.

ORGANIZATION OF THE HEALTH GUIDANCE PROGRAM

There are few school administrators who have completely ignored the health guidance program. This is not to say that all schools have acceptable health guidance because most schools do not have all the essential features of a good health guidance program. It is well, therefore, to point out a few basic features which can be used as criteria in assessing the total health guidance program. These can be divided into three major areas of concern: those features related to the administration of the program, those features related to school personnel, and, most important, those features related to students.

Administrative features. More than other aspects of the school's guidance program, a successful health guidance program depends upon complete administrative support and leadership. If this is forthcoming, it is more than likely that most or all of the following essentials can be achieved.

1. Records for each student can be kept up to date. When the student first enters high school, a health record for his previous school years should accompany him and should be continued through the twelfth grade.
2. Records should be kept in a place accessible to all school personnel responsible for any phase of health guidance. This may be encouraged during in-service sessions when the health educator or nurse discusses the proper use and interpretation of the records.
3. Sufficient funds should be budgeted and available to carry on the work

---

*Silverman, Margaret, and Silverman, Milton: Psychiatry inside the family circle, *The Saturday Evening Post*, July 28, 1962.

properly. Also, staff time should be allocated to keep the records up to date.

4. The health guidance program should satisfy the needs of all students.

5. A satisfactory health guidance office should be provided as part of the health service facilities.

6. The school personnel should be aware of other health guidance resources in the community and cooperate fully when the occasion demands. The local health department and the myriad of private health personnel available in all communities should be used as needed.

7. The school administrators should have final authority in the health guidance program.

Features related to the school personnel. A good health guidance program will display some or all of the following.

1. All teachers should accept the responsibility and extend the very best health guidance possible. This can be done through individual conference with students and also by displaying good personal example. A familiar story of Albert Schweitzer is appropriate in this regard. When once asked if he thought that personally setting a good example was one of the best ways of influencing people, he replied, "No! It's the only way."

2. All teachers should willingly participate in in-service meetings designed to increase their competence in health guidance. At least one school staff in-service meeting a month should be devoted to generalized health guidance problems. The need for such a program should be recognized and accepted by the school staff.

3. All staff members should honor the confidence of a student with a personal health problem. If more experienced help is needed, the student's permission should be sought. This is seldom a problem when the student senses an atmosphere of genuine confidence and sympathetic guidance.

4. Teachers who provide health guidance should try to learn all the facts pertaining to a specific case. This includes the student's home life, his school and community activities and companions, and all other environmental relationships. In a complex existence it is impossible to understand a single student out of context; all of the facts are necessary to make a wise judgment about health problems and their solution.

Features related to the student. As important as the foregoing principles are, it is those related to the student that are the most important; a health guidance program only exists to give service to the students. Here are some important points to remember.

1. A good halth guidance program should identify and assist those students who are not functioning at the peak of their physical endowment.

2. All students should be able to obtain competent health guidance at all times. Teachers and guidance personnel should not work only with the loudest, the brightest, and the best students; the reluctant and the reticent students, also, if not more so, should feel free to seek help.

3. The health guidance program should be client-centered. Certainly, there are long-standing differences in how counseling should be carried out, whether

it should be directive or nondirective,* but there can be no quarrel with the fact that it does not exist to solve faculty or other problems. Either way, it exists for the students.

4. The student should make the final decision himself, whether it be to visit the dentist, to stop biting the fingernails, to give up a foolish teen-age diet and eat sensibly, or to drive safely and honor the rights of others. Counsel and guidance will prove worthless unless the student fully accepts his own decisions and honestly understands the contribution that they will make to his immediate and ultimate life goals.

RESPONSIBILITIES OF THE SCHOOL PERSONNEL FOR THE HEALTH GUIDANCE PROGRAM

Because much of health guidance is less formal than health teaching, the setting within which it may take place is much more varied. The obvious settings include the school guidance department, the homerooms, and regular classes, especially the health education classes. Less obvious but just as vital in a progressive, organized program are health examinations, rehabilitation and special education classes, physical education and home economics classes, associations made through Parent-Teacher Association meetings, parental conferences in the school and community, extraschool activities such as school trips and athletic contests, and sometimes even during school bus transportation. This wide list of possibilities indicates that many members of the school staff may contribute to health guidance.

Board of education. The attitude of the board of education will determine the degree and quality of health guidance and teaching. If the board believes this phase of the program to be important, it will encourage in-service classes, the designation of a health guidance counselor, and other policy promotion decisions. The superintendent of schools, who usually serves as the secretary to the board, must be considered a part of this group. His opinions and those of the board's are usually reflections of each other on issues of broad policy. Acceptance or rejection of a thorough health guidance program that permeates all aspects of school life originates on this level.

School principal. One authority has written that the principal is "the key person in the whole situation, and how he works will determine the success of his efforts."† Among his responsibilities in the field of health guidance are the following:

1. To provide the leadership necessary to carry out a successful program
2. To provide sufficient funds for a program which meets the needs of all students
3. To designate one staff person to be responsible for directing the program and provide sufficient time from other school responsibilities to do an adequate job

---

*Breslow, A. P.: Adolescent guidance, a viewpoint, Journal of School Health **32**: May, 1962.
†From Schwartz, E. T.: Guidance: A cooperative venture, Elementary School Education **73**: April, 1953.

4. To support the program and encourage all staff people to participate actively
5. To schedule and support in-service sessions for the purpose of perfecting health observation techniques and informal counseling procedures
6. To favorably interpret the purpose of the program to the community and especially before the Parent-Teacher Association and the board of education

Director of guidance. In many high schools guidance is an accepted part of the total program, and one staff person fills the role of guidance director. A guidance director sees health guidance as only one aspect of the guidance process; his broader interest is in the over-all integration of academic, vocational, and social guidance problems in addition to health guidance. It is the wise guidance director who understands how directly the student's health is tied to other problems which he might have. This important staff person, then, is responsible for the following aspects of the health guidance program:

1. Meeting regularly with the health coordinator, health educator, or other designated head of the health program to discuss student problems of mutual concern
2. Being available and receptive to these same people for spontaneous problems that may arise
3. Including health histories and other similar data when guiding students
4. Developing an atmosphere of understanding among all staff members for the value of all aspects of guidance including health guidance

Health coordinator and/or health educator. Many schools have designated a staff member to direct, supervise, and coordinate all activities concerning the health of students. In some cases this has been an added responsibility for a

Fig. 3. Counseling is an important function of the high school nurse.

teacher already overburdened. More wisely, the health coordinator occupies a full-time post. He may or may not teach classes. He is usually a health educator when he does teach. The duties for either or both of these individuals with regard to health guidance include the following:

1. Coordinating reports, records, and findings from all phases of the school health program
2. Encouraging complete and accurate record keeping of all health forms adopted by the school and develop necessary and appropriate forms as needed
3. Initiating and directing in-service sessions relating to health matters for enlightment of the total school staff; major areas regarding health guidance would include observation, keeping of records, and proper referral
4. Conducting a continuous health observation campaign
5. Developing techniques that keep all staff members alert to student health needs without antagonizing or inadvertently questioning their intelligence

Health services personnel. The emphasis of this text is mainly on the education phase of the secondary school health program. Within this frame of reference, then, the physician, nurse, psychologist, and other persons in the health service program should be concerned with the following activities pertaining to health guidance:

1. Summarizing and directing information to the guidance department, teachers, and other persons in the school directly concerned with student health problems
2. Counseling and guiding students directly as needed and as opportunities develop
3. Referring special problems to available community resources

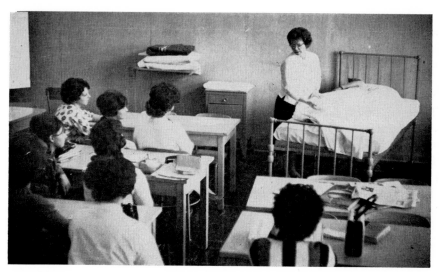

Fig. 4. The high school nurse may assume occasional teaching responsibilities. Here she is seen teaching a lesson in bed-making as part of a two-week unit in home nursing for high school girls.

4. Encouraging administrators to utilize health guidance resources; physicians and psychologists may be more influential in this regard than other staff members
5. Participating in the in-service programs concerned with health guidance
6. Administering group and individual medical and psychological tests to discover health needs
7. Conferring with parents and teachers about individual students with physical and emotional health problems

Other faculty members. Teachers not directly related to the health program are sometimes reluctant to concern themselves with the health of students. They frequently express the thought that nonqualified people should not be responsible. This is especially the case in the junior and senior high schools where each subject matter teacher may teach as many as 150 to 200 students every day. In such a mass education program in which each teacher is oriented to a single subject area or at the most to two or three areas, the expected responsibilities for health guidance are limited. Nevertheless, these teachers should at least do the following.

1. Develop techniques of health observation and referral of moderate to severe deviations; perhaps only gross screening is possible but conscious acceptance rather than denial of the responsibility is needed.
2. Take the time and interest to counsel on health-related matters when opportunities present themselves. Perhaps only listening to a student's problem, talking a few minutes about it, and sending the student on to a more qualified staff member will ease a serious situation that otherwise would go unattended.

Other school personnel. The maintenance superintendent and staff, the bus drivers, and the cafeteria workers are people who will also function cooperatively in a well-integrated health guidance program. These people do not have special responsibility for guidance, but they do influence students. Efforts should be taken to assure that their influence is constructive and that it be willingly and pleasantly offered when the opportunity arises.

EVALUATING HEALTH GUIDANCE

The American Association of School Administrators* developed a list of health educator responsibilities as a counselor-specialist. From this list it is possible to construct criteria that can be used effectively in evaluating a health guidance program. If we recognize that few programs are perfect and that most will fall on a continuum somewhere between excellent and poor, the following criteria may prove helpful. The better the health guidance program, the better it is able to perform the following:

1. Convey to students an understanding of their growth and health problems.
2. Help students to develop a sense of responsibility in meeting personal and family health problems.

---

*American Association of School Administrators: Health in schools, twentieth yearbook, Washington, D. C., 1951, National Education Association.

3. Interpret to parents the significance of health appraisal findings and assist them in obtaining appropriate health care for their children.
4. Contribute to the health education of both students and parents by utilizing the potentialities for education that are inherent in all health appraisal and counseling activities.
5. Assist all students with nonremediable defects to obtain programs adapted to their interests and needs with due consideration to their disabilities.
6. Work with community groups to assure the availability of treatment facilities for all students.

QUESTIONS FOR DISCUSSION

1. What personal characteristics of teachers attract high school students with health problems?
2. Define *guidance* in the broad educational sense and in the health sense.
3. What are the differences and similarities between health guidance and health teaching?
4. How does health guidance complement and supplement the more formal health teaching program?
5. How should an English teacher handle a student who asks for help with a serious acne problem in a school in which there is a good health guidance program? In a school in which there is no structured health guidance program?
6. If a school administrator asked you to justify a health guidance program, how would you answer?
7. What are the major problem areas that the health guidance program should provide counsel for?
8. What methods are most helpful in discovering health guidance problems? Discuss each of these.
9. Is health observation appropriate to the secondary school level?
10. What are the administrative problems of a health guidance program in the modern high school? How may these be compensated for in order to realize health guidance objectives?
11. The school health guidance program only exists to serve students. What issues can and do develop to cause some school systems to lose sight of this basic premise?

SUGGESTED CLASS ACTIVITIES

1. Discuss and construct an organization chart for the school health guidance program. Consider both large and small school situations and the differing responsibilities of the school personnel in each.
2. Analyze the use of several different record forms (for example, Meredith Physical Growth Record, Teachers Anecdotal Record Form, etc.) in the health guidance program.
3. Construct a checklist, simple yet complete, which can be used by the busy secondary teacher who is interested in assuming partial responsibility for health observation.
4. Have a small student group discuss the steps a newly appointed health coordinator would follow in setting up a complete health guidance program.
5. Develop a plan for an in-service program of 4 to 6 hours' duration. The following outline may serve as a rough guide which may be altered or expanded.
   (a) First meeting
      (1) Explanation of scope of program (health director)
      (2) Discussion of observation techniques
      (3) Practice of observation techniques using slides
   (b) Second meeting
      (1) Signs of a healthy adolescent and signs of possible health problems (physician)
      (2) Group discussion
   (c) Third meeting
      (1) Signs of dental health problems (dentist)
      (2) Signs of speech difficulties (high school speech teacher)
      (3) Signs of visual and hearing difficulties (school nurse)

    (d) Fourth meeting
        (1) Signs of emotional problems (guidance counselor)
        (2) Signs of posture condition (physical education director)
        (3) Group discussion
    (e) Fifth meeting
        (1) Recording observations (health director)
        (2) School policies
        (3) Actual observation of a group of students
        (4) Discussion of observations
    (f) Sixth meeting
        (1) Suggested teacher assistance with health problems (health director)
        (2) Review of previous programs
        (3) Group discussion
6. Survey several high school classes and compile a composite list of health needs.
7. Construct a checklist to evaluate a school health guidance program. Administer it as a class and analyze the results.

REFERENCES

1. Carroll, P. R.: School health and guidance services: a cooperative venture, Journal of School Health **30:** Jan., 1960.
2. Church, A. M.: Guidance, health and special education, Bulletin of the National Association of Secondary School Principals **44:** Oct., 1960.
3. Derthick, L. G.: Guidance and the nation's needs, Personnel and Guidance Journal **37:** Oct., 1958.
4. Geyer, M. A.: Counseling for physically impaired students in high school, Personnel and Guidance Journal **32:** Dec., 1953.
5. Henrie, B. S.: The high school home room program, Bulletin of the National Association of Secondary School Principals **45:** May, 1961.
6. Hoffman, F. P.: Health educator-counselor, Journal of Health, Physical Education, and Recreation **28:** Jan., 1957.
7. Humphrey, J. H.: The homeroom as a medium for health guidance, Journal of School Health **22:** Nov., 1952.
8. Klien, R. A.: School nurse as a guidance functionary, Personnel and Guidance Journal **38:** Dec., 1959.
9. Lantangne, J. E.: Health interests of 10,000 secondary school students, Research Quarterly **23:** Oct., 1952.
10. Long, J. R.: Guidance: a coordinated plan, Bulletin of the National Association of Secondary School Principals **45:** May, 1961.
11. Owens, L. E.: Counseling meets health needs, Journal of Health, Physical Education, and Recreation **26:** April, 1955.
12. Phillips, E. B.: Interprofessional communications in child guidance, Journal of School Health **32:** March, 1962.
13. Pupil personnel services in elementary and secondary schools, Washington, D. C., 1951, Federal Security Agency, United States Office of Education, Circular no. 325.
14. Rogers, J. F.: What every teacher should know about the physical condition of her pupils, Washington, D. C., 1945, Federal Security Agency, United States Office of Education, Pamphlet no. 68.
15. Roth, Arthur: Teenage concerns, Journal of School Health **31:** April, 1961.
16. Snepp, D. W.: An integrated guidance program in the high school, Bulletin of the National Association of Secondary Principals **34:** May, 1950.
17. Stoops, Emery, and Wahlquist, G. L.: Principles and Practices in Guidance, New York, 1958, McGraw-Hill Book Co., Inc.
18. Strang, Ruth: Every teacher's records, Bureau of Publications, Teachers College, Columbia University, New York, 1952.
19. Strang, Ruth: Techniques of counseling in regard to health programs, American Journal of Public Health **39:** July, 1949.

20. What is new in '52 for guidance and health? Coordinated Conferences on Guidance, Personnel Services, and Health Education, sponsored by the University of Wisconsin, Wisconsin Association of Educational and Vocational Guidance, Industrial and Education Counselors Association, The State Department of Public Instruction, The State Board of Vocational and Adult Education and The State Board of Health, July, 1952.
21. Wiebe, A. J.: High school guidance in 1970, Journal of Secondary Education 37: Jan., 1962.
22. Wheatley, G. M., and Hallock, G. T.: Health observation of school children, ed. 2, New York, 1956, McGraw-Hill Book Co., Inc.

Part II

FOUNDATIONS TO HEALTH TEACHING

Chapter 4

THE HEALTH
TEACHING PROGRAM

Individual needs and the demands of present-day society make it necessary for most people to make decisions concerning a lifetime occupation. For a few people the right or the ability to make occupational decisions is denied, but for most youth the time for decision arrives sometime between the fifteenth and twentieth year of life. The first such decision is not always the last, and even when final commitment is made, many youth are uncertain about their choice. Modern society is dynamic, complex, and changing. The number of career opportunities, which once were limited, today are seemingly numberless, and although several potential careers exist for every type of skill, ability, or personality, the possibility of making wrong decisions is high.

When a youth decides on a career of teaching, it is usually a generalized decision followed at some later date with the more specific choice of a subject area. Therefore, the first part of this chapter deals with the challenge offered by the teaching profession, and the second part considers the more specific challenge of health teaching as well as the place of health in the school curriculum and the various organizational plans for teaching health in the secondary school.

CHALLENGE OF TEACHING

Every year several thousand recent college graduates enter the teaching profession. At some point in the life of each beginning teacher a decision was made which in a general but final manner implied the following, "I have decided to make teaching my profession, and I will prepare myself for it." The how, why, and when of the decision to teach are crucial to the individual who makes it, to the teaching profession, and to the future of our country.

Decision to teach. Many studies have recently been completed in an effort to learn more about the factors that influence youth in selecting teaching as a career.

One such study was conducted with 488 students as subjects, 365 of them women and 123 men who were enrolled in a first year education course.* Among other questions, they were asked the age at which they first decided to become a teacher. For the women the answers ranged from 5 to 40 years of age, with a median age of 15.08 years. For the men the answers ranged from 10 to 28 years of age, with a median of 17.5 years. Another study was based on responses from 7000 beginning teachers.† The results indicate that 60% made the decision to teach between the junior year in high school and the sophomore year in college, whereas 16% decided prior to the junior year in high school and 24% some time after the sophomore year of college.

Once the choice of teaching as a career is made, the student is frequently confronted by a tremendous amount of social pressure from peer group members, parents, and favorite teachers concerning whether his decision is the wise one. The sum of these responses are likely to cause him (1) to change his mind, (2) to fluctuate between popular opinion and his own desires, or (3) to be reinforced in his decision. Results of one study show that 70% of the respondents reported unfavorable peer group reactions.‡ Typical responses of this group were the following: "You look like a teacher." "You're sick." "My classmates have told me that teaching just isn't for me, but I keep disagreeing with them."

In this same study, however, 82% of the respondents reported that parents reacted favorably, whereas 63% of other adults also reacted favorably. Surprisingly, only 48% of the experienced teachers approached offered a favorable reaction. Some responded by saying that the students should "set their sights a little higher." One student summed up the ambivalent teacher reactions in the following way, "In high school when I first thought about teaching and mentioned it to certain teachers, they didn't discourage me, but didn't really encourage me either."

Indifference and discouragement have challenged the teaching profession for centuries and find reinforcement in present circumstances. Because we are in the age of mass education, some persons subscribe to the thesis that it is necessarily also the age of mediocrity. Unfortunately, many persons who believe this are found on school boards and school committees and in other influential positions. Those who hold to this thesis contend that teaching is not an art, that it can be done by anyone, and that meaningful education is the fortune of those who wish to learn regardless of the ability of those teaching. Further, many people think that if science, philosophy, and other areas are really important, the relevant education is found in the institutions of higher learning; they feel that our "best" teachers belong there rather than in the public schools. The well-known Shavian statement "Those who can, do; those who can't, teach," summarizes well this unfortunate thinking.

But the age of mass education is also the age of science and enlightenment. Many leaders inside and also outside the field of teaching are asking such search-

---

*Riccio, A. C.: When do they decide to teach? Peabody Journal of Education 39: Sept., 1961.
†Editorial: Why do they teach? Overview 3: March, 1962.
‡Belok, M. V.: Social pressures and prospective teachers, Journal of Teacher Education 13: March, 1962.

ing questions as these: Are not our "best" teachers needed at all levels of the educational ladder? Can we settle for mediocrity in teaching and still keep pace with other cultures striving to get ahead? Need mass education result in mediocrity? Does not a free and open society have a responsibility to educate each citizen to the limit of his potential?

In the context of the present discussion we need to examine more closely the decision to teach.

Why teach? First, the decision to teach involves a desire to serve one's fellowman, although few persons are able to articulate this well when the decision is first made. Dedicated teachers, whom Cicero could have been describing when he said, "What greater or better gift can we offer the republic than to teach and instruct our youth?" have developed this philosophy and can express it with true feeling and belief. By contrast, the beginning education student is likely to express it in such terms as the following: "I like to work with other people." I'm interested in people, not money." "Teaching appeals to me." The young sophisticate is often embarrassed to go beyond this even though he has feelings which are every bit as genuine as the teachers he aspires to emulate.

Second, good teaching is of the utmost importance to the continuation and advancement of society. Aspersions are often made that link teaching to an ivory tower as if by this choice the teacher escapes the boresome responsibilities of life. Nothing could be farther from the facts. The practical bread-and-butter contributions made by the teacher in this scientific era rank far ahead of the contributions made by the Wall Street broker, the Madison Avenue advertiser, the Detroit assemblyman, or the Great Plains farmer.

Third, it must be said that a bona fide reason for teaching is because it is enjoyable. At times this fact seems extremely remote as, for example, when some students refuse to take part in the learning situation and are unruly and disrespectful, when the classes seem to get larger and larger with increased paper work and less time for individual student contacts, and when local taxpayers refuse requests for improved facilities, more equipment and staff members and larger salaries. In the face of all this and more, teaching is fun for those dedicated to it. There is a thrill in seeing a student grasp a new concept and assimilate it into his personality. There is a thrill for the teacher when a superior student wins a school contest in English composition, wins a debate against a rival school, or gets a scholarship at a university. These accomplishments are the teacher's "Christmas bonus" and help to salve the burns of conscience when other students are not quite as successful. The joys of teaching fall to the person who is able to build many small accomplishments into a successful lifetime of leading and encouraging others to fulfillment.

Fourth, persons who choose to teach do so because they believe that knowledge for its own sake is valuable and that the opportunity to help others see this is exciting. Learning should not stop at a specific commencement date. The teaching-scholar is thankful for the chance to broaden his own intellectual horizons. His quest for insight is infectious; he draws students along with him, many of them often learning without making a truly conscious effort to learn.

Responsibilities of the teacher. To elect to teach carries with it certain basic responsibilities, and one of the most important is implied in the last point mentioned. That is, the teacher should continue to learn throughout his teaching career. This means active participation in in-service programs, in which the greatest learning comes through personal contribution. Also, he should return to the classroom as a student himself, not only for required courses and credit, but also for some study that is of interest to him but not necessarily directly related to his academic responsibilities. Beyond this, he should communicate with his peers at professional meetings and through occasional publications.

The teacher should create an atmosphere in the classroom that makes learning not only possible but also efficient and effective. Important factors here are the mood of the teacher, the proper presentation of the material to be learned, a grasp of the prevailing attitudes of the class, and a recognition that other influences are competing for student interests.

Another responsibility of the teacher is to impart his learning to the student. Unless he is able to do this, he is not a good teacher. The phrase *master teacher* is often used to indicate native ability. Some teachers are naturally better than others, but much of successful teaching can be learned, practiced, and improved upon. One method by which teachers can improve is by determining the effectiveness of their teaching through the use of teacher rating forms which help to show some areas of strength and weakness in communication. It is surprising, when replies are anonymous, how astute and candid students will be. Several of these rating forms are available commercially.*

Finally, the teacher has the responsibility to conduct his own life in the manner he considers intelligent and by his example to encourage others to do likewise. Who has a greater obligation in this respect than the teacher of the health sciences.

CHALLENGE OF HEALTH TEACHING

Many educators, medical specialists, and laymen have questioned the place of health teaching in the schools at various times during the past few decades. Therefore, it is necessary for health educators and other persons interested in developing and maintaining acceptable and desirable health education programs in the schools to show clearly the need for extensive health teaching in all areas and levels of the school curriculum.

Why teach health? There are many things in the modern world that show very clearly the need for extensive knowledge of health and hygiene in maintaining individual and group health. A limited amount of thought, observation, and reflection concerning the health habits, practices, mistakes, and shortcomings of the adult population, particularly, makes it luminously clear that there is an urgent need for better education and understanding of health and healthful living if both individual and group health is to be improved and maintained on a basis commensurate with medical and scientific advancements in recent years.

---

*Teaching Appraisal Forms and Learning Appraisal Forms, Oregon State University Press, Corvallis. Ore.

The daily, monthly, and yearly statistics on national, state, and community bases concerning illness and death bring prominently to our attention the need for greater effort on the part of the individual and the group in not only reducing unnecessary illness and death but also improving and maintaining a high level of positive health among all segments of our population.

The rapid advancements in science, medicine, and public health make it necessary that the individual have sufficient knowledge to take advantage of and to understand and to make wise selections and decisions concerning the most recent developments.

The extensive and ever-growing amount of local, state, national, and international legislation pertaining to public health and medical care involving millions of dollars of tax money makes it necessary that the individual voter be able to understand the issues involved in order to participate intelligently in the democratic process. In this respect the public is frequently called upon to support pending legislation sponsored by medical and public health experts. Some modern legislation of this nature may be so extensive that it may tax the ability of the community, state, or nation to pay for it. Certainly, from the financial viewpoint of the taxpayer, the voting citizen must be well informed regarding health and hygiene needs. Also, laws pertaining to the maintenance of community public health departments, qualifications of health and medical specialists, and compulsory health insurance depend upon the knowledge and intelligence of millions of people comprising the voting group of communities and states throughout the country.

The gullibility of the public in spending millions of dollars each year on unnecessary and often harmful treatments, drugs, vitamins, and patient medicines shows a need for better understanding of health and healthful living. Also, reports from national nutrition groups state that approximately one-half billion dollars each year is spent by the American public on various kinds of food fads. In this case not only is the waste of money involved, but also many of the food fads and diets lead to malnutrition, ill health, and suffering for a gullible individual who follows advertising and incorrect advice suggesting the use of medication and faulty diets.

There is a need for greater health knowledge in preparing people to make the best and most intelligent use of available health services. Studies pertaining to the use of individual and group health services seem to show that there is a direct relationship between the level of knowledge and understanding of health and healthful living and the proper use of available health services.

The increasing number of both children and adults who are neurotic about their health points to another reason for better health education. It is frequently said that the number of people neurotic about their health increases almost in direct proportion to the amount and extent of *unorganized* and *haphazard* health instruction given to both children and adults.

The recent discoveries and developments in the area of the relationship of the emotions and physical health are extremely important in attaining and maintaining good health in the modern day. This rapid development in psychosomatic medicine brings to light one of the main reasons why it is so difficult for the individual to maintain optimum health under the stresses, strains, and tensions of present-day life. It is now known that a host of physical disorders are psychogenic in origin. That is, they are basically caused and brought on by the emotions. Furthermore, most illnesses which are physical in origin can become highly complicated by the emotions to a point at which recovery is greatly handicapped.

Specialists skilled in the science of psychosomatic medicine state that the more knowledge and understanding the individual has about the close relationship of emotional and physical health the easier it is to help either the child or the adult to recover and regain good health following a physical disorder brought on by the emotions.

But most of this has been a listing of adult ills. What meaning does this have for the secondary school? Does the secondary school have the responsibility to include health in its curriculum? Others have asked these questions and have turned to research for the answer. If health and safety problems prevail on the secondary school level, the educational system has the responsibility to correct this, else many students will become accident statistics, gullible food fadists, or neurotic health problems in their early adult years.

One study, limited in sample yet extremely meaningful, has been made to determine the prevalence of certain harmful health and safety misconceptions among a group of tenth grade girls.* When a health information inventory was administered, it was found that 25% or more of the girls subscribed to 111 of 126 harmful health and safety misconceptions. The information in tables 2 through 5 indicate these misconceptions and gives the percentage of girls who thought that the statements were true or sometimes true. A careful perusal of the information in these tables will reveal that there is good reason for serious concern.

Several other studies similar to the misconception study just discussed appear in the references at the end of this chapter. They, too, show the need for health education on the junior and senior high school levels.

There is little doubt that health education belongs in our secondary schools and that it can give deep satisfaction for those who teach it. The fact is, however, that when and how health education will be presented have been and still are deeply controversial.

Why is there a gap between the teaching and practice of health? In order to properly understand the place of health education in the schools, it may be helpful to consider briefly what has been done in the past and what is being done now. For many years some educators have considered health education an important part of the school program. During the past two or three decades in particular, health education has been offered in many secondary schools under varying circumstances. Unfortunately, in a majority of the schools in which health education was a part of the program the conditions under which health teaching was conducted were not particularly conducive to good results.

---

*Dzenowagis, Joseph G., McPherson, P. V., and Irwin, Leslie W.: Harmful health and safety misconceptions of a group of tenth grade girls, Journal of School Health 24: Nov., 1954.

Table 2. Prevalence of certain extremely harmful health and safety misconceptions among group of tenth-grade girls

	Extremely harmful health and safety misconceptions	*% T and ST*
1.	A person having a stomachache should usually take a laxative	62
2.	A person always comes up to the top of the water three times before he drowns	54
3.	The only good way to help a drowning person is to jump into the water and save him	54
4.	The best doctors always promise to make people healthy	54
5.	A bullet cannot go off unless it is fired by a gun	50
6.	All mad dogs foam at the mouth	46
7.	Bicycle riders should ride on the left side of the road to be safe	46
8.	It is usually safe to go swimming alone if you know how to swim	46
9.	It is a good idea to make an unconscious person drink something	36
10.	Most types of mental sicknesses cannot be helped by any treatment	36
11.	It is impossible to cure any cancer	30
12.	Oil, grease, and gas fires should be put out with plenty of water	28
13.	It is best to go to doctors who advertise in the newspapers	26
14.	It is all right to point a gun at someone if you are sure it is not loaded	26

Table 3. Prevalence of certain very harmful health and safety misconceptions among group of tenth-grade girls

	Very harmful health and safety misconceptions	*% T and ST*
1.	There are certain cough medicines that will cure or prevent the common cold	86
2.	People who exercise a lot live longer than other people	76
3.	There are some pills that people can take which will cure the common cold	72
4.	It is always impossible for a person with cramps to swim	70
5.	Any food that does not smell or taste spoiled is safe to eat	68
6.	Iodine is the best treatment for wounds caused by stepping on rusty nails	62
7.	Spring water that is clear and cold is always safe for drinking	60
8.	People should walk on the right hand side of the road if there are no sidewalks	60
9.	If you have any disease or sickness, you will always feel some pain	58
10.	All people with rosy complexions are very healthy	58
11.	Every disease needs a drug or medicine for its cure	56
12.	A great deal of exercise can never hurt anyone	56
13.	Persons can clean their blood by eating certain foods	54
14.	All radio advertising about what is good or bad for your health is true	48
15.	All persons should take laxatives whenever they are constipated	46
16.	Most people who get tuberculosis will die in a short time	46
17.	The best way to get a tan is by sleeping in the sun	42
18.	Measles is never harmful	40
19.	Mental illness usually happens suddenly	38
20.	There are special laxatives that will help prevent or cure the common cold	36
21.	All advertising on television about what is good or bad for health is true	36
22.	Most fat people are very healthy	36
23.	Most illnesses are caused by constipation	34
24.	Fresh raw milk is better food for your health than pasteurized milk	32
25.	Most accidents cannot be prevented	32
26.	All health advertisements in papers and magazines are true	26
27.	All children with heart murmurs will surely have heart trouble later on in life	26
28.	A good way to treat frostbite is to rub the frostbitten part with snow	26
29.	Everyone should take a laxative once a week	26
30.	A good safety rule for bicycle riders is the following: Ride on the sidewalk as much as possible	26

Table 4. Prevalence of certain moderately harmful health and safety misconceptions among group of tenth-grade girls

Moderately harmful health and safety misconceptions	*% T and ST*
1. Brushing your teeth every day is a sure way of stopping decay	92
2. Everyone who has weak feet should wear arch supports to strengthen them	90
3. A daily bowel movement is always necessary for a person to stay healthy	86
4. Nose drops will cure a cold which is causing a stuffy nose	82
5. The only good treatment for weak arches is to have arch supports placed in the shoes	80
6. Wearing bathing hats or ear plugs while swimming will give a person complete protection for his ears	74
7. Sugar diabetes is caused by eating too much sugar	72
8. Persons who have pimples or boils usually have bad blood	68
9. All persons should use nose drops and mouthwashes daily when they have a cold	64
10. Wearing eyeglasses will always make a person's eyes stronger	64
11. Most fat people are happy and jolly	64
12. The best way to treat a black eye is to put a piece of raw meat on it	62
13. The use of tooth powders and toothpastes is sure to make a person's gums firm	62
14. There are some pills that people can take which will prevent the common cold	60
15. Eating between meals causes most children to have bad health	60
16. You can be sure anything a scientist says about health is true	58
17. Wearing sunglasses will give your eyes complete protection from the sun	56
18. The use of skin creams and lotions will make any skin clear and healthy	56
19. Taking vitamin pills will guarantee good health	54
20. Bad breath can be stopped for good by using special mouthwashes	54
21. The use of skin lotion is a healthful way to make any skin beautiful	54
22. Most cases of baldness can be cured if treated early	50
23. The vitamins in certain pills are better than the vitamins in natural foods	50
24. Most persons who look thin are certain to be underweight and in poor health	50
25. Any exercise is bad for persons who have heart trouble	46
26. Pain near the heart is generally a sign of heart disease	40
27. Exercising regularly is a sure way to prevent disease	40
28. Taking vitamin pills is the best way to get your necessary vitamins	40
29. The only way to lose weight is by exercising	40
30. Missing a bowel movement for one day is always a sign of constipation	38
31. Good doctors usually advertise	38
32. Mouthwashes are sure to prevent or cure diseases of the mouth and throat	38
33. Any person who feels all right is sure to be in good health	38
34. Expensive food is always the best food to eat	38
35. If your eyes do not hurt, you can be sure they are healthy	38
36. Good health does not depend on what you eat	36
37. Food that tastes good is usually bad for your health	34
38. The first and best thing to do in caring for a cold is to take a laxative	32
39. People can never change their food likes and dislikes	32
40. A cold can usually be cured by eating raw onions	30
41. Most colds can be cured by taking vitamin pills	30
42. Wanting to eat candy and sweets is always a sign that your body needs sugar	30
43. It is very hard for thin persons to keep from getting tuberculosis	28
44. Bananas should be kept out of a good diet because they are hard to digest	28
45. An all-vegetable diet is the natural and best diet	26
46. You can always tell if a dog is friendly by his looks	26

Table 5. Prevalence of certain slightly harmful health and safety misconceptions among group of tenth-grade girls

Slightly harmful health and safety misconceptions	% T and ST
1. A mouthwash is healthful because it helps kill germs in the mouth and throat	80
2. Cutting or shaving a person's hair makes it grow faster and thicker	76
3. The use of tooth powders or toothpastes will always cure a person's bad breath	70
4. Most colds can be prevented by taking vitamin pills	56
5. Any person who sees clearly can be sure he doesn't need glasses	56
6. A pain in your right side usually means that you have appendicitis	54
7. It is a bad health habit to drink water while you exercise	48
8. Men with large muscles are always healthier than men with small muscles	48
9. Anyone who keeps his skin clean will never have pimples	48
10. Some people are born lucky	46
11. Persons can always prevent pimples by eating more raw foods	46
12. Everyone who is on a diet is trying to lose weight	44
13. There are no living germs in pasteurized milk	40
14. To go on a diet always means to eat less food	40
15. Fish is a food that is very good for the brain	38
16. People should protect themselves from catching cold by gargling with a mouthwash	38
17. People should eat only when they feel hungry	36
18. Friday the thirteenth is an unlucky day for most people	36
19. People are born with their food likes and dislikes	32
20. Most dogs do not remember the people who are mean to them	30
21. Using a toothpick is the best way to get things from between your teeth	28

The trial-and-error methods of teaching health in the past have revealed the difficulty in getting the proper attitudes and practices established. Consequently, there have been many criticisms by educators of the ways, methods, and means by which health has been taught. Frequently, one may hear a few educators say that health education cannot be justified if the students fail to form proper attitudes and proper health habits immediately following teaching. It should be clearly understood that a main purpose of health teaching, especially on the secondary level, is to impart knowledge regardless of whether proper attitudes and habits are immediately formed. It is granted at once, of course, that it is highly important to develop proper habits and attitudes, and strong emphasis should be placed on this phase of the program. There is no justification, however, for withholding knowledge concerning health and healthful living from students, even though the most desirable attitudes and practices are not immediately established following health teaching. There is no certain way of knowing just when students begin to practice desirable health habits following teaching. For example, senior high school students may be taught safe driving practices and the appropriate attitudes. Some will prove to be excellent drivers immediately, others will not demonstrate completely safe habits and attitudes until later, and a few perhaps never will. Nevertheless, the chances are great that if students never receive information regarding safe driving, they are not likely ever to give sufficient attention to it.

It should be kept in mind by teachers that following teaching some students may start at once to put into practice the most desirable health teachings in all situations. In other cases some students may practice proper habits a part of the time, particularly when circumstances are favorable, and in still other cases some of the students may not form the most desirable health habits and practices for some time following teaching. In some cases perhaps some of the students will never form the proper habits regardless of the knowledge they may gain through teaching. This, of course, is true of all learning and not just of health education.

A main point to be drawn from this discussion is that if students never receive instruction in health and healthful living the chances are great that they are not likely to ever give attention to and establish proper habits and practices. It follows then that knowledge is primary and basic. The students must be taught about health and healthful living; otherwise, there is little hope that they will ever develop the habits, attitudes, practices, and appreciations necessary to assist them in their life goals. They need this background to lead the good and full life.

It should be kept in mind that health knowledge and information are only a part of the process of helping students to establish proper habits, attitudes, practices, and appreciations. However, it is extremely difficult to form habits and attitudes without the proper knowledge and understanding. The statement of an able psychologist concerning learning applies in this case. He said, "By learning we may live better or worse but we are sure to live according to what we learn." Even though sound knowledge of health and healthful living does not assure the formation of habits and attitudes, without such knowledge there is little or no hope for improvement in habit formation and practices.

The question often is raised as to why it is so extremely difficult to get a large majority of youth to form the proper and correct health habits. On first consideration it would seem that with proper emphasis and motivation during teaching most of them should form the correct practices almost at once. One main reason why it is so difficult for the teacher to get immediate results is that a large part of teaching is dissipated when the students mingle in adult society. The students come in contact with adults who fail to observe even the most fundamental health practices. The example set by adults tends to minimize the importance and the need for proper health habits in the minds of youth. Too, the home conditions of some students are such that it is next to impossible to follow the teachings of healthful living.

Another point that should be kept in mind in attempting to get the proper health attitudes and habits established is that the laws and rules of health and hygiene can be too rigid. There come times in the lives of all of us when it is necessary to momentarily forego what we know is the best health practice. This holds true for both adults and students. For example, if because of some emergency situation such as illness in the family a person fails to get sufficient sleep, it would perhaps be best for his health if he could take time from his daily duties to get sufficient sleep. However, in many situations it would be impossible for him to take time from his daily duties to practice what he knows would be the best for his health. It is evident then that there are times in the lives of all people when it is a question of selecting and doing the best under the circumstances, even though it is not the best for the health of the individual.

HEALTH EDUCATION IN THE SCHOOL CURRICULUM

It was indicated in Chapter 1 that the need for health education in our schools today is almost universally recognized and accepted. There are, of course, many persons who oppose it, but nonetheless a majority of educators feel that health belongs in the curriculum. One of the main problems, however, is finding the place and the time for it. Examination of most school curriculums show that the school day is overcrowded with many subject matter areas in competition for time, space, staff, and money. The newer areas including health education are less able to compete than the more traditional areas. Persons responsible for health teaching are under continual pressure to improve content and methods and to develop accurate evaluation tools in order to justify a place in the sun.

A more complete presentation of placement, scheduling, content, and evaluation is the subject of the next three chapters. Of immediate concern here are the ways in which health subject matter is presented. Health instruction may be direct, correlated, integrated, or incidental.

Direct health instruction. The direct method of health instruction has proved by far to be the most satisfactory. Only through planned sequential teaching are students assured of receiving the breadth of health subject matter so vital to their well-being. Most of the methods, techniques, and procedures of health education in this book pertain to the direct method of health instruction.

Correlated health instruction. Correlation teaching has been defined as a course of study in which textual references or specific suggestions are made for relating materials in one subject field with pertinent materials in other subject fields.* Correlated teaching is most effective on the elementary level where the self-contained classroom still prevails, and it is perhaps unrealistic to expect that special subject matter teachers in the high school will develop health correlation techniques. Teaching by correlation requires sufficient background in the health sciences to build confidence as well as extensive preplanning of the desired correlated unit. Beyond these, there is the matter of teacher distinterest in and resistance to health correlation which may or may not be entirely or partially overcome by in-service sessions keyed to health.

Some subjects correlate more closely to health than others. A recent report has summarized some of the opportunities for correlating health with other subject areas.† In Table 6 are shown three subjects that correlate quite closely and in Table 7 are listed some of the items for which correlation is possible in three of the more remote subjects. The main purpose of this brief listing is to point

---

*Good, C. V., editor: The dictionary of education, New York, 1945, McGraw-Hill Book Co., Inc.
†Sliepcevich, Elena M., and Carroll, Charles R.: The correlation of health with other areas of the high school curriculum, Journal of School Health **28:** Nov., 1958.

Table 6. Possible items for health correlation in three closely related high school subjects*

Biological science
1. Cellular development and the formation of tissues and organs as related to physical growth
2. Scientific methods vs. superstition in treatment of diseases
3. Relation of genetics to human development and health
4. Biology of infectious disease, body immunity, and disease control
5. Communicable diseases and methods of control; antibodies
6. Basic structure and functions of animals, particularly mammals
7. Consideration of basic functions of digestion, assimilation, elimination, respiration and irritability
8. Aspects of sexual development; reproduction as exhibited in plants and animals
9. Sources of food—their processing and relation to good health
10. Protection and purification of water, milk, and foods
11. Body care as insurance for good health
12. Effects of alcohol, narcotics, and tobacco on the human organism
13. Danger involved in self-medication and need to seek appropriate medical attention
14. Survey of common injuries and emergency first aid measures
15. School and community health services; local, national, and international health agencies and their functions

Chemistry
1. Relation of fats, carbohydrates, and proteins to nutrition
2. Chemotherapy and disease treatment
3. Usefulness of antiseptics, anesthetics, and insecticides
4. Chemistry of detergents and other cleansing agents
5. Importance of water for proper body function; water purification methods and softening of water
6. Osmosis applied to physiological function
7. Colloidal chemistry as related to medicinal preparation and the precipitation of smoke impurities
8. Biological principle of the oxygen tent and the uses of oxygen relative to health
9. Physiology of the bends
10. Radioactive substances for disease control and the tracers in biochemistry
11. Relation between addition of fluorides to drinking water and dental health
12. Precautions in handling and use of chemicals, chemical apparatus, glass tubing, and thistle tubes
13. Laboratory safety, emphasizing precautions against fires and explosions; treatment of burns and cuts
14. Chemical analysis of the human body, and of common foodstuffs

Home economics
1. Relationship between proper diet and fitness
2. Sources of foods, their storage, processing and preparation
3. Sanitation of the cooking area; health of the cook; Typhoid Mary
4. Home nursing and child care
5. Safety in the kitchen and the prevention of accidents in the home
6. Importance of pasteurization of milk; proper methods of canning to preserve foods; examples and causes of food poisoning epidemics
7. Federal Food, Drug, and Cosmetic Act and its provisions
8. Value of personal grooming and social graces
9. Acquaintance with basic first aid procedures
10. Selection and proper wearing of clothes
11. Home management—ventilation, heating, planning, recreation, and marketing
12. Common problems of marriage and personality adjustment
13. Consideration of forming appropriate boy-girl relationships; courtship and marriage
14. Effect of decorating schemes and colors on human emotions

*Adapted from Sliepcevich, Elena M., and Carroll, Charles R.: The correlation of health with other areas of the high school curriculum, Journal of School Health 28: Nov., 1958.

Table 7. Possible items for health correlation in three less closely related high school subjects*

English and speech

1. Emphasis on health vocabulary and spelling of common health terms
2. Composition of essays and themes on health topics, especially current problems concerning health matters
3. Library reference and research on specific health topics, socialized medicine, and fluoridation of water; function of health agencies
4. Use of health heroes as subjects for biographical sketches
5. Oral reports and debates relative to health, personal adjustment, and group living
6. Writing of original health slogans, plays, and radio and television scripts in connection with local health drives and campaigns
7. Making adjustments through speaking with emphasis on getting along with others and with oneself; public relations
8. Explanation of normal change in male's voice at puberty, a secondary sex characteristic
9. Cultivation of reading as a means of relaxation and recreation
10. Use of selected reading lists based on books with a health or medical theme as a means of stimulating career interests

Mathematics

1. Calculation of statistical probabilities by projecting health data
2. Computing birth, illness, accident, and mortality rates
3. Mathematical relationships between illness and absences
4. Cost of illness, medical expenses, and hospital services
5. The use of statistics, such as population, life expectations, and stages of human growth to construct graphs, curves, and correlations

Problems of democracy

1. Study of official and voluntary agencies and their function in public health; U. S. Public Health Service and local health department
2. Functions of health officers, health commissioner, coroners, inspectors, and sanitation directors
3. Knowledge of available community health services
4. Consideration of health activities of clubs, labor organizations, and various other societies
5. Analysis of recreational facilities available in community
6. Legal requirements for driving, use of fire arms, and installation of certain machines and apparatus
7. Health status of community and nation
8. Study and discussion of current health legislation; fluoridation, socialized medicine, etc.
9. Discussion of family health problems; advisability of voluntary health insurance; cost of medical care
10. Health problems of nation's elder citizens
11. Relation of slum areas to physical and mental health
12. Sociological aspects of disability and disease
13. Effect of city zoning in promotion of community health
14. Problems of community sanitation and efforts to control communicable disease; inspection and adequate waste and sewage disposal
15. Importance of food preservation in interstate and international commerce
16. Health regulations and inspections relative to international travel

---

*Adapted from Sliepcevich, Elena M., and Carroll, Charles R.: The correlation of health with other areas of the high school curriculum, Journal of School Health 28:9, Nov., 1958.

out that most subject matter areas in the high school do relate to life and health, and the classroom teacher should strive at all times to make obscure subject matter meaningful to the everyday problems which the students face.

There is no question that correlation should continue in the school program and that health education should be correlated with other subjects and that it should be a reciprocal procedure. In certain of the areas such as the biological sciences a certain amount of correlation is evident regardless of whether it has been planned for. It remains for the teacher to place enough emphasis on the natural relationships between other subjects and health education to make it effective.

A word of caution is necessary. It has been learned through experience that the broad area of health knowledge cannot be imparted entirely by correlation means. If this is attempted, then there is not sufficient time left in the other subject matter areas to impart the relevant information. In other words, with all the correlation that can possibly be done with the related courses in the school curriculum, there remains a need for direct health teaching courses in order to properly educate youth in health for adult life.

Integrated health instruction. One difference between integration and correlation is that the integration of learning experiences centers around a core or group objective. However, it should be recognized at once that the term integration has been used in a number of ways in its application to the school curriculum. It has sometimes been used to refer to the procedure of integrating materials within a subject matter field. It has also been used to indicate the integration of the student as a whole. Then, the broader application and use of the term *integration* has had to do with the integration of the total school curriculum, as stated in *Education for All American Youth.** In this sense integration sometimes means the tendency toward the elimination of subject matter areas as such into a broader whole and on a problem basis. It is in this sense that teaching health through integration has been used most frequently—that is, the attempt to integrate health throughout all school areas, whether or not there are subject matter lines and division. There is a need for the integration of health materials in all school experiences. It should be planned for, the same as in other areas.

As with correlation, however, experience has shown that attempts to teach health *only* by integration have not been sufficient to impart the broad area of information the student should have for adult life. Furthermore, the teaching of health by integration through such procedures as the core curriculum shows that much of the teaching is left to chance and might be termed accidental, depending upon whether or not in the process of studying the greater areas problems of health will arise in sufficient numbers to give the proper amount of education and background. When plans for integrating the entire school curriculum are developed to the point at which they are considered successful enough to eliminate the subject matter areas, then perhaps health education will have

*Educational Policies Commission: Education for all American youth, a further look, Washington, D. C., 1952, National Education Association.

developed within the framework sufficiently so that the health knowledge of the students can be completed entirely on an integration basis.

Incidental health instruction. This approach to health teaching has been variously described as opportunistic teaching and taking advantage of the teachable moment. Meaningful experiences, joyous occasions, and traumatic events tend to be remembered for long periods of time. A wise teacher will take advantage of these when they occur to present a vignette of teaching which relates the important health principles. The physical education teacher is in an excellent position to develop this type of teaching as, for example, with injuries and menstrual hygiene, but all teachers should be alert to possibilities.

HEALTH TEACHING IN THE JUNIOR HIGH SCHOOL

The various plans of organization for education must be taken into account in the process of establishing the best possible health education programs in the junior high school grades. The traditional plan of organization in which the seventh and eighth grades are a part of the elementary school is still used in this country. The more modern junior high school plan which employs special teachers and which is organized along the lines similar to the high school is another established type of organization for students in the seventh, eighth, and ninth grades. Between the traditional organization in which the seventh and eighth grades are organized as a part of the elementary school and the more modern junior high school plan, there exists numerous ways of organizing education for students at this level. In some cases, a modified junior high school plan is used in which the seventh and eighth grades only are organized on a junior high school basis. The specialized subject fields are then handled accordingly, with specialized teachers in charge of the work. In some other schools the traditional classroom teacher organization continues but certain areas and fields of education are taught and handled on a specialized basis.

A more recent development in educational organization which affects the junior high school grades is the six-four-four plan. In this type of organization the first six grades of the elementary school form one unit, the seventh, eighth, ninth, and tenth grades form a second unit, and the eleventh, twelfth, thirteenth, and fourteenth grades form the third unit. The thirteenth and fourteenth grades correspond to the junior college level.

The plan of education in operation at the junior high school level in any community affects to some extent the organization and conduct of the health education program. In the more modern plan of junior high school education in which the teachers are specialized more along the lines of the high school teacher, it is possible to employ teachers who have had some specialized training in health education. It may be possible, particularly in some of the larger junior high schools, to have the services of health educators. In most schools, though, the responsibility for teaching health in direct teaching courses is more likely to be taken by science teachers, home economics teachers, physical education teachers, or other teachers who have had some basic preparation which tends to qualify them for the work. It should be mentioned at this point, though, that neither science teachers, physical education teachers, nor home economics teachers are qualified to teach the health education courses in the junior high school unless they have had specific preparation in health education.

In a majority of those schools in which the seventh and eighth grades remain a part of the elementary school, the classroom teacher will have to be responsible for teaching health the same as in other grades of the elementary school.

In the six-four-four plan of education the second unit is usually recognized as the high school level. In a majority of those communities in which this plan of organization is in operation usually there are sufficient resources to employ health specialists to assume responsibility for the health teaching program. There should be health educators on the faculties of these schools if at all possible to coordinate the health work and to teach the health education courses.

Most of the health teaching carried on at the junior high school level should be done through direct teaching courses. The health courses should be given sufficient time in the curriculum, and they should be conducted on the same basis as other school subjects if they are to be most successful. In addition to the health courses offered on a semester or yearly basis, there should be correlation and integration of health through other school subjects such as science, social studies, home economics, and physical education. One of the most successful ways of correlating and integrating health education through other school subjects is by the use of definitely planned units whereby the health factors are clearly evident.

In planning health education at the junior high school level, the previous education and background of the students should be taken into account. If the students have had the advantage of a broad program of health education in the elementary school grades, health education materials in the junior high school should be of an advanced nature. Overlapping of health content should be as carefully controlled in a junior high school as in an elementary school. If overlapping occurs in a form that is more than a brief review of the previously presented material, the students are likely to become bored and lose interest in health, which creates an unsatisfactory learning situation.

It is recommended for the junior high school level that the cycle plan described in Chapter 6 be used to prevent overlapping of health materials from one grade to another rather than attempt to teach all areas and units every year.

It is usually thought best that if at all possible a health education course be given at each grade at the junior high school level.

In ordinary circumstances the content of the health courses in the junior high school should be advanced study and exploration of many of the units offered in the upper grades of the elementary school. Usually, there should be a more intensive study of the fundamentals of hygiene and physiology in the junior high school grades in order that the students will have sufficient background to understand and appreciate somewhat more advanced health and hygiene materials. Also, there should be some time given to an introduction and study of community health and hygiene, particularly in the upper grades of the junior high school.

HEALTH TEACHING IN THE HIGH SCHOOL

It is extremely important to have a well-organized health teaching program at the high school level because the majority of the students will not have an opportunity for organized instruction of any kind after graduation from high school. It is the duty of persons directly in charge of the high schools to be certain that the health education of the students is as complete as possible by the time they graduate from high school. The plans and methods used in attempting to complete the health knowledge of students in preparing them for adult life depend materially upon the extent and background of health knowledge of the students when they enter the high school. Experience shows that students enter high school with widely varying backgrounds of knowledge in health and hygiene. If complete and comprehensive health instruction is given in elementary and junior high schools, the task of completing the education of the students in health in high school would be materially simplified. However, at the present time a high percentage of students reach high school lacking the health knowledge and information they should have acquired in the elementary and junior high schools.

The health courses in the high school should be organized on a semester or a yearly basis. It is usually recommended that at least one course be given at the ninth or tenth grade level and a more advanced course be given in the eleventh or twelfth grade. In some cases health specialists have recommended that a health education course on a yearly or semester basis be given at each grade at the high school level. This, perhaps, would be an ideal situation, but in most schools throughout the country time has not been made available for so much health teaching. Although a few schools have offered health courses at all grade levels in the high school, it is the exception rather than the rule. As a matter of fact, if a direct teaching course in health education is offered at the lower grades of the high school and another at the upper grades, there is no great need for health courses at all grade levels, provided that the students have had a satisfactory background in health in elementary and junior high school.

In the past, one common way in which health education was organized in the high schools was to alot a certain number of regular school periods each week to health and physical education. Then a part of the time was devoted to physical activities and a part to health teaching. An example of this was in those schools in which five class periods each week were given to health and physical education and in which two or three periods were devoted to health teaching and two or three to physical activities. When health and physical education were organized as a unit, it was usually the duty of the teacher of physical education to do the health teaching. This arrangement was sometimes satisfactory so far as the health teaching was concerned, provided that the physical education teacher had sufficient background, preparation, experience, and interest in health education. In many cases physical education teachers lack sufficient preparation in teaching methods of the kind necessary to conduct health classes satisfactorily and on a basis comparable to other academic courses.

The plan in which health and physical education are combined is not recommended because in the present day it seems best to completely separate physical education from health education as far as teaching is concerned and organize the health courses similarly to the way other academic courses are organized. Furthermore, because physical education teachers very often are not qualified to teach health education and because frequently they are not interested, the health education courses are far more likely to be successful if a teacher specifically prepared in health education is assigned to teach the courses.

There has been a misunderstanding concerning the qualifications of physical education teachers to teach health in past years. It should be kept in mind that of the more than 500 schools in the United States educating and preparing physical education teachers perhaps not more than 75 of these schools properly prepare teachers to teach both physical education and health education. It is estimated that approximately 75% of the physical education teachers in the United States have neither the background of training nor the experience to teach health education courses successfully. Some physical education teachers can teach health successfully, and they are now doing so, but these teachers are usually from the schools in which they have received a background of education and training which has prepared them more adequately to teach health. However, because in a large majority of the schools throughout the United States the physical education teacher must teach the health courses if they are taught at all, teacher education institutions for many years to come should try to properly prepare physical education teachers to teach health courses.

Perhaps the most satisfactory arrangement in the health teaching program in the high school is to have the courses taught by a health educator. In the absence of a health educator other health specialists such as physicians, nurses, science teachers, and home economics teachers may be assigned the duty of teaching health and hygiene. However, this arrangement is not wholly satisfactory because physicians and nurses, the same as many physical education teachers, lack education, training, and teaching methods of the kind so necessary for conducting health classes on a basis similar to other school subjects.

Perhaps the best solution to the problem of personnel to successfully teach health and hygiene courses in the high schools is to prepare sufficient health educators to accept the responsibility. A few health educators are now being prepared at the undergraduate level in some colleges in the United States. However, it will be many years before they are available in sufficient numbers to take the responsibility for a major part of the health teaching in the secondary schools.

A word of caution should perhaps be given here concerning the minimum amount of time that should be allotted to the health education courses. A common practice in the past has been to devote one class period weekly to health teaching. Experience with this over a period of many years has shown that it is not successful in a large majority of the schools in which it has been tried. Unsuccessful attempts to teach health on a one-day-a-week basis is one reason why many school administrators have been dissatisfied with the health courses. One of the main difficulties in the one meeting period per week for the health courses is that periods are so far apart that all continuity of instruction is likely to be lost from one class meeting to another. Under such circumstances it is extremely difficult for a teacher to organize and present materials on a basis comparable to other school subjects. So, very often the one-period-per-week health course turns out to be a period in which it is necessary for the teacher to try to do something to entertain the students in one way or another because it is practically impossible to do the proper kind of teaching.

The phases of health to be included and stressed at the high school level should be in advance of the program given in the junior high school. Some more intensive study of basic physiology and hygiene in relation to healthful living as well as to community hygiene is recommended for high school students. In connection with the teaching of physiology it should be remembered that the pure physiology courses at the high school level were common at the turn of the century. Largely because of the teaching methods used and the uninteresting features of the subject, physiology courses as such gradually passed out of the curriculum. The physiology included in modern health education courses should be more or less limited and largely for the purpose of preparing the students to understand health and hygiene.

At the high school level, as at other levels, precautions should be taken to prevent overlapping of health content. Again at the high school level the plan of arranging materials on a cycle basis is sometimes used. Ordinarily, however, it does not make too much difference at the high school level whether health materials are on a cycle basis or otherwise, for usually the study is far in advance of the health content presented in the junior high school.

There are certain things connected with the teaching of health courses that should be avoided. In past years as well as at the present time it has been a practice in some schools to have extremely large health classes. This situation has ordinarily come about because the health teaching program has been closely connected with physical education. For example, in many schools throughout the country students from all grades in the high school may be found in one physical education class. Furthermore, the classes in physical education sometimes have as many as 150 or more students. It is evident at once then that a classroom instruction course cannot be conducted successfully on such a basis. If the health teacher is expected to take the total physical education class with the mixture of students from the various grade levels on alternating days with physical education, it is readily evident that successful health teaching cannot be done under the circumstances.

Another condition that has been responsible for poor health teaching is that in which a physical education teacher attempts to teach health to a class only on days when the weather is too inclement to be outdoors for physical education. It is evident at once that under such conditions the teacher cannot plan the proper kind of a health teaching program and conduct it any more successfully in health education than he could for other academic subjects, in which such a situation would not be tolerated.

In the absence of direct health teaching courses, some health education has been done on a limited basis in areas such as social studies, general science, home economics, biology, and other related courses. In some cases, special health units have been included in other courses. The health units in related courses can be successful. However, it should be realized that there is not much chance of covering the field of health education as it should be by placing isolated units in other subject matter fields. Experience with this plan throughout the country has shown that it is practically impossible to include sufficient health materials in science instruction or other related courses to prepare the students properly for adult life. It has been shown that if a science teacher attempts to present the amount of health materials the students should have, he has practically no time left for teaching science.

QUESTIONS FOR DISCUSSION

1. List the criteria you consider important in selecting a lifetime occupation. Have you consciously or unconsciously used any of these in arriving at your decision to enter the teaching profession?
2. What are the positive values of the teaching profession? Do you feel there are negative values? If so, what are they?
3. What responsibilities go with the decision to teach?
4. A successful teacher needs several characteristics. List and discuss a few of these. What are a few negative characteristics?
5. Why must we be content at present to impart sound knowledge and understanding of health rather than to insist upon immediate improvement in health attitudes and practices in all cases?
6. Little has been said up to this point about the values of direct health teaching. Before proceeding further, what do you think are its advantages and disadvantages?
7. Does the study of misconceptions among tenth grade girls appear valid to you?
8. What difficulties arise when health courses are combined with physical education at the high school level? With science?
9. Who should be responsible for the teaching of health at the high school level?
10. List what you consider to be the advantages and disadvantages of correlated, integrated, and incidental teaching.
11. How would you concisely describe the philosophy of a person dedicated to teaching health education on the secondary school level?

SUGGESTED CLASS ACTIVITIES

1. Discuss each class member's decision to teach. Consider such points as when it was made, precipitating events, opposition to the decision by other persons, and doubts, both past and present, if any. Summarize.
2. Ask several respected teachers for the reasons they decided to teach and why they remain in teaching.
3. As a class, develop your own teacher appraisal form. Write for some sample copies of those available commercially and compare them with the form you develop.
4. Discuss the crucial question of how to make health teaching meaningful and how to reduce the gap between teaching and practice. Keep notes of your discussion and see if you are more certain of your ability in this respect at the end of the course.
5. Debate the virtues of direct health teaching versus correlation and integration.
6. Select several courses in the high school curriculum other than those in Tables 6 and 7 and suggest items of potential correlation.

REFERENCES

1. Anderson, G. W.: Health education—a one-world challenge, Journal of Public Health **50:** Feb., 1960.
2. Davis, L. B.: Integrating health education, Journal of Health, Physical Education, and Recreation **26:** Nov., 1955.

3. Dzenowagis, J. G., McPherson, P. V., and Irwin, L. W.: Harmful health and safety misconceptions of a group of tenth grade girls, Journal of School Health **24**: Nov., 1954.
4. Fischer, J. H.: Why teach? National Education Association Journal **51**: April, 1962.
5. Garrison, R. H.: Why do we teach? Improving College and University Teaching **9**: Summer, 1961.
6. Garvas, E. G.: Searching for the truth: evaluation of evidence in health education, Journal of School Health **32**: March, 1962.
7. Irwin, L. W.: Some areas of needed research related to health teaching in secondary schools, Journal of School Health **31**: March, 1961.
8. Irwin, L. W., and Staton, W. M.: Health concepts at the secondary level, Research Quarterly **22**: March, 1951.
9. Haskew, L. D.: This is teaching, Chicago, 1956, Scott, Foresman & Co.
10. Johns, E. B.: Forecast for the future, health education, Journal of Health, Physical Education, and Recreation **31**: April, 1960.
11. Lewis, C. G.: Teaching—an island of excellence, Journal of Health, Physical Education, and Recreation **31**: Jan., 1960.
12. Muldoon, M. W.: Learning to teach, New York, 1958, Harper & Brothers.
13. Patton, R. D.: Teaching, Journal of Higher Education **33**: May, 1962.
14. Reckham, D. R.: High school seniors' opinion of teaching, California Journal of Educational Research **13**: Jan., 1962.
15. Rosenthal, M.: Why we teach, High Points **43**: Oct., 1961.
16. Streit, W. K.: Health education from kindergarten through high school, Journal of School Health **24**: Nov., 1954.

Chapter 5

SAFETY EDUCATION IN SECONDARY SCHOOLS

R apid progress has been made in medical care and public health, particularly in recent years. Life expectancy has increased to beyond 70 years, in comparison to approximately 49 years at the turn of the century. Common diseases and disorders of the past are now under control, and many former diseases that caused disability and death are now curable or preventable. The control and prevention of death and disability from accidents have not kept pace with the progress made in the field of medicine and public health.

An accident is defined by the National Safety Council as follows, "that occurrence in a sequence of events which usually produces unintended death, injury, or property damage." Of all the major causes of illness, permanent or temporary disability, and death, accidents are considered the easiest to prevent. The main point is to keep the sequence of events from beginning or break the sequence short of an accident.

Many people think of accidents largely in terms of catastrophes in which many people are injured or killed. This is a natural reaction since catastrophic types of accidents such as airplane crashes and bus, ship, and railroad accidents are usually highly publicized. Although catastrophes in which people are killed and injured are serious, they do not account for a substantial percentage of the deaths and injuries through accidents. As a matter of fact, catastrophes account for less than 3% of all accidental deaths and injuries. Even so, investigation of many catastrophes shows that they result from some type of human failure or negligence.

It is very important that parents, teachers, and administrators clearly understand the problem of safety and the relationship of health and safety in the school program. Most schools now accept at least some responsibility for the health welfare of students. In taking this responsibility, the schools have attempted to do as much as possible in helping to maintain the health of students as well as to protect them from illnesses and disabling diseases and disorders. It is now realized that safety and accident prevention are in the same category as health education in the attempt to assure the optimum welfare of students.

If parents and members of the school personnel are committed to protecting and providing for the optimum health, growth, and development of students, then certainly they are committed to assuming responsibility for safety and accident prevention the same as for health education. The main reason for this is that accidents rank high as a cause of death and injury among youth of school age.

WHAT IS THE PROBLEM OF ACCIDENTS?

The number of deaths and injuries in the United States each year is appalling. Although the yearly statistics indicate that the accidental death rate has declined slightly in recent years, nevertheless from 90,000 to 97,000 people continue to lose their lives in accidents each year, and from 300,000 to 350,000 persons receive some type of permanent disabling injury. In addition to the accidental deaths and disabling injuries, statistics of the National Safety Council indicate that between 9,000,000 and 10,000,000 people are injured severely enough to require medical attention as well as to lose time from work and school.

In regard to accidental injuries, the National Safety Council statistics do not seem to reflect the total seriousness of the situation when compared with the results of the United States Public Health Service National Health Survey conducted from July 1957 through June 1960. The survey included 108,000 households. The results showed the average yearly number of accidental injuries to be approximately 45,000,000. There seems to be a wide discrepancy between the statistics of the National Safety Council and the United States Public Health Service. However, the difference in the total yearly number of accidents indicated by these two organizations results from their methods of classification. The National Health Survey statistics included injuries that restricted the individual for one day, including the day of the accident, and people who received some type of medical care. The National Safety Council statistics included only injuries that restricted and disabled the individual longer than the day of the accident.

A better perspective of the accident situation can be gained if consideration is given to the number of people killed during the past two decades. On the basis of the National Safety Council statistics, approximately 2,000,000 people lost their lives in accidents during the past twenty years; 7,000,000 persons were permanently disabled in some way, and more than 180,000,000 persons were injured.

Cost of accidents. According to the National Safety Council, accidents resulting in death and injury, combined with noninjury motor vehicle accidents, work accidents, and fires, cost the nation more than $15,000,000,000 in a recent typical year. These costs are distributed as follows:

Wages lost during temporary inability to work; lower wages after $4,400,000,000
   returning to work due to permanent impairment; value of future
  earnings lost by those totally incapacitated or killed

Medical fees; hospital expenses	$1,500,000,000
Administrative and claim settlement cost of insurance	3,400,000,000
Property damage in motor vehicle accidents	2,400,000,000
Property destroyed by fire	1,265,000,000
Property destroyed and production loss due to work accidents	2,500,000,000

Accidents versus illness. There are no statistics available by which to compare accurately the extent of ill health and disability caused by accidents and diseases. However, death rates are available. In Table 8 are shown the leading causes of death for different age groups in a recent typical year. These statistics show that although accidents are the fourth leading cause of death among people of all ages they are the greatest killer in the age group 1 to 36 years.

In Table 9 are shown the number of deaths by leading causes among youth 15 to 24 years of age in a recent typical year. Accidents cause approximately seven times more deaths than the next leading cause in this age group.

Safety hazards. Safety hazards have become so numerous that it is difficult to live safely in the world today. During the early history of the United States, life was comparatively simple. The main occupation of farming was carried on with simple hand tools. Travel was slow and limited. There were many hazards during colonial days, of course, but life was simple compared to our present-day standards. In many ways, though, life is far easier today than in the early days. Nevertheless, modern machines and complex equipment have become part of the hazards of daily life for everyone. The ways which present-day hazards can be encountered are so complicated and varied and the intellectual and emotional preparation needed to live safely with the hazards are so demanding that safety and accident prevention have become major unsolved problems of our day.

Risk and exposure to accidents. One basic principle in our democratic society is that everyone shall live under equal rights. This principle includes equally safe living conditions for all. Present-day hazards, however, have assumed such proportions as to challenge the ability of society to assure and pro-

Table 8. Order of leading causes of deaths for all ages and for various age groups in recent typical year*

All ages
Heart disease (including rheumatic fever)
Cancer
Vascular lesions (affecting the central nervous system)
Accidents (such as motor vehicle, falls, fires, burns, and drownings)

Under 1 year of age
Immaturity
Postnatal asphyxia
Congenital malformations
Pneumonia
Birth injuries
Accidents (such as mechanical suffocation, ingestion of food and other objects, motor vehicle, fires, burns, and falls)

---

*Data from National Safety Council; Accident facts, Chicago, 1963 edition, The Council.

Table 8. Order of leading causes of deaths for all ages and for various age groups in recent typical year—cont'd

---

1 to 4 years of age

Accidents (such as motor vehicle, fires, burns, drownings, poisons (except gas), and ingestion of food and other objects)
Pneumonia
Congenital malformations

5 to 14 years of age

Accidents (such as motor vehicle, drownings, fires, and burns)
Cancer
Congenital malformations

15 to 24 years of age

Accidents (such as motor vehicle, drownings, firearms, and railroad)
Cancer
Homicide

25 to 44 years of age

Heart disease (including rheumatic fever)
Accidents (such as motor vehicle, drownings, fire, burns, and falls)
Cancer
Suicide

45 to 64 years of age

Heart disease (including rheumatic fever)
Cancer
Vascular lesions (affecting central nervous system)
Accidents (such as motor vehicle, falls, fires, burns, and drownings)
Cirrhosis of liver
Diabetes mellitus

65 to 74 years of age

Heart disease (including rheumatic fever)
Cancer
Vascular lesions (affecting central nervous system)
Diabetes mellitus
Accidents (such as motor vehicle, falls, burns, fires, and drownings)
Pneumonia
General arteriosclerosis

75 years of age and over

Heart disease (including rheumatic fever)
Vascular lesions (affecting central nervous system)
Cancer
General arteriosclerosis
Pneumonia
Accidents (such as falls, motor vehicle, fire, burns, ingestion of food, objects, drownings, and railroad)
Diabetes mellitus
Hypertension

Table 9. Number of deaths by leading causes among youth 15 to 24 years of age in recent typical year*

Cause	Number of deaths		
	Total	*Male*	*Female*
All causes	25,268	17,887	7,381
Accidents	13,269	11,015	2,254
Motor vehicle	8,969	7,527	1,712
Cancer	1,991	1,205	786
Homicide	1,375	1,048	327
Suicide	1,152	898	254
Heart disease (including rheumatic fever)	1,008	550	458
Congenital malformations	655	345	310

*Data from National Safety Council; Accident facts, Chicago, 1962 edition, The Council.

vide equally safe living conditions. Even when society exerts the greatest effort to protect its members, some occupations and activities are more hazardous than others. Regardless of the differences in hazards involved in various activities and occupations, it remains the responsibility of the social order to provide as safe living conditions as possible for all persons, regardless of rank, status, or occupation.

Cooperation and understanding must exist if safe living conditions are to be attained. Many people believe that risk and exposure to accidents are the concern only of the person involved. This is a fallacious attitude, for accidental death or injury practically always involves more than one person. Employees, employers, families, and society are all affected by any death or injury.

All risk or exposure to accidents cannot be avoided. Some occupations necessary to maintain society have greater risks than others. The ideal situation would be to have the safest possible conditions relative to the risk involved. There are activities, too, which are not necessary to the proper function and maintenance of society in which great hazards are involved. The question arises as to whether the more hazardous activities that are not necessary to maintain society should be carried on. Naturally, this brings up another question about the risk involved in activities in relation to their contribution to society. An example of this is football in the secondary schools. It is readily granted and statistics show that football is more hazardous than many other sports. Because football is not necessary to the function and maintenance of society, it is the contention of some people that football should be abandoned and that a less hazardous game should be established to take its place. On the other hand, persons opposed to this opinion argue that there are developmental features in the game of football that justify the risk taken and the hazards involved. The decision regarding an activity such as secondary school football cannot be made with a clear-cut and definite conclusion. There will always be those persons who believe that the secondary school boy would be better off without the game of football and those persons who believe that the hazards involved are not too great for the values received. It is quite possible that the determination of risk in such cases should be left to the persons who control a particular situation. There are some schools in which football with all its hazards would be highly desirable because of the particular type of boy involved. There might be a need in a particular situation to develop more rugged individuals which could be brought about in no other way than through exposure to the hazards of more rugged activities.

Perhaps in all cases in which risk is involved, two phases should be given careful consideration: (1) the effect the risk or possible injury might have on a particular individual his immediate family and associates and (2) the effect that possible injury might have on society as a whole. It should be kept in mind, however, that persons responsible for prevention programs do not expect all risk and exposure to accidents to be completely eliminated. There will always be a certain amount of risk involved in all activities. A main objective of safety programs is to avoid and prevent *needless* risks. A positive safety and accident prevention program recommends neither a course of needless risk nor safety at any price.

One of the main reasons why society has not been able to provide a completely safe environment is largely because of constantly changing conditions and progress. Consequently, it is necessary for people to control and modify their actions when necessary and to learn to adjust to the environment as it exists. People must constantly strive to keep up with scientific advances and changing conditions if they are to avoid unnecessary risk and unsafe acts that lead to accidental death and injury.

The ability to adjust to the complexities of modern life varies greatly among persons. Some individuals seem to adjust more readily and better than others. Also, statistics show that people in certain age groups seem better able to avoid death and injury by accidents. In the age group 15 to 24 years, for example, statistics show that the injury and death rates from accidents are much higher than in other age groups. The implications are that boys and girls 15 to 24 years of age take more risks which result in accidents. However, many people think that the higher death and injury rates among the members of this group are due to the greatly expanded activities of youth and because they lack understanding and proper education in safety and accident prevention.

PUBLIC APATHY TO THE ACCIDENT PROBLEM

Many people in the United States are indifferent and apathetic to the accident problem. Unquestionably, one of the reasons for this public apathy is that people are not conscious of the seriousness of the situation. Because of public apathy it is very difficult to elicit the attention and support of people for accident prevention programs. It is not difficult to get the attention of the public to the accident problem when a catastrophe happens in which a large number of people are killed or injured. For example, an airline accident in which a large number of people are killed gets radio and television publicity as well as newspaper headlines throughout the entire country. Yet, as previously pointed out, deaths and injuries in catastrophes make up less than 3% of the total number of people killed and injured in the course of a year. The many less spectacular deaths and injuries that happen each day throughout the year get little or no publicity. For example, on the same day that a catastrophe occurs in which upward of

100 people are killed, on the average more than 250 people are killed in accidents throughout the country which do not receive headlines. But this happening of 250 people or more being killed on the same day as a catastrophe is almost a daily occurrence; yet insufficient attention is given to the much greater problem.

Another factor which shows the apathy of the public is the inconsistency in emphasis placed on causes of deaths, injury, and permanent disability. This inconsistency seems to be due to a lack of information and illogical thinking. For example, in the years before the discovery of immunity to poliomyelitis, parents were likely to become more or less panic stricken in the presence of an epidemic. Their fear, of course, was of death or permanent crippling of their children. These same parents, however, who could so easily become panicky because of a poliomyelitis epidemic, remained more or less apathetic or indifferent to the much greater possibility of their children's being permanently disabled or killed in accidents. Yet, the chances were twenty to thirty times greater that a child would be permanently disabled or killed in an accident than by poliomyelitis. The attitude of most persons concerning diseases and accidents remains largely the same today.

People abhor wars and will go to any length to prevent a war because of the death and destruction it brings. Yet they remain apathetic to the accident situation which is infinitely worse over a period of time in terms of death and injuries. A comparison of deaths and injuries resulting from accidents and with those resulting from previous wars shows that in the same period of time more people are injured, permanently disabled, or killed in accidents than in wars. For example, during World War II from December 7, 1941, to August 14, 1945, there were 275,338 deaths and 670,548 wounded in the United States military services. Among civilians during the same period of time, accidents were responsible for 36,000,000 injuries, 1,250,000 permanently disabling injuries of some type, and 355,000 deaths.

SECONDARY SCHOOL STUDENTS AND ACCIDENTS

Accidents are the greatest killer of students of secondary school age. Also, disability from accidents ranks higher than disability from illnesses. The statistics given in Table 9 show that more boys and girls lose their lives from accidents than from all other causes combined. These statistics also show that a majority of the accident victims among secondary school youth are boys. Motor vehicle accidents are most prevalent among secondary school students, followed by drownings and firearms accidents.

Since secondary school students are in the age group having one of the highest accident rates, strong emphasis should be placed on safety education programs for them. They should be thoroughly familiar with the accident problem, and they should learn how to avoid and prevent accidents without restricting their activities. The more the student knows about accident hazards, the more likely he will be to avoid accidents. Furthermore, secondary school students should realize that they have a responsibility, not only for their own safety, but also for the safety of others. A sense of responsibility to both self and to others should be developed on the part of all secondary school students. The responsible student is likely to work and play without taking undue risk if he thoroughly understands that by persisting in risky practices he is very likely sooner or later to be involved in an accident resulting in injury or death to himself or to others.

ACCIDENT STATISTICS

Statistics concerning accidents are recorded and compiled by local, state, and federal governments as well as by some voluntary and private organizations. Also, many industrial organizations keep very careful records of accidental deaths and injuries among employees.

Statistics are the basis upon which organized efforts are founded for combatting accidents. Although statistics are often criticized for being inadequate, nevertheless, they continue to be the basis upon which organized efforts are founded. One of the first steps in safety education is to know where and how accidents happen. This information must be known before intelligent efforts can be made to prevent accidents.

The National Safety Council compiles accident statistics on the basis of four general divisions. These four main divisions are motor vehicle, home, work, and public accidents exclusive of accidents in which motor vehicles are involved. The four main divisions of accidents designated by the National Safety Council represent the first step in the breakdown of statistics for analyzation and clarification of the situation. Although it is helpful to know the number of deaths and injuries occurring in each of the four main divisions, many more classifications within each division are necessary to learn specifically

Table 10. Deaths and disabling injuries by principle classes of accidents for recent typical year*

Type of accident	Deaths	Disabling injuries
Work	13,700	2,000,000
Motor vehicle	40,900	1,500,000
Home	28,500	4,300,000
Public	17,000	2,100,000

*Data from National Safety Council: Accident facts, Chicago, 1963, The Council.

Table 11. Accidental deaths in recent typical year*

All accidents	97,000
Motor vehicles	40,900
Falls	19,800
Fires, burns, and deaths associated with fires	7,500
Drowning	6,400
Railroad accidents	2,200
Firearms accidents	2,000
Poisons, solid or liquid	1,700
Poison gases	1,400
All other types	16,300

*Data from National Safety Council: Accident facts, Chicago, 1963, The Council.

how and under what conditions accidents happen. Nevertheless, the four main divisions are a good perspective of the accident problem.

The statistics given in Table 10 show the number of deaths and disabling injuries on the basis of four main divisions of the National Safety Council. The statistics in Table 11 indicate another way of breaking down statistics to give more detailed information about accidents that cause deaths and injuries.

CAUSES OF ACCIDENTS

Although the information given in Tables 10 and 11 show how yearly accidents happen, no indication of the factors involved is included. Many of the causes of accidents are associated with the emotional and physical makeup of people, with environmental hazards, and with understanding and knowledge concerning safety and accident prevention. Immediate causes of accidents involve such things as environmental hazards, poor safety habits, emotional maladjustment and immaturity, social maladjustment, lack of skill, improper use of alcohol and drugs, mental and physical fatigue, carelessness, illness, and undeveloped or poor attitudes concerning safety.

Many people involved in accidents in which someone is killed or injured are socially maladjusted and emotionally unstable, selfish, and reckless or careless. Some of these people have physical handicaps that contribute to the accidents. People who are emotionally unstable or socially maladjusted are more likely to drive a motor vehicle with excessive speed, to be inattentive, to show poor judgment, to be discourteous, to drink alcoholic beverages excessively, or to permit themselves to become mentally or physically fatigued. Any of these factors or a combination of them can result in an accident in which someone is killed or injured.

EMOTIONAL AND PHYSICAL FACTORS
IN SAFETY AND ACCIDENT PREVENTION

Although physical factors sometimes contribute to the cause of an accident, recent research and experience indicate that psychological factors are more often basic causes of accidents. Experts in accident prevention estimate that 80 to 85% of the accidents that result in death or injury can be prevented.

The prevention of many accidents would require the elimination of hazards. Nevertheless, accident prevention remains largely a problem of individual and group attitudes, behavior, and reactions. Partial proof of this is shown by statistics which indicate that only a very small percentage of motor vehicles involved in accidents had a faulty mechanism. This seems to indicate that motor vehicle accidents are caused largely by the driver and not by the machine.

Another fact which seems to indicate that poor judgment and emotional instability are frequently responsible for accidents is the proposal by safety groups that the granting of motor vehicle drivers' licenses be based on tests of emotional stability as well as on physical fitness. Safety groups have learned that motor vehicle drivers who are involved in accidents in which someone is killed or injured are likely to be impulsive, irresponsible, intolerant, aggressive, and often maladjusted. Other studies seem to show that drivers who have the best records are emotionally stable, reasonably conservative, have good judgment, and are socially well adjusted.

In industry and occupations the marked reduction of accidents during the past four or five decades indicates that the problem is largely one of attitudes and practices. Although employers have gone to great expense and trouble to be sure that all machines and working conditions are safe, many accidents occur each year because of the human element involved. It is apparent, then, that even though all conceivable types of safety devices may be provided for society in building and constructing safe living and working conditions a large percentage of accidents cannot be eliminated merely by the use of safe machinery or of foolproof safety devices. In late years, engineers in all fields of human endeavor have been striving to make safer conditions for the individual and for society. Unless the individual and the group cooperate and know how to make intelligent use of the safety devices provided, there is not likely to be any material reduction in the present accident rate, regardless of the emphasis placed on the removal of hazards.

Attitudes are especially important in accidents. This is particularly true in motor vehicle safety. Everyone is more or less familiar with the different attitudes among motor vehicle drivers. Reckless drivers who do not give consideration either to themselves or to others are in far too great numbers. State laws have been enacted whereby youths below certain ages cannot drive cars. A factor in the development of state laws regarding age limits for drivers is the emotional nature of the adolescent. What is not given consideration is that many adults never seem to progress beyond the emotional level of an adolescent.

Emotional stability is certainly one of the most important factors in the cause of accidents. More and more time and attention are being given to the study of the emotions in an effort to lower the accident rate. There are, admittedly, many physical attributes related to the problem of the psychology of safety. Such physical attributes as age, race, sex, native coordination, skill, reaction time, vision, stimulation, fatigue, physical condition, and many others are directly related to the safety of both the individual and the group. Practically all of the physical attributes are, however, so closely related to emotional and psychological aspects of human behavior that it is usually impossible to separate them as causative factors in accidents. It is usually next to impossible to determine the particular mental or emotional attribute responsible for an accident in which it is clearly evident that a mental or emotional factor is at fault. More often, a combination of a number of mental and emotional attributes are involved in a particular situation. Some of the mental and emotional attributes important in safety are native intelligence, knowledge in relation to safety, judgment in relation to safety, experience, attention, memory, absentmindedness, imagination, concentration, boredom, decisiveness, worry and mental balance.

Closely correlated with the numerous mental and physical attributes affecting safe conduct is emotional stability. Both the mental and physical attributes of the individual can be highly conducive to safety, but if the emotions are not reasonably stabilized, the mental and physical qualities may be rendered ineffective, particularly in situations in which emotional control may be easily lost. After a review and study of the many psychological factors involved in accidents, it seems impossible to determine clearly why people have accidents. It is clear, however, that the answer is as complex as the psychology of human behavior.

During the beginning of the safety movement in the United States, it was assumed that if a person had a broad knowledge of safety and accident prevention, he would avoid accidents. However, it has been learned through experience that it is not enough to know about safety. Proper attitudes and habits are necessary as well as safety knowledge. Proper habits and attitudes cannot be formed, though, unless a person first possesses knowledge.

ACCIDENT-PRONENESS

The terms *accidentitis, accident repeater,* and *accident-proneness* are frequently used more or less synonomously in describing the individual who seems to have more than the usual number of accidents. At the present time there is no clear-cut explanation of the physical and psychology factors involved in accident-proneness. In times past it was attributed to poor physical and sensory characteristics. More recently research seems to indicate that poor attitudes, maladjustment, emotional instability, and lack of knowledge concerning accident prevention and safety are associated with accident-proneness. It is likely that the physical and psychological components vary from one accident-prone person to another.

Only a very small percentage of the population are classed as accident-prone. Nevertheless, they account for a disproportionately large share of the accidents resulting in death and injuries. Also, it is likely that a large number of people who are seriously injured or die in accidents had not had a serious accident before. At the present time there are no satisfactory ways of identifying accident-prone people. The only certain test for an accident-prone person is his continual repetition of accidents, provided that he does not have a fatal accident early in life. It is not known how many accident-prone people were killed early in life as the result of their first and only accident. They do not live to be classed as accident-prone although death may have resulted because of accident-proneness.

OTHER PSYCHOLOGICAL EXPLANATIONS OF ACCIDENTS

It is common knowledge that even temporary emotional upsets may lead to accidents. Although anyone can be involved in an accident as a result of a temporary emotional upset, such conditions as emotional instability, stress, and strain over a long period of time are thought to be more serious positive causative factors of accidents.

Some psychiatrists and psychologists feel that accident repeaters often actually try to have accidents to escape from seemingly intolerable psychological situations in which they are emotionally involved. These victims of accidents unconsciously or subconsciously want to have accidents. Such people often take risks and suffer repeated injuries which seem wholly unnecessary and even foolish but which serve a real purpose to them. However, they do not or cannot profit by their experience. Psychiatrists have stated that accident-proneness, at least in some persons, results from an unconscious desire to inflict self-punishment or destroy oneself. Also psychiatrists have noted excessive guilt feeling among people who are considered accident-prone.

MOTOR VEHICLE ACCIDENTS

Statistics show that since motor vehicles were first used in the United States more than 1,000,000 people have lost their lives in traffic accidents. Approximately 38,000 people are killed in traffic accidents, and more than 2,000,000 persons are injured each year in the United States. Many injured persons receive some type of permanently disabling injury. This is due particularly to the fact that motor vehicles are classed as heavy equipment and are more likely to cause excessive physical damage in accidents.

It is very difficult to determine the cause of many motor vehicle accidents because in most cases there are a combination of causes and because few accidents are investigated carefully enough to learn the exact causes. Excessive speed for existing conditions is perhaps one of the greatest single contributing factors to motor vehicle accidents. This does not necessarily mean high speed but too great a speed for the conditions of the roadway. For example, a speed of 60 miles an hour on an open highway where there is little or no traffic and the pavement is dry in clear weather would probably be a safer speed than that of 20 miles an hour in a congested area on icy streets. Other things which contribute to accidents are improper and reckless driving, violation of the right-of-way, improper passing, and driving on the wrong side of the road.

Unsafe acts by pedestrians bring death and permanent injury to many persons each year. It should be pointed out at this time that a large number of pedestrians who are killed or injured are children and youth of school age. Many of the pedestrians killed by motor vehicles each year either violate a traffic law or act in an obviously unsafe manner. The violation which most frequently results in death or injury to pedestrians is crossing streets between intersections. This is particularly true of youth of school age.

Many fatal accidents involve either a driver or a pedestrian who has been drinking. The problem of alcoholic drinks in relation to accident frequency seems to grow in importance not only so far as motor vehicle accidents are concerned but also in practically all phases of human endeavor. Fatigue on the part of drivers is a common cause of accidents. Drivers and pedestrians with physical defects such as bad vision and hearing are responsible for some accidents. Defective motor vehicles are reported as a cause of a few accidents. Although unsafe machines may be a contributing factor in some cases, the cause of accidents usually can be traced to the driver or to a pedestrian rather than to a defective machine.

Darkness is a major contributing factor to motor vehicle accidents in that the fatal accident rate per mile of travel is much greater during the hours of darkness. More than half of the fatal motor vehicle accidents occur at night. Although road and weather conditions have considerable bearing on motor vehicle accidents, the yearly statistics show that more accidents occur during clear weather than during times when it is raining or snowing or when the weather is cloudy or foggy. Apparently, drivers are more careful when road and weather conditions are unfavorable.

ALCOHOL AND TRAFFIC ACCIDENTS

The drinking driver has become a major problem as a cause of motor vehicle accidents. Studies conducted throughout the United States indicate that approximately 50% of the drivers of motor vehicles involved in fatal accidents had been drinking alcoholic beverages. The results of these studies seem to indicate that the drinking of alcoholic beverages on the part of the driver is a contributing cause of traffic accidents.

The question frequently arises as to the extent to which the drinking of alcohol affects driving ability. Studies show that when the concentration of alcohol in the blood reaches 0.15% the chances of involvement in an accident are at least ten times greater than when no alcohol has been consumed. From five to eight ordinary drinks of an alcoholic beverage will cause the concentration of alcohol in the blood to reach 0.15%. With a blood alcohol level of 0.10%, which is about three to six ordinary drinks, the chances of involvement in a traffic accident are about three times greater than with no alcohol consumption. When the blood alcohol level reaches 0.05%, which is about two or three ordinary drinks, the chances of an accident are approximately twice as great as when no alcohol has been consumed.

Many people think that it is the drunken driver who is involved in accidents when, in reality, it is not the *drunken* driver but the *drinking* driver who is the most dangerous. The completely drunken driver is usually unable to drive, but if he does attempt to drive, his condition is so obvious he is halted or other persons notice his condition immediately and keep out of his way. The completely drunken driver is not a big problem on streets and highways. It is the drinking driver who creates the biggest problem, that is, social drinkers, who greatly outnumber the drunken drivers. The social drinker may have the ability to talk fairly intelligently and coherently and to maintain a bearing that gives the appearance of sobriety while at the same time being sufficiently under influence of alcohol to be considered in an intoxicated condition. These drinkers are not usually considered drunken drivers in that they do not exhibit behavior such as slurred and unintelligible speech and staggering gait. Nevertheless, social drinkers are the ones who are the greatest concern in the traffic. The social drinker may not show signs of being influenced by the alcohol he has consumed; yet his driving ability is impaired. Even after the consumption of small amounts of alcohol, the drinker is not alert, and he loses some of his self-control.

Many people think that a few drinks of an alcoholic beverage do not effect their driving ability. This is a risky fallacy, for persons who drink are seldom able to clearly judge their driving ability. Research has clearly established that the judgment of the drinking driver and his ability to respond quickly in emergency situations are greatly impaired after the consumption of a few drinks of alcohol. Of course, an individual under the influence of alcohol can carry out the usual mechanical processes of driving to the extent of starting the motor, getting the car started, and steering it even though he does not have the proper judgment and reflex actions to drive safely. Another misconception held by many people is that alcohol is a stimulant and thus will result in better driving. However, alcohol depresses rather than stimulates the nervous system.

Such factors as body weight, food in the stomach, kinds of food, type of alcohol consumed, and drinking habits affect the absorption of alcohol into the bloodstream. However, none of these things prevent the alcohol from reaching the brain. The amount of alcohol absorbed into the bloodstream and the time allowed for its elimination are important factors in its influence on the body. Alcohol is eliminated from the body at a relatively slow rate. It is common for a person to have an accumulation of alcohol in the body that requires several hours for elimination. Alcohol is excreted through the lungs and kidneys after being detoxified in the liver. This process consumes approximately three hours for each ounce of pure alcohol. Under ordinary circumstances it takes about one hour for the body to eliminate the alcohol in a bottle of beer or an ounce of whiskey.

The question often arises as to how many drinks an individual can take and still drive safely. Naturally the answer to this question varies with individuals, the time between drinks, and the time lapse between the last drink and the driving. If you want to be absolutely certain that alcohol will not affect your driving, then do not drink. This does not necessarily mean that you cannot take a drink with your dinner and then an hour later cannot drive safely. In the one hour after you took the drink and before driving most of the alcohol will be eliminated from your body.

Because of such things as differences in body size and weight, degree of fatigue, emotional stability, and other individual characteristics, one person may show fewer visible signs of the effect of alcohol than another. This should not be interpreted to mean that an individual who shows few visible signs of alcohol consumption is any less impaired so far as safe driving is concerned. Good drivers can properly judge speeds and distances, react safely to traffic patterns, make satisfactory adjustment to the flow of traffic, and react safely to hazards and emergencies. After the consumption of a few drinks of alcohol, a good driver can no longer do these things well; he is likely to become a hazard to himself and to other persons while driving a motor vehicle.

HOME ACCIDENTS

The modern home is no longer the safe haven it was once considered, for thousands of men, women, and children are killed and millions are injured in home accidents each year. From 4,000,000 to 5,000,00 people are injured and approximately 26,000 are killed in home accidents yearly. The cost of home accidents is approximately $1,000,000,000 per year. Falls are responsible for about two thirds of home accident fatalities, and fires and burns account for more than one fifth of the deaths.

Three basic factors are involved in home accidents. First, the many hazards which include such things as power equipment and electrical appliances which are dangerous if not handled safely. Second, the lack of understanding on the part of both children and adults concerning hazards in the home. Third, people seem to be prone to carelessness about the home.

Ignorance concerning safety practices, poor judgment, physical defects, fatigue, and hurry are responsible for many home accidents. Human failure is more often the cause of accidents than mechanical factors. Many accidents occur in the kitchen of the home largely due to carelessness in handling the many different kinds of equipment. The more serious accidents occurring in the living room of the home are burns and falls. Falls are often caused by slipping on waxed floors or small rugs. The modern bathroom is a particularly dangerous place in the home due to the danger of falls, electric shock and poisoning. Many falls happen in halls and on stairways. Going up and down stairs, particularly in the dark or in a dim light, frequently lead to serious falls. In recent years power lawn mowers have been responsible for many injuries. The rapidly moving blades are particularly hazardous for hands and fingers. Fires and burns often occur in the home due to carelessness. The majority of the fires in the home are caused by careless smokers. Smoking in bed seems to be particularly hazardous.

WORK ACCIDENTS

The National Safety Council statistics show that from 13,000 to 16,000 people are killed and approximately 2,000,000 people are injured each year in occupational accidents. Many injured persons are permanently disabled in some way. Approximately 230,000,000 man-days are lost each year through work accidents. The cost of these accidents exceeds $4,600,000,000 per year.

When the number of people working and the extent of exposure to accidents are considered, it would seem that work accident death rates should be greater than in any other area; yet they are much less than either motor vehicle or home accident fatalities. A main reason why the occupational accident rate is lower than the motor vehicle and home rates is that there has been an organized and controlled effort to reduce accidents in industries and occupations which has been highly successful. Whereas in a modern industrial plant it is possible to eliminate hazards on an organized basis and to some extent to control safety practices, it has been next to impossible to control the safety practices of individuals in the home or the acts of individual drivers of motor vehicles. In order to overcome the tendency of people to become careless and to expose themselves unduly to hazards within a given occupation, employers have established rules and regulations in regard to safety which employees are expected to follow. Because an employer must pay the cost involved in accidental death or injury, it is to his advantage to prevent accidents. Often the penalty for not observing the safety rules and regulations is that the worker who fails to obey is discharged.

Even though the death and injury rate in occupations is lower than motor vehicle and home accidents, nevertheless, the time lost from work and the costs are staggering as a result of the accidents that do happen. In addition to the time lost from work by the injured workers, there is also a loss by other persons. Time lost by workers other than those injured results when they stop work to help the injured and also to discuss the accident. Also, suspension of work caused by damaged equipment and the time to replace or repair damaged machinery often results in much loss of time and production.

Another way in which employers have reduced the accident rate is through safety education programs. Although the rules and regulations established by employers have been helpful, they would not be too effective unless accompanied by safety education. In some cases in which the accident rate has been greatly reduced, it has been estimated that from 50 to 75% of the reduction resulted from safety education and approximately 25% from the elimination of hazards and the use of mechanical safeguards.

PUBLIC NONMOTOR VEHICLE ACCIDENTS

From 14,000 to 16,000 people are killed in public nonmotor vehicle accidents each year and approximately 2,000,000 people are injured. Many of injured persons are permanently disabled in some way. Drownings rank high as a cause of accidental death in public accidents. Approximately 5000 to 6000 people drown each year. A high percentage of the number of fatal drowning accidents each year occur among children and youth under 24 years of age. Railroad and airline accidents as well as falls in public places also rank very high.

SAFETY IN SPORTS AND RECREATIONAL ACTIVITIES

Increasing amounts of leisure time as well as the modern emphasis on physical fitness are inducing increasing numbers of people to take part in sports and recreational activities. Most secondary school students today participate in a variety of sports and recreational activities. Furthermore, they look forward to continued participation throughout their lifetime. Participation in physical activities is particularly valuable to the student from the viewpoint of physical development, social adjustment, and psychological satisfaction and enjoyment. Also, it gives the student an opportunity to explore many activities from which he can select those he wishes to continue to participate in after school life.

Secondary school students should become aware of the particular hazards of different activities. They should learn not only the techniques of activities but also the unsafe hazards involved and the procedures most effective in preventing accidents. Everyone knows that many sports can be hazardous, particularly those in which speed, force, body contact, and strenuous effort are involved. Learning how to participate in an activity safely increases the enjoyment for the student. When students know of the hazards of sports and recreational activities and learn to compensate for those hazards without creating new ones, they are then in a position to benefit most from their participation.

The hazards in physical and recreational activities differ greatly. Statistics show that the number of injuries in some activities is larger than in others. Sometimes this is because a greater number of students participate in a certain sport. Statistics show that sprains, muscle contusions, strains, fractures, and dislocations are the most common types of injuries received during participation in sports and physical activities.

The following precautions should be taken to help assure safe participation in sports and recreational activities.

1. Have a periodic medical examination to determine physical fitness for vigorous and strenuous sports.
2. Be in good physical condition before fully engaging in a strenuous activity.
3. Have proper and adequate equipment and use it correctly for a particular activity. Participation in sports such as football, skiing, and water activities without proper equipment is conducive to accidents.
4. Be thoroughly familiar with and know how to compensate for the hazards of a particular activity.
5. Do not participate alone in such activities as hunting, boating, or swimming. Serious accidents can happen sometimes because help is not available.
6. Take adequate rest periods when participating in strenuous activities.
7. Participate in strenuous activities only with other persons with about equal skill and strength.
8. Practice moderation in all physical and recreational activities.
9. Keep within the limitations of your strength and capabilities.

ORGANIZATION AND SUPERVISION OF THE SECONDARY SCHOOL SAFETY PROGRAM

Because safety is a comparatively new area in the school program and because it has not yet become well established in many schools, there is widespread misunderstanding concerning the organization, supervision, and responsibility for the safety program. The entire safety program, the same as other programs, should be under the direct control of the board of education and the school administrators. Community organizations may be called upon to assist with the school safety program; yet they should not be permitted to have final control or responsibility for any phase of the safety program.

Although the kind of organization for safety may vary from one school to another, every member of the school personnel has a responsibility for the safety welfare of secondary school students. The organization of a safety program may vary greatly on the basis of the size of the school system. Consequently, no single organizational pattern is suitable for all schools. In city school systems there is usually a director or supervisor of safety who coordinates the entire program. In smaller communities the safety organization, direction, and supervision may be the responsibility of some member of the school staff such as the director of health, physical, education and recreation. Many junior and senior high school academic teachers feel that safety is the responsibility of safety specialists or specialists in related fields. It should be clearly understood that all teachers in the junior and senior high schools have certain responsibility for the safety welfare of the students.

There is usually a need for a safety director or coordinator in the junior high school. In the traditional junior high school, which is usually located in communities in which resources are available for the most desirable programs of education, there is more likely to be a specialized safety education teacher on the faculty. One of the main reasons why a director or coordinator of safety is needed in the junior high school is that safety units are frequently included in very specialized courses in the junior high school curriculum. Obviously, then, teachers of a number of academic courses in the junior high school must take some responsibility in the actual safety education of students. In many of the more modern junior high schools health courses, as such, are offered. In recent years part of the time alloted to health teaching is devoted to safety instruction, and the two are coordinated in a direct teaching course. This is usually a good arrangement in most cases in that the person teaching health education usually has some background in safety education as well. Also, in some schools, a safety education course, as such, is offered. This is to be recommended, of course, if time and qualified teachers to handle the course are available. When direct safety education courses are offered, they are usually on a semester or yearly basis at some one of the grade levels in the junior high school.

The organization for safety in the high school is quite similar to that for junior high school. If the school does not have the services of a director or supervisor of safety, or if no teachers with safety training are available, the responsibility for coordinating safety may be assumed by a special teacher in a related field such as health education, industrial arts, or physical education, provided that the specialized teachers have some background of training and experience in safety. In small high schools in which it is impossible to find anyone on the faculty who can act as safety coordinator, it is usually the responsibility of the high school principal to see that at least a minimum amount of safety is taught and observed. In the small schools it is likely that safety knowledge will have to be imparted through units in other high school subjects and through various types of safety projects. If there are no teachers in the high school who have had sufficient education in safety to act as coordinator, the school administrator should look forward either to employing a teacher with training in safety or to designating some member of the faculty, preferably one with an interest in safety, to acquire the necessary education.

TEACHER LIABILITY AND RESPONSIBILITY FOR STUDENT INJURIES

Many secondary school teachers are not fully aware of the extent of their responsibility and liability for school accidents involving students. Under certain circumstances teachers can be held financially liable for injuries to students. In other cases they can be held responsible for the accident even though they are not held financially liable. In recent years there has been a greater tendency for parents to attempt to hold teachers financially liable for injuries to students. One reason for this is that the present-day public in general has come to expect the accidents will be paid for by insurance of some type. In the absence of state legislation, school boards and the school funds raised by taxation in most cases and administered by school boards cannot be held financially liable for student injuries. Consequently, under ordinary circumstances this leaves the teacher the only source of financial remuneration.

The question is frequently asked concerning the circumstances under which a teacher can be held financially liable for student injury. Teachers can be held financially liable in case of negligence. The law of negligence implies that safe living is the right of everyone and that society must protect the individual from the negligence of others in this right. So far as the schools are concerned, teachers owe a duty to the students. Sometimes even the failure to act to prevent injury to a student would be classed as negligence on the part of the teacher.

The trend in modern times is to arrange for society as a whole to pay the cost of injuries rather than the individual. Since most states lack legislation for boards of education and the education funds they administer to be held liable for accidents, there is no way the group as a whole can bear the cost of student injuries. In those states lacking the proper legislation, school boards cannot legally spend tax-raised funds to purchase liability insurance to cover students. Legislation is needed in most states to correct this situation.

It was mentioned previously that teachers may be held responsible for accidents even though they cannot be held financially liable. In such cases the school administrators might consider a teacher negligent and perhaps censor or even discharge him for failure to use reasonable precautions in preventing an accident.

SAFETY EDUCATION IN THE JUNIOR HIGH SCHOOL

The safety topics and units in the junior high school grades may include many that were introduced in the upper elementary school grades. The number of safety topics offered at the junior high school level that are first introduced at the fourth, fifth, and sixth grade levels is governed largely by the extent of exploration of the topics in the intermediate grades. A topic having to do with some phase of traffic safety, for example, may be introduced as low as the primary grades in the elementary school. Additional teaching of the topic may be done at each grade level in the intermediate grades. If the topic is only briefly stressed at these grade levels due to a lack of time or for other reasons, it will be necessary to explore the topic further in the junior high school. If sufficient time is given to the teaching of safety in the primary and upper elementary grades, safety education in the junior high school may be established on a much more advanced level. These considerations underscore the need for curriculum planning which takes into account the program at both the elementary and the secondary school levels.

It is highly desirable that sufficient time be devoted to the teaching of safety at the primary and upper elementary grades in order that the safety work in the junior high school can be of an advanced nature. Then, the units in safety can be arranged in such a way as to bring out the relationship of safety to society as a whole. That is, instead of placing the greater emphasis on a type of safety education directed largely toward the knowledge of specific safety situations and the formations of proper habits and desirable attitudes in those situations, the emphasis can be placed more on the appreciation of safety in relation to life in general and the entire social order.

The following safety topics are suggestive of those which may be used in the junior high school.

Safety topics for the junior high school

School safety

1. Review of safety taught in the intermediate grades
   - (a) Pass to the right in halls and on stairs
   - (b) Avoid pushing, shoving, and running in the school building
   - (c) Know the location of exits and fire escapes
   - (d) Go through doors carefully
2. Gymnasium safety
   - (a) Equipment in good condition
   - (b) Skill in the intelligent use of equipment
   - (c) Play under the direction of trained supervisors
   - (d) Safe shower room conduct
   - (e) Proper dress for activities
3. Vocational shops
   - (a) Care in the use of machines and tools
   - (b) Proper and safe storage of tools
   - (c) Working under supervision
4. Home economics
   - (a) Development of skill and care in handling of equipment
   - (b) Safety in the use of flammable materials and substances
5. Laboratories
   - (a) Care in the use of equipment and chemicals
6. Safety on the athletic field
   - (a) Safety skills in organized athletic activities
   - (b) Intelligent and safe use of equipment
   - (c) Knowledge of the importance of medical examinations
   - (d) Knowledge of the rules of the game for safety
7. Activities on the playground
   - (a) Safety in free play
   - (b) Importance of immediately reporting injuries
8. Safety en route to school
   - (a) Safety as a passenger in a car, bus, or streetcar
   - (b) Safety as a pedestrian
   - (c) Safe and unsafe habits
   - (d) Knowledge and practice regarding systems of traffic control
   - (e) Community traffic enforcement
   - (f) Statistics concerning accidents en route to and from school

Fire prevention

1. Fire
   - (a) Nature of fire
   - (b) Causes of fire—careless use of such things as cigarettes, matches, kerosene, and gasoline; careless use of equipment and apparatus such as chimneys, stoves, furnaces, and electrical appliances; spontaneous combustion; incorrect disposal of ashes; accumulation of rubbish and litter.
   - (c) Fire escapes—understand their purpose and correct use
2. Effects of fires
   - (a) Statistics on injuries and loss of lives
   - (b) Statistics on the economic loss through fires
   - (c) Hospitalization due to burns
   - (d) How the cost of fires is met
   - (e) First aid for burns
3. Controlling the fire menace
   - (a) Safety inspection of homes and public buildings
   - (b) Individual responsibility for fire prevention such as carefulness, knowledge of first aid, use of fire extinguishers, fire drills, and emergency exits

4. Forest conservation in relation to fire
   (a) Knowledge of the work of forest rangers
   (b) Economic loss through forest fires
   (c) Individual responsibility for fire safety on the part of campers, hikers, fishermen, and lumbermen

Transportation safety

1. Traffic laws
   (a) Why traffic laws are needed
   (b) Who makes traffic laws
   (c) Community regulations
2. Regulations and requirements for drivers
   (a) Regulations pertaining to drivers' licenses
   (b) Different types of drivers' licenses
3. Enforcement of traffic regulations
   (a) Direction of traffic, inspection of vehicles, examination of individuals for drivers' licenses, traffic courts, and effects of public attitudes
4. Organization for traffic safety
   (a) Knowledge concerning the work of local, state, and national organizations
5. Safety in using public conveyances
   (a) How to ride public conveyances safely
   (b) Safety with respect to all phases of school bus transportation
6. Safety in railroad transportation
   (a) Statistics regarding railroad accidents
   (b) Railroad safety regulations
   (c) Grade crossings
   (d) Dangers of trespassing on railroad property
   (e) Organized efforts of national and private agencies for railroad safety
7. Water transportation safety
   (a) Extent of water transportation
   (b) Statistics of water transportation accidents
   (c) Safety methods and regulations pertaining to water transportation
   (d) Work of the United States government in water transportation safety such as weather bureaus, warnings, inspections, licenses, lighthouse service, and Coast Guard
8. Air transportation safety
   (a) Kinds of air service
   (b) Statistics on aviation accidents
   (c) Causes of aviation accidents
   (d) Prevention of aviation accidents

Safety in activities

1. Skating and coasting
   (a) Recognition of dangers related to skating and coasting
   (b) Precautions to take in assuring safety in skating and coasting
2. Snowballing
   (a) Recognition of dangers involved
   (b) Rights of pedestrians
3. Holiday safety
   (a) Christmas—safe and unsafe gifts; dangers of firearms

Safety in the home

1. Present status of home accidents
   (a) Statistics on the various types of home accidents
2. Causes of home accidents
   (a) Personal factors such as skill, judgment, fatigue, hurry, worry, age, personal characteristics, and physical handicaps

(b) Mechanical factors such as arrangement within the home, equipment in the home, and safety habits of the occupants

(c) Places in the home in which accidents occur such as stairs, kitchen, bedroom, basement, porch, yard, bathroom, dining room, and living room

3. Types of home accidents
   (a) Burns, conflagrations, and explosions
   (b) Falls of all types
   (c) Poisoning, including gas poisoning
   (d) Firearms and fireworks
   (e) Mechanical suffocation

Work accidents

1. Welfare of the individual student in a particular community
   (a) Survey of community occupations and the health and safety hazards inherent
   (b) Consideration of physical and mental capacities of students in relation to hazards of occupation
2. Effects of industrial accidents on the family
   (a) Economic, social, and psychological
3. Preventive measures employed in occupations and industry
   (a) Education, machine protection, regulations, inspection, protective personal equipment, medical service, supervision for safety, publicity, and rewards
4. Results of safety work in the industrial field
   (a) History, statistics, and methods of safety

First aid

1. Advanced knowledge concerning supplies needed for first aid kits
   (a) Various articles to be included
2. Basic principles of first aid
3. Symptoms and care of specific injuries
   (a) More extensive knowledge and practice of the first aid taught in the intermediate grades plus an understanding of other less usual injuries
   (b) More specific knowledge and practice of artificial respiration

How safety protects the individual and the group

1. Bicycle safety
   (a) Statistics pertaining to the bicycle accidents
   (b) Extensive knowledge of bicycle safety such as care of the safety devices on bicycles, skill in riding, safety habits on the streets, employing proper signals, and obeying all rules and regulations
2. Swimming and boating
   (a) Causes of drowning
   (b) How to prevent accidental drowning—water skill and safety, knowledge and, practice of safety habits in the water, safe use of boats, and understanding of weather conditions
3. Hiking
   (a) Extensive knowledge of hazards of hiking
   (b) Knowledge concerning the prevention of hiking accidents
4. Camping
   (a) Observance of safety in swimming, boating, and hiking
   (b) Knowledge of safety concerning safe camp sites, fire prevention, and weather conditions
5. Firearms and fireworks
   (a) Statistics regarding firearm accidents
   (b) Safe storage of firearms
   (c) Recognition of dangers of fireworks

SAFETY EDUCATION IN THE HIGH SCHOOL

Safety education in the high school depends greatly upon the program offered in the elementary and junior high schools. If sufficient time and attention are devoted to the teaching of safety in the grades below high school, the problem of safety education is materially simplified. Therefore, determination of the safety program in the high school must be on the basis of the previous education of the students. The development of a safety program in any high school usually must be done on an individual school basis because of the varying amounts of safety training offered in the elementary and junior high schools.

It is conceivable that the program of safety in the high schools should be largely the fundamentals of safety practices. This would be true when little or no safety instruction was given in the grades below the high school. On the other hand, a student may enter high school with enough knowledge and training in safety so that a minimum of time need be devoted to safety instruction in specific situations. In such instances the time allotted can be given to an appreciation of safety in society as a whole. Although it is entirely possible that sufficient time and attention might be devoted to safety at the elementary and junior high school levels to eliminate the need for a highly organized program of safety in the high school, there would remain the need for emphasizing certain types of safety that are beyond the capacity of students of elementary and junior high school age. Furthermore, the ideal situation wherein students below the high school level are brought to a high degree of development in safety and accident prevention seldom exists. Therefore, in a large majority of the high schools of the country there is a definite and distinct need for a well-organized program of safety.

The problem of organizing and conducting an effective safety education program in the secondary school is quite different from that in the elementary school. In the elementary school the traditional organization of classroom teachers lends itself readily to the efficient conduct of an effective safety program. In the high school, teachers are largely specialized in definite fields or subjects, without more or less total responsibility for a given group of students. Although the homeroom organization in the secondary school does provide to some extent for a teacher to assume some responsibility for a particular group, under ordinary circumstances the amount of time given to homeroom activities is insignificant in comparison to the time available in the elementary school classroom teacher organization.

Another factor that makes the secondary school problem of safety education more difficult than in the elementary school is explained by the psychological nature of high school students. Characteristics of students of secondary school age include their desire for adventure which at times may border on recklessness, particularly from the viewpoint of safety. Also there is a tendency for students of high school age to ridicule restraint which is seemingly negative. Often, the teaching of safety may appear to the students to be negative and inhibitive and in direct contrast to the spirit of youth in that it appears to place restraint on their natural ways of reacting to life.

For many years high schools lagged behind elementary schools in providing a well-balanced program of safety education. However, high schools have stressed and taught safety in certain specific fields and areas. In vocational and industrial arts, the teachers have stressed safety in their courses largely because of the more hazardous nature of the work. Also, for obvious reasons, safety has been stressed in science laboratories, home economics classes, gymnasiums, and swimming pools and on the athletic field.

With the development of safety education, high school educators came to realize the need for a broader and more comprehensive program of safety throughout the high school. Experience with various methods of organizing, teaching, and presenting broader programs of safety has led to the following ways of offering curriculum material.

1. Organizing safety as a separate subject
2. Teaching safety as a unit included in other subjects
3. Teaching safety through the homeroom organization
4. Arranging a safety education program around pupil organizations and special projects
5. Correlating and integrating safety with many other subjects and activities
6. Combining safety teaching with health teaching

Perhaps the greatest need for the organization of general safety as a separate subject is found in those schools in which the students have not had the benefit of a broad safety program in the elementary school. When a separate course in safety is offered in the high school, it should be organized on a unit basis, with due consideration for the past education and experience of the students enrolled in the course. The content of the unit should embody advanced safety materials. Considerable stress should be placed on activities of a practical nature. Activities in which students participate in the high schools should be analyzed, and the safety elements should be incorporated in the units. Also, the relationship of safety to community and adult life should have a prominent place in the safety course.

The inclusion of units in safety education in other school subjects can be an effective way to offer safety education in the high school when it is necessary. In the absense of a separate course in safety, there is a distinct need for the inclusion of safety units in other fields. When safety units are included in other subjects, they should be arranged to embody material not usually given as an integral part of courses such as industrial arts, home economics, health education, and physical education. Some of the subjects in which distinct safety units may be readily included are health education, social studies, science, English, and home economics.

In the absence of a separate course in safety or units included in other school subjects, it is possible to impart a reasonable amount of safety education through the homeroom organization, provided that the material is well-organized and arranged and the teaching is closely supervised by someone competent in the field of safety education. At best, however, the homeroom plan of safety education is inferior to the separate course or units in other subjects.

The arranging of safety education through pupil organizations and through special projects is considered largely a supplementary procedure. With any type of organization for safety it is deemed desirable to capitalize on student organizations and special projects to broaden the scope of safety education, but these methods are insufficient in themselves. However, in the absence of other means of imparting safety knowledge, they are at least helpful. Some of the student organizations and special projects through which safety can be taught are assemblies, school newspaper, posters, school safety patrols, school clubs, driver education and training, and field trips.

When safety education is properly correlated and integrated with other school subjects and activities, there is an advantage in presenting it in connection with situations as they arise. This precludes the necessity of adding and introducing a subject into the curriculum. On the other hand, there is a disadvantage in diffusing the safety responsibilities so that there is a possibility of the complete neglect of vital safety material by some teachers who lack proper safety consciousness. When a total safety education program is conducted through correlation and integration, definite responsibilities in the teaching of safety should be assigned. That is, teachers of specific subjects within fields should be held responsible for the safety knowledge that should be imparted in relation to their subjects and the accompanying activities. For example, teachers in physical education should teach safety having to do with participation in physical education, athletics, and games and sports. Teachers in science should teach safety in relation to the usual activities surrounding the science laboratory. Shop teachers should teach shop safety, and home economic teachers should stress safety in relation to the performance of activities in home economics.

Although the correlation and integration of safety education with other subjects and activities are desirable and helpful regardless of other ways of imparting safety knowledge, they are not entirely satisfactory in giving a complete and comprehensive education in safety. Therefore, they must be considered largely as supplementary means of imparting safety knowledge.

Some of the areas and topics that should be taught and explored at the high school level are street and highway accidents, water safety, railroad safety, water transportation, home accidents, use of electricity and electrical appliances, use of gas and gas appliances, burns, falls, use of flammable materials, school accidents, fire prevention, safe use of laboratories, safety in aviation, safety in industry, forest conservation, first aid, psychological aspects of safety and accident prevention, safe use of firearms, safety practices in farming, dangers of contaminated food, poisons, injurious plants and animals, alcohol and narcotics, and driver education and training.

SCHOOL AND COMMUNITY COOPERATION FOR SAFETY

It is a fundamental obligation of every community to provide living conditions that are as safe as possible for everyone. In providing and assuring the safest environment for youth, there is a need for community organization. Every community should recognize and plan for youth safety in such ways as protection against physical dangers and disease and provision of safe and wholesome places for play and recreation. To furnish maximum protection for youth, cooperation between school and community agencies will prove advantageous since the greatest percentage of accidents to the school age population occurs in places other than school. Some of the community organizations and agencis that should be expected to cooperate with the schools are police departments, fire departments, recreation departments, and health departments.

Police departments should provide protection at school crossings by regulating vehicular and pedestrian traffic, by helping to train and supervise school safety patrols and auxiliary guards, by restricting traffic in designated coasting areas, and by blocking off certain streets and congested areas as play streets. Fire departments should provide the following kinds of aids: (1) inspect schools and buildings and recommend changes to assure safety, (2) plan with schools for fire and civil defense drills, (3) demonstrate care and proper use of fire extinguishers, (4) help promote special fire prevention and protection activities, and (5) assist in home inspection campaigns. Community recreation departments should perform the following functions: (1) maintain safe play and recreation areas, (2) furnish skilled supervision for all recreational activities, (3) train and furnish lifeguards for pools and swimming areas, (4) make first aid supplies and services available when necessary, and (5) furnish instruction in the safe use of recreational equipment, apparatus, and play areas. Community health departments should do the following: (1) provide health services such as examination and treatment of injuries in emergency cases, (2) maintain sanitary conditions in swimming areas, and (3) post and enforce sanitary regulations.

It should be recognized that the school is only one of many agencies in the community interested in the common problems of safety. The safety of the school population, moreover, is a single but inseparable phase of this common problem. As a community is rendered safer for all, so will it be safer for youth. For this reason, as well as for the broader reason that education is maintained by society to serve society, the school administrator should view himself as a community leader in safety and should accept the responsibility for assisting in any appropriate projects of other community agencies. In this respect he may be guided by considerations such as the following.

1. All cooperative activities planned for the school should be sound from an educational point of view.
2. Activities which provide for student participation should be welcomed in community projects.
3. There are good public relations values in having school staff representation at safety council meetings, parent-teacher meetings on community safety, and other programs of a public nature in this field.
4. Students should be utilized to make parents aware of home and traffic hazards and the need for correction and control of these hazards.
5. Use of such media as the newspapers, radio, and television as well as special meetings for adults can be very helpful in both adult and youth safety and accident programs on a community-wide basis.

QUESTIONS FOR DISCUSSION

1. How do the yearly number of deaths caused by accidents compare with those caused by diseases each year in the United States?

2. What are some important factors in the historical evolution of safety education?
3. Why is safety education so closely allied with health education?
4. How is it justifiable to provide potentially dangerous activities such as sports in schools?
5. What are some implications of mental and emotional factors for safety and safety education?
6. What is meant by the statement that proper safety habits and desirable safety attitudes are based upon safety education?
7. What are some major causes of youth accidents?
8. Who should be responsible for the school safety education program?
9. What are the major functions of the school safety program?
10. To what extent is the home a factor in the total accident problem?
11. What are the major causes of traffic accidents?
12. What are some important steps which may be taken to reduce the frequency of accidents in school?
13. Under what conditions is the teacher liable in the event of a serious accident involving a student?
14. Who is responsible for teaching safety in the junior and senior high school?
15. What groups are ordinarily involved in city safety councils or committees?
16. What are some special problems related to teaching safety at the high school level?
17. What are the advantages of viewing school safety as a phase of total community safety?

SUGGESTED CLASS ACTIVITIES

1. Obtain figures showing the numbers of accidents caused by various factors (a) in the home and (b) in the community.
2. Form a committee to prepare a sample check list of possible home hazards, room by room, which may be used by students in evaluating the safety status of their own homes.
3. Form a committee to prepare a sample checklist to guide the inspection of the school plant and grounds for safety hazards.
4. Prepare a list of safety measures employed in a school that is well known to you. Evaluate this list and indicate how it might be made more adequate.
5. Form committees to outline teaching units on home, traffic, and other community safety subjects which might be used.
6. Prepare a list of major sources of safety materials suitable for use in the secondary school.
7. Form a panel to discuss and evaluate the various plans for teaching safety, that is, as a separate subject, by integration and by utilizing opportunities (teachable moments) as they arise.
8. Prepare a plan for teaching safety in a school that is well known to you. Take into account the special circumstances of that school which are likely to influence the type of safety education program that would be most feasible, at least in the first stages of its development.

REFERENCES

1. Bishop, Richard: How did they happen? Safety Education **42**: April, 1963.
2. Dzenowagis, Joseph G., and Irwin, Leslie W.: Prevalence of certain harmful health and safety misconceptions among fifth and sixth grade children. Research Quarterly **25**: May, 1954.
3. Dzenowagis, Joseph: College sports—accidents, injuries, Safety Education **41**: March, 1962.
4. Florio, A. E., and Stafford, G. T.: Safety education, ed. 2, New York, 1962, McGraw-Hill Book Co., Inc.
5. National Safety Council: Accident facts, Chicago, published annually, The Council.
6. Rosenfield, Harry: Guilty, Safety Educaton **42**: April, 1963.
7. Spadafora, Jennie: Accidents: the number one killer, Safety Education **42**: May, 1963.
8. Stack, Herbert J., and Elkow, J. Duke: Education for safe living, ed. 2, New York, 1957, Prentice-Hall, Inc.
9. Weedon, Vivian: Home is where the parents aren't when their children need them, Safety Education **42**: Feb., 1963.

Chapter 6

PLANNING HEALTH INSTRUCTION IN THE SECONDARY SCHOOL

This chapter deals with materials that are essential to a comprehensive understanding of the health instruction program on the secondary school level. Consideration is given to the various health areas, placement of these areas within the total school program, various plans of scheduling within a single year's program, the characteristics of secondary school students, and finally, suggested secondary school health content.

HEALTH AREAS

The particular grouping of health areas that follow is only one of many ways that have been proposed by groups and individuals doing research in health curriculum planning.

Fig. 5 gives a simple yet comprehensive way of grouping health content areas. It was developed in a health workshop* attended by a number of experienced health teachers.

The purpose of Fig. 5 is to show that the four major health areas and the subareas within each all share equally in the development of the healthy individual. If one or more areas are not included in the school health curriculum, the students are likely to be adversely affected in regard to total physical, mental, social, and emotional development. Timely emphasis on each area is considered a necessity.

For the sake of uniformity, the following outline plan of the health content

---

*Workshop in Health Education Curriculum Planning, Oregon State University, July, 1958; sponsored by the Oregon State Department of Education.

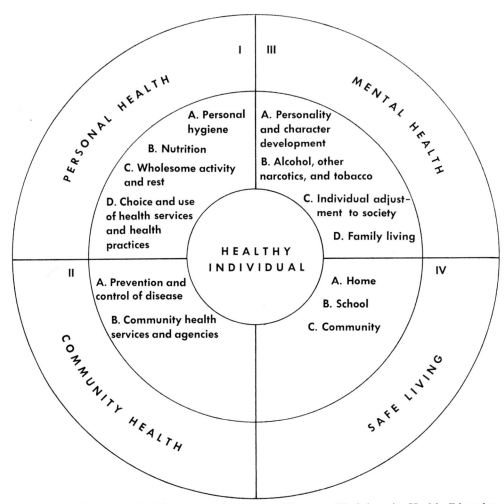

Fig. 5. The four major health areas and subareas. (Courtesy Workshop in Health Education Curriculum Planning, Oregon State University, July, 1958; sponsored by the Oregon State Department of Education.)

areas suggested in Fig. 5 will be used throughout this book when reference is made to the various health areas.

I. Personal health
   A. Personal hygiene
   B. Nutrition
   C. Wholesome activity and rest
   D. Choice and use of health services and health practices
II. Community health
   A. Prevention and control of disease
   B. Community health services and agencies
III. Mental health
   A. Personality and character development
   B. Alcohol, narcotics and tobacco
   C. Individual adjustment to society
   D. Family living

IV. Safe living
    A. Home
    B. School
    C. Community

GRADE PLACEMENT OF HEALTH AREAS

The grade placement of health content areas has not fully crystallized. The placement of the several health areas in the curriculum of grades one through twelve in schools throughout the country may be nonexistent, may be carefully planned and coordinated, or may be at some point of development between these two extremes.

State legislation pertaining to health teaching. Twenty of the fifty states have neither laws nor regulations by the state departments of education pertaining to health instruction in the public schools. Most schools within these states do not have well-organized health instruction programs. In most cases, health instruction depends largely on the initiative of individual teachers. Furthermore, when planning is absent, there is ordinarily very little continuity from one grade to the next, and it is not uncommon for excessive overlapping of subject matter to occur.

Fortunately, there seems to be a trend developing which indicates that a greater number of states are beginning to give more attention and support to the school health instruction program.

Continuous emphasis plan. In some schools, health is taught by a plan that is best described as continuous emphasis. In this plan all areas are con-

Table 12. Health instruction by continuous emphasis for school systems in which health course is taught only once in junior high school and once in senior high school

Area	Grade							
	1	2	3	4	5	6	8	11
I. Personal health								
A. Personal hygiene	x	x	x	x	x	x	x	x
B. Nutrition	x	x	x	x	x	x	x	x
C. Wholesome activity and rest	x	x	x	x	x	x	x	x
D. Choice and use of health services and								
health practices	x	x	x	x	x	x	x	x
II. Community health								
A. Prevention and control of disease	x	x	x	x	x	x	x	x
B. Community health services and agencies	x	x	x	x	x	x	x	x
III. Mental health								
A. Personality and character development	x	x	x	x	x	x	x	x
B. Alcohol, other narcotics, and tobacco	x	x	x	x	x	x	x	x
C. Individual adjustment to society	x	x	x	x	x	x	x	x
D. Family living	x	x	x	x	x	x	x	x
IV. Safe living								
A. Home	x	x	x	x	x	x	x	x
B. School	x	x	x	x	x	x	x	x
C. Community	x	x	x	x	x	x	x	x

sidered of equal importance, and the teacher must cover all of them during the designated health course.

The continuous emphasis plan is most often used in those school systems in which a health course is offered only once during the three years of junior high school, as either a semester or full-year course, and once again in the senior high school. With teaching done most often through integration in the elementary grades, a plan of continuous emphasis for the twelve grades in a school with the areas already discussed would be like that shown in Table 12.

The advantages of continuous emphasis method are the following.

1. It assures that the student receives some instruction in all health areas.
2. It discourages a teacher from teaching only in favorite areas.
3. It supports the contention that all areas are important for the development of the healthy individual.

Among the disadvantages of continuous emphasis are the following.

1. It does not recognize the increased needs of students for certain areas at specific periods during their growth and development.
2. It gives emphasis to certain areas that students show little or no need for at specific times during their school life.
3. It permits for excessive overlapping in health learning situations.
4. It can lead to student criticism that health is boring and pointless.

Despite the disadvantages of the continuous emphasis method, it has substantial merit for those school systems in which health is limited to a course given only one semester or a year in the junior high school and again in the senior high school. When instruction is conducted for longer periods, one of the following three plans is more preferable.

Cycle plan. The cycle plan was first introduced a number of years ago to offset the mounting criticism that health teaching was too repetitious. This plan divided the twelve-year school program into four three-year cycles. Each of the health areas was taught once during each cycle, with attempts to place each at the point within the cycle which most satisfactorily met the needs of the students. In Table 13 is indicated the possible placement of the health areas on a cycle plan.

It should be noted that most grades have an equal number of health areas and each area appears only once every three years. Those who support this plan are careful to point out that teachers at other grade levels than those at which the indicated areas are taught by direct instruction are free and in fact are encouraged to employ incidental teaching when opportunities arise in areas not directly their responsibility.

The advantages of the cycle plan are the following.

1. It eliminates the criticism of constant repetition in some areas and thus tends to reduce student boredom.
2. It ensures that all subjects will be taught at least once every three years.
3. It permits the teacher to develop more complete units in the designated areas with full knowledge that the area will not be taught for another three years.

The disadvantages, while not so extreme as those of the continuous emphasis plan, are significant. These include the following.

1. It is too rigid to meet the needs of students satisfactorily.
2. It fails to recognize that some areas may require continuous emphasis if knowledge is to be retained and good health and safety habits are to be developed.

Table 13. Health instruction by cycle plan

Area	Cycle I Grades 1 2 3	Cycle II Grades 4 5 6	Cycle III Grades 7 8 9	Cycle IV Grades 10 11 12
I. Personal health				
A. Personal hygiene	x	x	x	x
B. Nutrition	x	x	x	x
C. Wholesome activity and rest	x	x	x	x
D. Choice and use of health services and health practices	x	x	x	x
II. Community health				
A. Prevention and control of disease	x	x	x	x
B. Community health services and agencies	x	x	x	x
III. Mental health				
A. Personality and character development	x	x	x	x
B. Alcohol, other narcotics, and tobacco	x	x	x	x
C. Individual adjustment to society	x	x	x	x
D. Family living	x	x	x	x
IV. Safe living				
A. Home	x	x	x	x
B. School	x	x	x	x
C. Community	x	x	x	x

Table 14. Placement of health areas using both cycle plan and continuous emphasis plan in combination*

Area	Cycle I Grades 1 2 3	Cycle II Grades 4 5 6	Cycle III Grades 7 8 9	Cycle IV Grades 10 11 12
Structure and function	x x x	x	x	x
Personal hygiene	x x x	x	x	x
Physiological effects of exercise		x	x	x
Nutrition	x x x	x	x	x
First aid and safety	x x x	x x x	x x	x
Control of communicable diseases (including non-communicable diseases)	x x x	x	x	x
Community health and sanitation	x x x	x	x x	x
Choice and use of health services and products		x	x	x
Mental health†	x x x	x x x	x x	x
Alcoholic beverages and narcotics		x	x	x

*From State Department of Education: Health instruction in Oregon secondary schools, Salem, 1954, The Department.

†Teacher will place emphasis in this area as the emotional needs of the individual student may determine.

Cycle plan-continuous emphasis plan. A plan for placement of health subject matter which combines the advantages of the cycle plan with those of continuous emphasis seems the logical result of the problems so far presented. This plan provides for cycling but also takes into account the fact that certain areas need to be emphasized on a continuing basis.

The information in Table 14 shows that certain areas are on a cycle pattern without deviation, whereas others are taught by the continuous emphasis plan in the early years and are then taught by the cycle plan in the secondary school years.

The advantages of a plan combining the cycle approach with continuous emphasis are several.

1. It provides for continuing emphasis in the areas in which it is considered important that the student receive direct instruction at the risk of excessive repetition.
2. It is not considered repetitious when the successive units are carefully constructed and integrated.
3. It meets the needs of students at important age periods.
4. It assures that all subjects will be taught at least once by direct instruction every three years, commencing at the cycle of maturation. That is, for example, the area of Choice and use of health services and products is not taught until the sixth grade but then appears twice more on three-year cycles.

There are fewer disadvantages to the cycle-continuous emphasis plan than to the others presented. Two points should be considered, perhaps more as criticisms than as disadvantages. One is the unfortunate fact that few school systems teach health in all twelve grades. When a health course is taught only once or twice at the junior and senior high levels, it would be inappropriate to teach only those subjects suggested by this plan. If, for instance, a teacher of a ninth grade health class knows that his students have had no direct instruction since the sixth grade and will have none again until the twelfth grade, he would feel obligated to teach more than the three areas indicated. The second is the fact that even this plan has received criticism for not meeting the needs of students. There is the belief that any plan which includes cycling is arbitrary and tends to defeat the objectives of health teaching. As a consequence of these criticisms, another plan for the placement of health areas has developed in recent years. This has most often been described as the scope and sequence method.

Scope and sequence plan. In recent years some local school districts as well as state department of education curriculum committees have developed various plans for placement of health subject matter. Many of these plans are impossible to classify under one term such as the continuous emphasis method or cycle plan. When this has been the case, there is pointed concern for the scope and sequence of the several areas of subject matter. The philosophy of these committees has been to plan subject matter in depth (scope) and breadth (sequence) so that the needs which students have at any and all levels of maturation will be met. Such a philosophy rejects the arbitrariness of cycling but recognizes the potential danger for repetition inherent in continuous emphasis.

Nonetheless, there is much in the philosophy of the scope and sequence plan that bespeaks of continuous emphasis, and perhaps the placement of health areas has made the full circle and has returned almost to where it was approximately 30 years ago. Certainly examination of Table 15 will indicate similarities between the two approaches to health subject matter placement.

There are basic differences, however, which make the two plans quite different. The first is the fact that the scope and sequence concept groups the several health areas into four major categories, thus relating all health areas to a greater extent than has been the case under previous plans. Second, there is a greater concern in the scope and sequence concept for the needs of students. The continuous emphasis plan is concerned with needs but solves the problem by teaching all areas every year. On the other hand, the scope and sequence method meets the needs as they arise. Thus, certain areas will be taught in consecutive years with increasing depth, whereas others will be taught considerably less often.

Since absolute or even partial cycling largely ignores developing health needs of students, an examination of Table 15, developed on the basis of the scope and sequence philosophy, indicates that there has been no attempt to cycle subject matter.

A recently adopted course of study which follows a scope and sequence

Table 15. Placement of health areas using plan most often described as scope and sequence

Area	Grade											
	1	2	3	4	5	6	7	8	9	10	11	12
I. Personal health												
A. Personal hygiene	x	x	x	x	x	x	x					x
B. Nutrition	x	x	x	x	x	x		x				
C. Wholesome rest and activity	x	x	x	x		x		x		x		
D. Choice and use of health services and health practices				x					x		x	
II. Community health												
A. Prevention and control of disease	x	x	x			x						x
B. Community health services and agencies	x	x	x	x			x					x
III. Mental health												
A. Personality and character development	x	x	x	x	x				x	x		x
B. Alcohol, other narcotics, and tobacco							x			x		
C. Individual adjustment to society	x	x	x	x	x				x	x		x
D. Family living	x	x	x	x	x							x
IV. Safe living												
A. Home	x	x	x		x		x					
B. School	x	x	x		x		x	x		x		
C. Community	x	x	x	x	x	x	x	x	x	x	x	

plan very similar to that indicated in Table 15 describes the aims of this type of plan as follows:

"1. To provide each student with a basic education in personal health prac-tices, community health services, mental health development, and good safety habits

"2. To try to instill in students a pride in healthful living and an apprecia-tion of the human body—its capabilities and limitations

"3. To provide for the joint responsibility of home, school, and community for the health education of the school age child

"4. To teach within the comprehensive ability of each child so that all are challenged to develop and utilize critical thinking"*

SCHEDULING

When a school determines the grade levels at which direct health instruction will be presented and the areas to be taught, there still remains the question of scheduling.

Total time devoted to instruction is often prescribed by law or regulation as in the following example.

"The Superintendent of Public Instruction has stipulated that approximately one sixth of each school day in the high schools be devoted to health and physical education instruction and activities and that the minimum amount of this time allotted to health instruction be 45 one-hour periods per school year."†

Since there are many variations to the way in which this minimum amount of time or more if the school should so decide, is scheduled, consideration should be given to the merits of scheduling plans.

Regular course. The average public school year is approximately thirty-six weeks in length. The most acceptable scheduling of health instruction within this period is as a full-year course which meets five days a week. A frequent but less acceptable alternative is a half-year course, eighteen weeks, still meeting five days a week.

Scheduling health on a regular basis has important values for the student. It indicates to him that the school administration considers the subject matter important; health becomes as prestigious as other subjects in the curriculum. Also, it permits the student to develop concepts without interruption. Learning is more complete and interest is maintained more satisfactorily when health is taught five days a week rather than only two or three times. Learning is also enhanced because students feel less need for daily review of important concepts when they receive daily health instruction.

Equally as important are the benefits which accrue to the teacher. When a teacher has a health course which meets five days a week, he is able to present content more adequately; assignments are more easily made and are more likely

*From Health education guide K through grade 12, Corvallis, Oregon, School District, No. 509J, 1961-1962.
†From State Department of Education: Health instruction in Oregon secondary schools, Salem, 1954, p. 4.

to be completed by the student; visual aids, films, outside speakers, and field trips can be planned and presented more satisfactorily; evaluation procedures may be used more as learning situations, rather than as enforcement to press for assignment completion, as is likely when the course meets less often.

Perhaps most important to the success of the program, there is increasing administrative acceptance for the health course scheduled on a regular basis. School administrators recognize that teachers hired to teach health will be better qualified than if health teaching responsibilities are assigned haphazardly. This becomes more true as our knowledge in health sciences increases along with the tremendous need to translate technical facts into relevant health attitudes and habits. In addition, the administrator is able to schedule a regular course in his crowded curriculum more easily than one meeting on an irregular basis. Also, standards for student learning and accomplishment are improved. Finally, the administrator is justified in counting the regular health course as a unit toward the number required for high school graduation, and he is able to point out to students that the course is acceptable as a credit toward college entrance. This fact has been substantiated by a study which drew the following conclusions.

"1. Institutions of higher education will in general, accept credit in health education as a college entrance unit when the subject has been taught as a separate course.

"2. Most colleges will accept credit in health education as one of the electives in the sixteen units required for admission.

"3. Most colleges which accept credit in health education prefer that health education be taken in high school for a full year with one credit or for one semester with one-half unit. Fewer institutions accept the plan when credit it accumulated fractionally over two or three years, or when the credit in health education is combined with that for physical education."*

Thus it is seen that the regular health course is certainly the most acceptable type of scheduling from all points of view. The fact is, however, that there are several other scheduling patterns to which health is subjected. Each such pattern represents some sort of a compromise or adjustment necessitated by local problems and differing philosophies. The several other scheduling patterns that are most prevalent are now presented in brief, and the disadvantages of each become obvious when comparison is made with the regular health course.

Block plan. Health and physical education are often scheduled in alternating blocks of time. In one such state-adopted plan, for instance, the school year is divided into four nine-week blocks. All students take physical education the first and fourth nine-week period. During the second nine-week period half of the students take health while the remaining students take physical education; in the third nine-week period the two groups change. The classes meet five days a week. Thus, the students receive forty-five class hours of health instruction in

---

*From Kilander, H. J.: Health education as a college entrance unit, Journal of School Health 21: May, 1951.

a single block of time. The advantages of the longer health course may still apply, although reduced proportionately.

Other scheduling plans on the block basis exist. These include blocks of six, four, three, two, and even one week, still meeting the five days a week. When the students alternate with physical education throughout the school year, they end up with a half year's course in health education, but as the alternating blocks become smaller, the benefits that derive also diminish. There is serious question as to how much value the student receives from a health course that meets only a week at a time or even two and three weeks at a time.

Alternating three-two plan. With this plan the students are scheduled for health one day and physical education the next day, disregarding vacation periods and other interruptions. For maximum benefit the same teacher should be responsible for both health and physical education in order to relate important facts and to best capitalize on incidental teaching situations as they may arise.

The three-two plan, as it is known, is found particularly in those school systems in which boys and girls are segregated for physical education. Because of this common practice, arising from the differing physical skills and interest of boys and girls, the belief developed that health, also, is best taught with the sexes segregated. Whereas this may be true for one or two units, such as menstrual hygiene and reproduction on the junior high level, the developing philosophy is that health teaching provides the grestest student benefits when the classes are mixed. As more educators on the administrative level come to accept this, we should witness a gradual reduction in those systems using the three-two plan of health scheduling.

One period each week. A few scheduling plans exist wherein health is scheduled for one day a week. When health and physical education are under the direction of the same teacher, this one day of health is often determined by rain or other restricting factors. Occasionally health will alternate with home economics, industrial arts, music periods, study halls, and other less than regular activities.

Correlation with other subjects. A few states permit the health education requirement to be completed through correlation with other subjects. When this is the case, it is usual to designate the grade level, health area, and necessary number of class periods.

For example, we can transfer the units found in grade twelve shown in

Table 16. Correlation of health with other courses in twelfth grade curriculum

Area	Correlated with	periods
Personal hygiene	Orientation	10
Family living	Family life education	25
Individual adjustment to society	Social studies	15
Personality and character development	American problems	10
Prevention and control of disease	Biology	20
Community health services and agencies	American problems	10

Table 15 into a plan which calls for correlation of these same units within other courses in the twelfth grade curriculum. A plan to assure this would be similar to that shown in Table 16, based on ninety class hours or a half-year requirement.

With the plan shown in Table 16, a file card should be kept for each student for grades one through twelve which contains completion date of each health unit and the subject with which it was correlated. In addition, all lessons plans, including content and time allotment for health instruction with the correlated subject, should be kept on file with the administrators.

IMPORTANT CHARACTERISTICS OF SECONDARY SCHOOL STUDENTS

There are many important characteristics of secondary school students that should be taken into consideration in the health education program.

Junior high school students

If we think of the junior high school as consisting of seventh, eighth, and ninth grades, the students in these grades will range in age from slightly less than 12 to more than 14 years. This is an age period of extremely rapid growth, especially for girls, and the developing characteristics of both girls and boys create a multitude of needs. Brief consideration is given here to their physical, mental and emotional, and social characteristics.

Physical characteristics. Between the ages of 12 and 14 years, growth is rapid. Girls develop at a faster rate than boys, and most will enter puberty by the age of 13½ years, whereas boys lag by approximately two years. Rapidly accelerated growth, triggered by glandular changes, is likely to result in problems of personality adjustment and postural defects. Desire for activities requiring extreme expenditures of energy places further stress on the body frame and supporting systems, thus increasing the need for sleep and rest. Awkwardness and poor coordination are not uncommon. Skin disorders and acne plague large numbers of youth in this age group.

Mental and emotional characteristics. The widely divergent growth patterns among students is frequently a cause for worry and anxiety. Most boys and girls make satisfactory adjustments during this rapidly changing period, but some are likely to show one or more of the deviant characteristics indicated in Chapter 3. Adults should be alert to offer counsel and guidance to those who need it.

At 12 to 14 years of age it is typical for boys and girls to first seriously question their relations with adults. Status with peer groups is more important than adult approval. Cliques, clubs, and societies become all-important. The junior high school age youth receives great satisfaction in individual accomplishments which are recognized by the peer group. Independence from family in most respects is frustrated by continuing economic dependence. Ambivalence and tension often result. Adult behavior is imitated as well as dress and language; the desire to be treated as an adult conflicts with the need for continuing family security and status within a family group.

Intellectual development is striking during this period. Abstract thought comes easily, and personal experiences are intellectualized. The meaning of life and reality take on importance. Interest in mental health increases.

There is an awakening interest in the opposite sex, which has been dormant previous to this period. Girls' interest in boys is kindled first because of their earlier maturation. For both sexes, however, tensions and anxiety will occur as they slowly build confidence in their interpersonal relationships.

Social characteristics. The initial problems of dating become a prime interest, especially for girls. Both sexes reflect interest in manners, appropriate behavior in different situations, and acceptable social values. Care for personal grooming almost becomes an obsession.

The 12- to 14-year-old student projects personal social problems to the larger scene of the world around him. Solving his own life problems is done partly in terms of large social groups. The larger social problems of housing, sanitation, venereal disease, and community relationships take on significance. The problems of our present culture become real and dramatic.

Senior high school students

The period of concern here is usually between 15 and 18 years. The students in this period are most often referred to as youth, and they are said to be in the period of adolescence.

Physical characteristics. At 15 to 16 years of age physical maturation has been achieved by about 90% of the girls and 60% of the boys. At 17 to 18 years of age all but approximately 10% of the boys have matured. Girls, who have been as much as two years in advance of boys in physical development since the early junior high school period, discover that most boys have grown taller and more mature physically. The awkward period for both sexes is behind them, posture improves, and most girls become more graceful by the end of the senior high school years.

Adult characteristics are developing. The long bones have nearly completed their growth, and adult height is reached by the twelfth grade. The heart, slow to develop during the years of rapid structural change, still continues to grow in size; by the twelfth grade it, too, is near adult size.

Appetite is often cavernous, especially for boys, and between-meal eating is common and is often a serious problem. Sweets have a strong appeal. Faulty eating habits and need for large carbohydrate supplies result in an unstable energy level and a tendency to frequent fatigue.

Mental and emotional characteristics. The adolescent's concern for being like others and being accepted greatly influences his level of mental and emotional well-being. He needs to be popular, if only in a limited sense. He fears ridicule, and he is often over-sensitive to the opinions of others.

The 15- to 18-year-old youth presses for independence. He seeks to remove the last obstacle, the economic dependence, by taking after school and summer jobs. Adults continue to supply him with the needed moral support. Most youth display a front of assurance and self-sufficiency, but adult help is still needed and accepted. Judgment among senior high school students varies widely.

Social characteristics. Acceptance by a social group is a consuming objective of most adolescents. The gang interests of earlier years give way to the need to be accepted by the opposite sex. The social graces that win approval assume more importance. As the adolescent wins acceptance, he responds by an intense loyalty and gives much time and interest to group activities. Cliques tend to form as the adolescent seeks further demonstration of support from the peer group.

HEALTH CONTENT BY GRADE LEVELS

The content of health courses and units on the secondary school level is constantly changing. Exactly what will be included in any single course or unit is likely to be largely determined by the experience and background of the person teaching; the geographic location of the school; the needs of the students; the facilities and time available; and the state legislative and board of education requirements. Because of this wide variation, it would be presumptive to recommend a single course outline for all situations.

The suggested content which follows, however, is presented as an example of what might be included at the various grade levels. It was developed originally in a workshop by a group of experienced teachers and administrators.* It demonstrates the result of cooperative efforts in curriculum building. Subsequent committee work under the direction of the Oregan State Department of Education has resulted in several changes and incorporation of this content into the revised state health education handbooks.†

Health content areas by grade levels may be listed as follows.

Grade 7

I. Personal health
   A. Personal hygiene
      1. Human growth and development
      2. Individual differences
      3. Grooming
II. Community health
   B. Community health services and agencies
      1. Contributions of organizations and agencies
      2. Disposal of waste materials
III. Mental health
   B. Alcohol, other narcotics, and tobacco
      1. Nature and effects of alcohol, tobacco, narcotics, and other drugs
      2. Analysis of advertising
      3. Laws and regulations
IV. Safe living
   A. Home safety
      1. Personal and mechanical causes of accidents
   B. School safety
      1. Safety in school activities (for example, physical education, shop, athletic, etc.)
   C. Community safety
      1. Safe use of firearms
      2. Hunter safety
      3. Safety relating to explosives, fire works, rockets, and blasting caps

---

*Workshop in Health Education Curriculum Planning, Oregon State University, July, 1958; sponsored by the Oregon State Department of Education.
†State Department of Education: Health education in Oregon schools, K-grade 8 and Health education in Oregon schools, grades 9-12, Salem, Oregon, 1964, The Department.

Grade 8

    I. Personal health
       C. Wholesome activity and rest
          1. Relationship of wholesome activity to the development of skeletal, muscular, circulatory, respiratory, and excretory systems
          2. Need for rest, sleep, relaxation, and recreation
   III. Mental health
       A. Personality and character development
          1. Making friends
          2. Getting along with members of family
          3. Courtesy and good manners
   IV. Safe living
       B. School safety
          1. Civil defense (taught with first aid)
       C. Community safety
          1. American Red Cross junior first aid course

Grade 9

    I. Personal health
       B. Nutrition
          1. Review nutrients
          2. Food and dietary fads
          3. Effects on personal appearance
          4. Hygiene of digestion
       D. Choice and use of health services
          1. Food and drug advertising
          2. Health appraisal
   III. Mental health
       A. Personality and character development
          1. Physical basis of behavior
          2. Heredity and environment in determining behavior
          3. Desirable attitudes toward mental and nervous illness
          4. Good mental health practices and attitudes relating to personal and social maturity
   IV. Safe living
       C. Community safety
          1. Occupational safety
          2. Recreational safety

Grade 10

    I. Personal health (thirteen class periods)
       C. Wholesome activity and rest
          1. Effects of exercise
          2. Sound principles of body conditioning, emphasizing muscular activity to accomplish the desired purposes of the individual
          3. Need for rest, sleep, relaxation, and recreation
   III. Mental health (fifteen class periods)
       B. Alcohol, other narcotics, and tobacco
          1. Mental and emotional aspects of use of alcohol, tobacco, other narcotics, and other drugs
   IV. Safe living (seventeen class periods)
       B. School safety
          1. Safety in school and home
       C. Community safety
          1. Traffic safety

Grade 11

    II. Community health (fifteen class periods)
        A. Prevention and control of diseases
            1. Communicable and noncommunicable disease
            2. Factors in prevention and control
            3. Modern medical care
    IV. Safe living (thirty class periods)
        C. Community safety
            1. American Red Cross standard first aid course
            2. Disaster and civil defense

Grade 12

    I. Personal health (twenty class periods)
        A. Personal hygiene
            1. Individual self-appraisal
            2. Future health planning (introduction to family living)
        D. Choice and use of health services and health practices
            1. Consumer selection
            2. Federal Food, Drug, and Cosmetic Act
            3. Health, accident, and hospital insurance plans
            4. Health vocations
    II. Community health
        B. Community health services and agencies
            1. Health agencies and organizations (taught with Choice and use of health services and health practices)
    III. Mental health (twenty five class periods)
        A. Personality and character development, individual adjustments to society, and family living
            1. Family as a basic social unit
            2. Preparation for marriage
            3. Marriage adjustments
            4. Planning for family
            5. Adjustments for unmarried persons
            6. Later life adjustments

QUESTIONS FOR DISCUSSION

1. Do you feel that there is another more efficient organization of health areas than that suggested in this chapter? Briefly outline your thoughts.
2. What are the similarities and differences between the several plans for placement of health areas throughout the twelve grades? Which plan do you favor? Why?
3. What are the advantages and the disadvantages of the following scheduling plans?
    a. Regular course
    b. Block plan
    c. Three-two plan
    d. One period a week
    e. Correlation with other subjects
4. What are the administrative problems when health is taught by correlation?
5. What health needs do junior high school students have? Senior high school students?
6. Is the suggested health content realistic?
7. In the content areas just given, are there any areas that appear too early for developing student needs? Do any come too late?

SUGGESTED CLASS ACTIVITIES

1. Have each class member analyze a different state course of study and report on the placement and scheduling plan proposed. Consider the dates of publication of the courses of study for possible trends.

2. Debate the scope and sequence plan considering such facets as adequacy of coverage, correct placement for meeting student needs, and place of health in the total school curriculum.
3. Have four committees investigate and report in class on the health needs of boys and girls at the junior and senior high school levels. Summarize the reports by indicating similarities, differences, and trends throughout grades 12 through 12.
4. Have groups of three or four students analyze the suggested content for a specific grade and make class reports on their findings. Consider such points as coverage of subject, grade placement, time necessary to cover the outline adequately, presentation to mixed classes, and relationship to health areas in other grades.

REFERENCES

1. Breazier, E. E.: Community expectations and school health curriculums, Journal of School Health **31:** Jan., 1961.
2. Byrd, O. E.: The health curriculum: 500 topics, Journal of School Health **28:** March, 1958.
3. Childs, V. R.: High school biology: its contribution to health education, Science Education **43:** Dec., 1959.
4. Gesell, Arnold, Ilg, F. L., and Ames, L. B.: Youth—the years from ten to sixteen, New York, 1956, Harper & Brothers.
5. Gmur, Ben: A comparative study of three common curriculum plans for organizing health instruction, unpublished Doctor of Education dissertation, 1959, University of California, Los Angeles.
6. Grout, R. E.: Health teaching in schools, ed. 3, Philadelphia, 1958, W. B. Saunders Co.
7. Haag, J. H.: Health content of the future, Journal of School Health **32:** April, 1962.
8. Harnett, A. L.: Scope of health education, National Association of Secondary School Principals Bulletin **44:** May, 1960.
9. Harnett, A. L., and Shaw, J. H.: Effective school health education, New York, 1959, Appleton-Century-Crofts, Inc.
10. Hayes, R. F.: The construction of a course in health education for secondary schools, Education **61:** Dec., 1940.
11. Jensen, A. M.: Experimental evaluation of two different programs of teaching health in the sixth grade and the administrative implications involved, Journal of Experimental Education **27:** March, 1959.
12. Ludwig, D. J.: An analysis of the health information in selected health education textbooks for grades seven and eight, Journal of School Health **27:** Feb., 1957.
13. Schaller, W. E.: Health needs and interests as a basis for selecting health content in secondary schools, Research Quarterly **31:** Oct., 1960.
14. Shaw, J. H.: Emphasis and sequence in health teaching, National Association of Secondary School Principals' Bulletin **44:** May, 1960.
15. Snyder, R. A.: Developments in school health education, California Journal of Secondary Education **34:** Dec., 1959.
16. Vavra, Catherine: Recent trends in school health education, Journal of School Health **31:** May, 1961.

Chapter 7

EVALUATION IN HEALTH EDUCATION

Evaluation is frequently an afterthought in the teaching process; yet it is extremely important to satisfactory progression in health subject matter and in the attainment of health outcomes. Therefore, evaluation is given a prominent place in Part II, Foundations to Health Teaching, to underscore our conviction that evaluation should be an integral aspect of the teaching process; evaluation should begin with the teacher's first consideration of health content and should never be forgotten throughout the full presentation of units, areas, or courses.

In this chapter consideration is given first to the over-all purpose of evaluation. This is followed in order by a discussion of general and specific health education evaluation, a consideration of teacher-prepared evaluation materials, and a summary of the standardized materials available to assist the secondary teacher in his evaluation program. The related material found in Appendix B should prove valuable to the health teacher in training. Appendix B contains an objective test based on the table of specifications on p. 150. Analysis of this material should be delayed, however, until Chapter 9, covering health unit theory and construction, has been studied along with the units of Appendix A.

PURPOSE OF EVALUATION

The term *evaluation* in a purely literal sense means "to estimate or place a value on." Evaluation in health education is concerned ultimately with the extent to which learning has occurred. In other words, it is a means of estimating the educative growth of students with respect to health learning experiences.

It has been stated previously that the health education program provides teaching and learning experiences and activities for the purpose of favorably influencing knowledge, habits, attitudes, practices, appreciations, and conduct pertaining to individual and group health. This implies that learning is concerned with changes in behavior and that teaching involves guidance, direction, and supervision of learning. Therefore, evaluation in health education makes

133

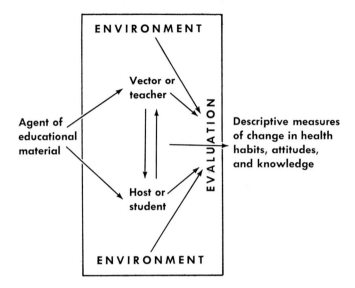

Fig. 6. Model patterned after the epidemiologic approach depicting the interrelationship of educational material, teacher, student, and environment.

possible a determination of behavior changes as a result of learning. A valid estimate of the educative growth of students is considered an essential phase of the teaching-learning cycle.

The purpose of evaluation in health education, then, is to determine the nature, kind, and extent of learning that have taken place. More specifically, evaluation should indicate whether students are educated in health to the extent that they have accumulated sufficient, appropriate, and meaningful health knowledge to influence present as well as future health behavior. Without a satisfactory evaluation program, all talk of the values of a health instruction program become hollow utterances since there is no other way of knowing whether or not health teaching has had an influence on behavior.

It is necessary and important to point out that the evaluator should be alert to those factors which act to reduce the validity of his evaluative procedures. Estimates of educative growth so far as health knowledge, attitudes, and practices are concerned are estimates of the effectiveness of the teacher as well. Beyond this, concern must also be given to the environment because a rating of a particular student or class may, more correctly, be a rating of the environment as it favorably or unfavorably influences the student or class. An excellent description of this relationship has been developed using the classical epidemiological approach which considers the host, agent, vector, and environment.* This epidemiological approach, when applied to the school situation, may be represented as in Fig. 6. In this analogy the host is the student, the agent is the educational material, the vector is the teacher, and the environment is the class-

*Leonard, A. R., and Arnold, M. F.: An epidemiologic approach to health education, American Journal of Public Health **51:** Oct., 1961.

room including the physical conditions such as lighting, acoustics, temperature, and size.

The model in Fig. 6 is designed to serve two basic purposes: first, to indicate the interdependent relationships of the several factors that make up the educative process and, second, to caution that evaluation of student progress may, in fact, be evaluation of the environment or teacher and not much more or may be an assessment of both of these factors. Likely, however, evaluation will reflect some aspects of all factors involved. The wise teacher will consider this point and will make use of those scales, inventories, and tests which are most appropriate to the specific purposes of the evaluation.

The remainder of this chapter strives to assist the reader in making necessary delineations.

GENERAL EVALUATION IN HEALTH EDUCATION

The general evaluation of a health education program is frequently conducted by any one of three groups. Most often the faculty members of a school or school district decide to rate their program, and they develop what is called a self-evaluation study. Occasionally, too, the school or school district will invite evaluation of their health program by an outside group, such as state department of education personnel or team from a teachers' college or university. A third approach is to invite an expert group to work with the local faculty so that the evaluation is actually instructional for the participating teachers. The recent Los Angeles School Health Education Evaluation Study* is an example of this combined approach.

In all approaches to general health education evaluation the initial task is to decide upon the specific measurement techniques that will be applied. Although a few scales are available, both in the literature and commercially, the participating teachers derive much more value if a part of their task is to develop the scale themselves. No matter what group prepares the general evaluation scale, the purpose is always the same, that is, to create preciseness out of the abstract. Therefore, although the proportionate numerical values developed by other groups in other locales may save time, these values are not likely to to reflect the needs and interests of both teachers and students in the local situation. Thus, while there is merit in considering what others have done, there is greater value through discussion and study and in developing a scale locally that will be most appropriate to the school district under examination.

How does a group of teachers attack the problem of conducting a general evaluation of the school health education program? First consideration might be given to the importance of the instruction program in relation to health services and healthful school environment. This concern for all three aspects is important only if the evaluation seeks to assess the total school health program. Certainly all are interdependent and important in the attainment of school

---

*School Health Education Evaluative Study, Los Angeles, 1959, Los Angeles County Tuberculosis and Health Association.

health program objectives although the relative weight attributed to each varies both within actual programs and within the philosophies of school health program experts. However, if the starting point of a general health program evaluation is the instruction area alone, the responsible committees will first need to determine the major aspects of the program. It was pointed out in Chapter 4 that health may be taught by direct, integrated, correlated, and incidental instruction. The committee might start by accepting these as four major areas of their scale and perhaps make the fifth area an assessment of the teachers conducting the program.

The second step is to assign gross numerical values to each of the five areas with appropriate weighting. If 500 total points is considered sufficiently large to produce whole numbers for even the smallest aspect of the instruction program in the final scale, the committee might arrive at the following proportionate weights for each of the five major areas.

Direct instruction	200 points
Integrated instruction	75 points
Correlated instruction	75 points
Incidental instruction	50 points
Teacher preparation	100 points
	500 points

It would then be necessary to determine the constituent parts within each of these five major areas and to assign appropriate weights. For example, important aspects of direct instruction might be the presence or absence of progressive health instruction, inclusion of necessary health areas, use of a course of study in each grade, scheduling of health classes, frequency and length of health classes, quality of the textbooks used, variety of teaching methods used, classroom evaluation procedures, and the inclusion of local speakers, agencies, and source materials. Within each of these there are subareas that need to be considered, and varying weights should be assigned according to the best opinions of those developing the scale.

When a scale such as the one just outlined is completed, the self-evaluation may continue to the next stage. In this stage either the original creative committee or selected members of the school or school district staff apply the scale to the school health education program. The results are most satisfactory when several faculty and staff members determine a rating, and an average for each subpoint is computed before the points are totaled. With this procedure a fairly high degree of objectivity is realized, and because many staff members are involved, the results are more likely to have widespread acceptance.

If one approach to general health education evaluation is to be recommended, it is the evaluative study which includes both local school employees and outside experts with members of the latter group participating as consultants. Studies of this type combine the enthusiasm of the local participants with the experience of the outside experts, and the results are generally most satisfactory. Teachers who participate in such an evaluation ordinarily derive much personal benefit.

SPECIFIC HEALTH EDUCATION EVALUATION

The challenge of specific health education evaluation is to accurately measure progress in the health knowledge of students as well as to show changes in health habits and attitudes. The task involved is as difficult as that encountered in general health education evaluation, if not more so.

Techniques for objective evaluation of educative growth in habits, attitudes, and knowledge are presented in the remainder of this chapter. It is important at this point to indicate the various philosophical approaches to the evaluation of health outcomes.

One philosophical approach to specific health education evaluation places emphasis on acquisition of knowledge. Information in the health sciences has multiplied at a tremendous rate in recent years, and to stay abreast of it is diffi-cult and time-consuming. Because of this vast accumulation of factual and scien-tific material, teachers and students often feel that the acquistion of this ever-accumulating knowledge is an end in itself. For them facts and statistics are all important, and little thought is given to change in habits or attitudes. This ap-proach is further strengthened by the fact that evaluation of health knowledge is considerably more objective, valid, and reliable than evaluation of habits and attitudes. Certainly, the acquisition of health knowledge is important, but it is only one part of the school health instruction program.

On the other extreme, is the point of view held by some educators that health instruction programs are wholly unsuccessful unless positive changes in habits and attitudes can be objectively and accurately determined. Such a philosophy implies that an increase in health knowledge is followed closely by a change in health habits and attitudes and puts the pressure on teaching methods which at present are much too inadequate to provide completely satisfactory results. It is obvious to any observer of human nature that accurate knowledge does not necessarily guarantee desirable action. For example, probably *all* male drivers between the ages of 15 and 24 years know that their age-sex group has the highest automobile accident-fatality rate, but knowledge of this fact does not seem to materially alter their behavior. The reasons why the members of this group drive recklessly will remain more important than life itself until the related objectives of health habits, attitudes, and knowledge can be made more meaningful.

Between these two extremes is the philosophy of health evaluation which recognizes that not all recently acquired knowledge is applied immediately. The results of habit and attitude evaluation are often discouraging even within a group of students who possess sufficient to superior health knowledge. The behavior of individuals is a reflection of the values which they hold. Adoles-cents reveal conflicting values, and positive health attitudes are often sacrificed, for what appear to them to be more important values because health is taken for granted by this age group. Fortunately, these values change, and as the high school student develops insight, he adopts health habits and attitudes based on knowledge acquired at an earlier time. Even though there is frequently a lag between the time knowledge is acquired and the time it is put into prac-tice, health teaching, nevertheless, strives to have attitude changes follow closely the acquisition of knowledge. One main purpose of specific health education evaluation is to objectively reveal the success of this phase of the health teaching program.

TEACHER PREPARED EVALUATION MATERIALS

The classroom health teacher has an excellent opportunity to make evaluation an integral and continuing part of the teaching program. A first step in assuring this is in the development of a table of specifications.

Table of specifications

A table of specifications is defined as a preliminary plan which proportionately relates the objectives and content of a health unit or course to the techniques of evaluation available and thereby ensures fair representation of content areas and a variety of evaluation procedures. As an example, students will often state that they were tested over material which the teacher never emphasized or perhaps never presented in class. Another justifiable student criticism is that teachers do not use a variety of evaluation procedures but instead emphasize a favorite procedure. A third but related criticism is that teachers do not develop sufficient quality in their evaluation; it tends to be an afterthought—quickly developed, poorly constructed, and unfairly interpreted. As a further example, teachers are often aware when they develop health tests or scales after teaching a unit or course that their testing emphasis is not in harmony with the emphasis of presentation. Too, they may acknowledge the criticisms of their students as valid, but since evalaution has been delayed to the last, little if anything can be done about it. Evaluation should precede, parallel, be a part of, and follow health instruction. Consequently, a table of specifications serves as a continual reminder of this important relationship.

The first step in the construction of a table of specifications for a unit or course is to consider the outcomes or objectives expected and the content to be taught and to decide on the time to be spent on each of the several parts. In doing this the teacher is required to consider the total material and to arrive at decisions of emphasis. Even these decisions may not be perfect, but such preliminary thought will bring order to the teaching process and will establish goals which otherwise might not be attained. Table 17 (p. 150) has been developed from the eighth grade health content for personal health outlined in Chapter 6. The per cent assigned to each of the main areas and subareas of content in Table 17 indicates a decision to spend that proportion of the total availabel time teaching those areas. How this relates to evaluation of subject matter will become clearer after a discussion of the construction of test items and test refinement.

Construction of tests

There are several types of test questions which the teacher may use in constructing a comprehensive and thorough examination. A brief discussion of five frequently used and abused types is included in this section. Also, several examples of each are included in the sample objective test included in Appendix B.

Essay test. The essay test perhaps has the greatest potential of all forms for contributing to the educational process. It requires the student to respond with much more than rote memory and a few checks or letters from his pencil. It offers an opportunity to the student to express himself, to react to a broad area of subject matter, and to involve himself in the response.

Development of satisfactory essay test items is ordinarily not an easy task, and it should not be considered so. In the construction and scoring of subjective essay test items, the following suggestions should be kept in mind.

1. The intent of the question should not be obscure and vague. Specific points sought should be clearly indicated, and students should be encouraged to underline these in their answer.

2. Descriptive answers may be desired, but the student also should be required *to react to and criticize* the situation described. The essay question should be more concerned with the *how* and *why* rather than with the *who, what, when,* or *where.*

3. The teacher should have clearly in mind the answer he seeks as he makes out the essay question. He should write out the answer and should then be sure the question accurately seeks the answer he wants.

4. When the test is scored, all answers to a single question should be read and assigned to successive levels of quality. This will reflect relative competency to answer each question. Once all answers to a particular question have been read and placed on this continuum, the score given to each can be quite arbitrary. If 10 points is the perfect score decided on for an item, and if the best paper contains a near perfect answer, the teacher might assign a value of 9 points. As the quality of other answers diminishes, fewer and fewer point values are assigned. When all test items are handled in this way, the results will be as nearly objective as it is possible to make an essay test.

5. Papers which contain quantity of answer without quality should receive little credit. If the teacher follows suggestion no. 3 (above), the scoring of a verbose answer will offer little difficulty.

6. Samples of the best answers may be read in class as the test is being reviewed so that all students will have an opportunity to evaluate their own answers in light of one or two superior answers. Such a procedure helps to eliminate the misunderstandings that often accompany the scoring of essay questions.

Matching test. This type of test is best described as a group of multiple choice items, all of which are satisfied by the same responses. Like the true-false test to be discussed shortly, a great deal of subject matter can be tested in a limited space and time with a matching test.

When a series of test items are organized in the matching form, there is considerably more compactness than in the lengthy multiple-choice test, and time of construction is much less. The serious disadvantage of this test, however, is that it is not well adapted to testing interpretative or complex ideas and like the true-false test, excessive memorization is required.

When matching test items are constructed, the following suggestions may be helpful.

1. The student should clearly understand the basis of the matching. This can be assured by providing proper and accurate directions to precede each matching item.
2. The terms in the numbered column should be no less than three and no more than seven or eight. The responses in the matching column should number three or four more than the numbered items, and it should be possible to use some of the responses more than once.
3. All items in the numbered column should be homogeneous. If there is a mixture, the student is forced to sift before he can match. This becomes frustrating and time-consuming, and effective evaluation is sacrificed.
4. Scoring is facilitated if each item in the numbered column has a short blank directly before the number of the item and close to the left edge of the paper.

Multiple-choice test. A test composed of multiple-choice items, each with three, four, or preferably five alternatives, is considered the most satisfactory type of test from practically all points of view. A well-constructed multiple-choice item contains alternatives which look alike yet differ in quality under careful examination. It measures understanding and breadth of knowledge more completely than any of the other four methods discussed here.

There are a variety of forms from which multiple-choice items may be adapted.

1. A direct question or an incomplete sentence may be followed by five (preferable) possible responses of which only one is correct or one is more nearly correct (best answer) than the others.
2. The multiple-choice item may be accompanied by a table, map, graph, or diagram which is numbered at several locations, the numbers representing the responses from which the correct choice is to be made.
3. The student may be asked to select the least satisfactory response or the exception to the other four responses.
4. More than one and possibly all of the responses may be correct, or none may be correct. This is less desirable than the other forms. It permits for successful guessing. Allowance should be made to offset this weakness (right minus wrong).

Few teachers take time to construct multiple-choice examinations. The statistical value attributed to this type of test, however, is seen in the fact that most commercial tests are of the multiple-choice type.

The following suggestions may be helpful in constructing multiple-choice tests.

1. The direct question is superior to the incomplete sentence form; there is greater clarity and less ambiguity to a direct question.
2. The five alternatives should come at the end of the incomplete sentence and not within the statement.
3. Irrelevant clues should be avoided. These include textbook phraseology that serves as a guide to the correct response, correct answers consistently

longer than the other responses, and similar words in both the introductory statement and the correct response.

4. All responses to a single item should be homogeneous and should appear plausible.

5. Multiple-choice items of a particular variation should be grouped together and should be preceded by clear and accurate directions. If more than one variation is used, the student should be made aware of this to avoid confusion.

Short answer and completion test. The short answer and completion test is usually considered the weakest of the five tests discussed here with regard to diagnostic potential. However, because the items are easy to construct, this type of test is used excessively. The weaknesses of this type of test are that (1) too often, the objective in its use is fact-finding, thus placing emphasis on rote memory, (2) the real intent is often ambiguous, and (3) there is usually little opportunity to judge the student's capacity for interpretation, analysis, and discrimination.

Although the weaknessess cannot be disregarded, the short answer and completion test has diagnostic value. For this reason the following suggestions for construction, use, and scoring should be kept in mind:

1. The column of blanks should be arranged consistently at one side of the page. This facilitates scoring.

2. It is best to avoid direct textbook sentences which place a premium on recall rather than on understanding.

3. When the item is developed, all possible correct alternatives should be considered, and full credit should be given for equivalent meaning.

4. It is well to guard against the possibility of long phrases being used as answers since they reduce objectivity.

5. No part of an item should contain leads which suggest the correct word or phrase.

True-false test. This type of test is perhaps the most widely used as well as the most seriously abused of all tests. To many people the term *objective test* suggests a test of true-false items which have been gleaned from a textbook, repeating the textbook phraseology and placing undue emphasis on memorization. Properly used, however, the true-false test can be a valuable testing tool. The advantages of this type of test are that the techniques of construction are fairly easy to learn; it permits a wide sampling of the material within a limited time; it is valuable for testing misconceptions although it is hazardous in that it may create some also; scoring can be easily and quickly accomplished.

The competent teacher will consider the following important points in constructing a true-false test.

1. Ambiguity should be avoided at all times. Be sure that the statement has one and only one meaning to several people.

2. Qualitative terms such as *many, few, great,* and *small* should not be used. It is best to specify the exact quanitity.

3. The true-false items should be divided in a 60 to 40 proportion. It is

preferable that approximately but no more than 60% of the items be true; this will tend to reduce the possibility of developing false concepts through use of the items.

4. The purpose of the statement should be clearly obvious to the student, and he should be encouraged to look for this as he reads the statement.

5. Test items should not be unusually long. Items of excessive length tend to be true or are unfair if written false since their very length distracts the student's thought processes.

A modification of the true-false test is the corrected true-false test. This type of test reduces the role of guessing and is more discriminating than the simple true-false test. In the items in this kind of test, one or more words or phrases are underlined. The student places the T or F on the blank indicated just as he would for an ordinary true-false item. If the statment is true, he then proceeds to the next statement. If it is false, he must make the necessary changes so that the sentence reads true. He can change only the underlined words or phrases, but he cannot alter the sentence simply by changing it from positive to negative or vice versa. The following two statements are given as an example.

_T_   The circulatory system is a cell's single source of _nutrient_ supply.

        Diabetes
_F_   ~~Tuberculosis~~ is thought to be a hereditary disease caused by failure of the Isles of Langerhans to produce insulin.

True statements count one point, whereas false statements count two points, that is, one point for recognition that it is false (**F**) and one point for the correction which makes the statement read true.

Statistical significance

Most classroom teachers make little use of statistical techniques once they are caught up in the day-to-day routine of teaching. The reasons for this are twofold. First, there is lack of time. Second, and perhaps more important, statistical usage appears involved and difficult to persons unfamiliar with statistical techniques.

The material which follows presents brief definitions of the more necessary terms, and short methods for computing standard deviation, reliability, and validity are discussed in the hope that more teachers will consider standardizing their own material occasionally and thereby upgrading their evaluation.

Definition of terms. The mean or arithmetic mean is equal to the sum of the measures divided by their number.

The median (mdn.) is the middle measure in a series of measures which have been arranged on a continuum from low to high. This middle score is also referred to as the fiftieth percentile.

The mode is that measure which recurs most often in the distribution. If there are two such measures, the distribution is duomodal; if there are several, the distribution is multimodal.

The mean, median, and mode are described as measures of central tendency and represent only one of the important characteristics of a distribution.

It is equally as important to know how closely all the measures are distributed about the measure of central tendency. Other terms which refer to this second characteristic of a distribution are *spread, scatter, deviation, dispersion,* and *variability*. There are several ways in which this variability may be described. Most simple but of little practical use, especially as the number of measures increase, is to indicate the total range of measures. This shows only the distance between the two extreme scores and tells nothing of how the remaining scores are distributed.

A second method which is more descriptive than the range of scores is the use of percentiles. The tenth and ninetieth percentile and/or the twenty-fifth and seventy-fifth percentile are important indicators of variability. Although the statistical computation for these is more detailed, a rough approximation of say the tenth percentile may be arrived at quickly in the following way. Divide the total number of measures by 10, and starting at the lowest score of the ordered distribution, count up to this score, representing one tenth of the total distribution. The point at which the lower one tenth of all measures falls below and the upper nine tenths of all scores falls above is the tenth percentile.

Another measure of variability is the median deviation which is described as the median amount that all scores deviate from the mean in a frequency distribution. By the definition of median, the range described by the median distribution will include exactly half the measures of any distribution.

A statistical method including slightly more measures of the distribution than the median deviation is the mean deviation. The mean deviation is the mean of the deviation from the mean in a frequency distribution.

The standard deviation is the most accurate and widely used of all measures of variability. It is defined as the square root of the mean of the squared deviation from the mean of the distribution. In the normal or bell-shaped distribution one standard deviation on either side of the mean will include approximately two thirds (68.26%) of all the measures in the distribution.

Determining standard deviation. Most classroom teachers have access to an adding machine, a mechanical partner that makes computation of the arithmetic mean and standard deviation simple and rapid. Although it is necessary to order the measures of a distribution to compute the median, it is not necessary to order or group them when computing the arithmetic mean and standard deviation. The formula for the mean is as follows:

$$M = \frac{\Sigma f}{N} \text{ where } M = \text{mean}$$

$$\Sigma = \text{sum of}$$
$$f = \text{frequency of measure or score}$$
$$N = \text{number of measures or scores}$$

The formula for the standard deviation from unordered scores is as follows:

$$\sigma = \frac{\sqrt{\Sigma d^2}}{N} \text{ where } = \text{standard deviation or sigma}$$

$$\Sigma = \text{sum of}$$
$$d = \text{deviation from mean}$$
$$N = \text{number of measures or scores}$$

The computation of both arithmetic mean and standard deviation is made clear in the following example. A teacher gives a health education test to a twelfth grade class and in the group of 36 the scores attained are 75, 54, 53, 53, 24, 45, 39, 57, 59, 68, 74, 22, 31, 33, 81, 58, 61, 60, 72, 56, 61, 53, 50, 49, 80, 24, 42, 47, 52, 59, 56, 45, 48, 53, 72, and 78. The M and σ of this distribution are arrived at by a simple six step procedure as follows.

1. Add the scores and divide by the number (N) to arrive at the arithmetic mean.
2. Determine the amount each score deviates from the mean and place it in a column headed d.
3. Square each of these deviations and place in a column headed d².
4. Add the d² column.
5. Divide the sum of d² column by the number (N).
6. Extract the square root.

Following these steps, the teacher will derive the M and σ thus:

Scores	d	d²	Scores	d	d²	Scores	d	d²
75	21	441	31	23	529	80	26	676
54	0	0	33	21	441	24	30	900
53	1	1	81	27	729	42	12	144
53	1	1	58	4	16	47	7	49
24	30	900	61	7	49	52	2	4
45	9	81	60	6	36	59	5	25
39	16	256	72	18	324	56	2	4
57	3	9	56	2	4	45	9	81
59	5	25	61	7	49	48	6	36
68	14	196	53	1	1	53	1	1
74	20	400	50	4	16	72	18	324
22	32	1024	49	5	25	78	24	576
Totals						1944		8373

$$M = \frac{f}{N} \qquad\qquad = \frac{\sqrt{\Sigma d^2}}{N}$$

$$= \frac{1944}{36} \qquad\qquad = \sqrt{\frac{8373}{36}}$$

$$= 54 \qquad\qquad\qquad = 15.25$$

The mean is 54. The first score above is 75 and deviates from the mean by 21, which is entered in the d column, and (21)² is entered in the d² column. The sum of the d² column is 8373. When 8373 is divided by an N of 36 and the square root is extracted, a standard deviation of 15.25 is obtained.

An earlier statement indicated that with a normal distribution approximately two thirds of all the scores would fall within one standard deviation of the mean. In this distribution under consideration it is seen that 54 ± 15.25 (M ± σ) describes a range from 38.75 to 69.25. Examination of the scores indicates that 24 or 66% fall within the M ± σ. It would seem that this distribution approximates the normal distribution, at least so far as the standard deviation is concerned.

The standard deviation makes it possible to describe the limit of variability for the scores and the students. When two or more tests or groups are to be compared, the standard deviation is a quick but meaningful statistical method. Two tests answered by the same group or two groups tested by the same test with the same approximate mean and standard deviation are considered comparable tests or groups in regard to central tendency and variability. Thus the teacher may make meaningful comparisons between this year's class and last year's class, between a test given at the start of the year and one given at the end, and between the present level of health knowledge and the level of health knowledge six months later.

Measures of central tendency and variability summarize the record of response to a particular evaluation tool. They tell nothing of the tool itself—the validity, reliability, or objectivity for the total test or scale or for the individual items within. Again, while more statistical experience is recommended, the important troika of test construction—validity, realiability, and objectivity—need not be completely ignored by uninformed persons.

The suggestions which follow may prove helpful in this regard.

Validity. Validity is the degree to which an evaluation procedure measures what it purports to measure. Validity may be considered from a subjective viewpoint, curricular validity, and from an objective viewpoint, statistical validity.

Curricular validity is established through early consideration and development of the table of specifications, a subject which is the frame of this section of the chapter. By way of brief review, the essentials in the determination of curricular validity are as follows:

1. Development of a list of objectives for the course or unit of subject matter to be covered by the test
2. Development of a detailed outline of the subject matter to be covered in the test
3. Determination of a proportional value or ratio of emphasis for each of the subheadings
4. Determination of the appropriate test items to be used and the percent of the final test each will represent

Curricular validity is said to exist to the extent that the course outline is representative of what the student should know, to the extent that the proportionate emphasis is correct, and to the extent that the test items are carefully constructed. Table 17 (p. 150) and Appendix B represent the establishment of curricular validity in light of the selected health content areas.

Statistical validity is arrived at after the test has been administered once and before its revision for later use. It is at this point that many teachers fail to take advantage of further statistical investigation, and yet careful analysis of individual test items would reveal some items that discriminate well and could be used again with profit as well as some that should be discarded or altered considerably.

The index of discrimination is a tool which permits rapid analysis of individual test items. It is defined as the degree in which a test item differentiates between levels of abilities of different individuals, that is, the degree in which a test item discriminates between those who know and understand the material and those who do not.

Test validity is the cumulative reflection of the validity of individual test items. As the validity of each test item is improved, the validity for the complete evaluation scale or test is improved.

Although there are several procedures for determining statistical validity, a procedure which does not demand excess amounts of time nor an extensive statistical background is the Flanagan Index of Discrimination.* The Flanagan index yields a coefficient of correlation which reflects the success a single item has in differentiating between students of low and high ability. If the item distinguishes levels of ability well, the correlation will be high; if poor students do as well on an item as good students, the correlation will be low. When the teacher gives a test of 100 items and wishes to apply the Flanagan index, he must figure a correlation for each item. Thus standardization by the teacher which includes validation will be lengthy the first time a test is refined. Thereafter, assuming that only the poorer items are removed or altered, the index need only be applied to those few items that are being improved.

A Flanagan index is determined in the following manner.

1. On the basis of total test scores, the upper and lower 27% of the papers are removed. For best results there should be at least 25 to 30 papers in each group. The middle 46% of the papers are not considered in this statistical computation.

2. On a worksheet (see accompanying example) the per cent of students answering items 1, 2, 3 . . . .n successfully in both high and low groups is entered.

	SUGGESTED WORKSHEET FOR COMPUTING THE FLANAGAN INDEX OF DISCRIMINATION		
Item	% in upper group answering correctly	% in lower group answering correctly	Index
1	⊹⊹⊹ ⊹⊹⊹ ⊹⊹⊹ ⊹⊹⊹ ‖‖‖ 80	⊹⊹⊹ ⊹⊹⊹ ‖‖ 40	.42
2	⊹⊹⊹ ⊹⊹⊹ ⊹⊹⊹ 50	⊹⊹⊹ ⊹⊹⊹ ⊹⊹⊹ ⊹⊹⊹ 66	−.17
3	⊹⊹⊹ ⊹⊹⊹ ‖‖ 40	‖‖‖ 10	.40
n	⊹⊹⊹ ⊹⊹⊹ ⊹⊹⊹ ⊹⊹⊹ ⊹⊹⊹ ‖‖ 90	⊹⊹⊹ ⊹⊹⊹ ⊹⊹⊹ ⊹⊹⊹ 66	.34

3. These percentages are then located on the horizontal (upper group) and vertical (lower group) margins of the special table prepared by Flanagan, and the coefficient of correlation is read at the point of convergence within the table. The resulting coefficient of correlation (the index) is an estimate of the relationship of success on the item and success on the criterion. If the item is to be retained without alteration, it should have an index of 0.20 or higher.

---

*Flanagan, J. C.: General considerations in the selection of test items and a short method of estimating the product moment coefficient from data at the tails of distribution, Journal of Educational Psychology **30**: Dec., 1939.

If an item has an index lower than 0.20, several possibilities of action are suggested. First, the item can be removed and is not used again. Second, it can be analyzed for ambiguity, distracting phrases, advanced terminology, and other factors related to poor construction. Third, if it is a multiple choice item of any form, the number of responses to each alternative can be totaled to determine those alternatives not operating as foils. Perhaps refinement of one or two of these will improve the item's index.

Reliability. Reliability of a test refers to its internal consistency. A reliability coefficient is a description of the degree to which a test or scale measures whatever it is that it is measuring or the degree to which it is internally consistent. When a test is composed of well-constructed items, has good curricular and statistical validity, and is objective, reliability is also assured. However, once the classroom teacher has worked over the test items, improved some, discarded others, and administered the test to a second or third group of students, it is interesting and rewarding to compute a reliability coefficient.

The procedure recommended here for determining reliability is the simplified Kuder-Richardson procedure. In order for this formula to be applied the investigator must make three assumptions, as follows:

1. That the test measures only one factor
2. That all intercorrelation between items are equal
3. That all items are equally difficult

Although few tests meet all three of these criteria, the use of this formula is justified in the context of the present discussion. The formula presented here is simply and quickly applied, will err on the underside which is on the side of safety, and will be satisfactory for most classroom teachers carrying out their own test refinements. The authors state concerning the following formula that "it may be considered as a foot rule method of setting the lower limit of the reliability coefficient or the upper limit of error."[*]

$$r_t = \frac{n}{n-1} \cdot \frac{\sigma_t{}^2 - \frac{M_t}{n}(n - M_t)}{\sigma_t{}^2}$$

where n is the number of items in the test:
M_t is the mean of scores on the total test
σ_t is the standard deviation of the test

Objectivity. Objectivity is the degree to which a test may be administered to the same group by different individuals and still obtain the same results. Objectivity improves as the experience of the teacher increases, as the teacher's understanding of the student increases, and as both teacher and students completely understand the test directions. Further, objectivity improves as the possibility for individual interpretation regarding the answers is reduced. When all graders judge the merit of an answer in the same way, the item or the test has achieved objectivity. High objectivity is important to high reliability and validity, but it does not guarantee either.

---

[*]From Richardson, M. M., and Kuder, G. F.: The calculation of test reliability coefficients based on the method of rational equivalence, Journal of Educational Psychology **30:** Dec., 1939.

Teaching in the high school may easily tend toward the subjective involvement of the teachers in the learning process. For this reason, it is vital that the teacher maintain objectivity in the area of evaluation. Test results should be arrived at without the influence of normal human empathy for the developing adolescent. If they are, the interpretations derived and the academic counseling and guidances which should follow will be all the more meaningful.

Measuring attitudes

Accurate and predictable measurement of health attitudes continues to elude researchers and classroom teachers. The reason for this is largely in the very definition of attitude. Typical definitions of attitudes include the following: (1) a predisposition to act, (2) a feeling or belief toward an object, person, or thing, (3) the tendency of a person to react positively or negatively to a situation, and (4) potential behavior. Thus it is seen that attitudes represent an inner force and are not readily accessible to direct objective measurement. They are mental in origin yet dynamic in operation. The psychologist and behavioral scientist often refer to them as "hypothetical constructs" or "intervening variables."

Many attitude scales in the general fields of education and social science have been developed in the Thurstone or Likert tradition. Each of these asks the student to evaluate the degree of his feeling toward a particular subject in question and by his response to position himself along a continuum ranging from most favorable to least favorable. The basic assumptions underlying this kind of attitude scale construction are the following.

1. Attitudes are effectively organized as motivational, emotional processes.
2. Attitude responses reflective of these processes vary within and between individuals.
3. These responses are not revealed accurately or successfully by direct questioning or observation of behavior.
4. Measurement can be accomplished though employing written tests scaled on a positive or negative and favorable or unfavorable attitude continuum.

The reader will recognize that in the points listed, it is assumed that the subject or student is aware of his attitudes, that he will reveal what he believes or feels, that he can attach verbal labels to these beliefs or feelings, and that these verbal labels can be evaluated. Whether these conditions are achieved by most or any of the scales available is debatable. As attitude is defined, it is questionable whether the individual can objectively define his feelings toward a person, object, or thing. Assuming that he can, will he do so in light of conflicting pressures to conform to existing social patterns, to please his teachers, friends, and parents, or to agree just for the sake of not becoming controversial? Conformity surely will be the only result if the teacher indicates that the results of attitude evaluation are to contribute to grade determination.

Attitudes may be likened to the seven eights of an iceberg that rides below the surface of the water. The complex pattern of attitudes held by an individual are the cumulative result of his past experience and education. The teacher would like to understand that which is below the surface and to use this understanding as a starting point to build, alter, and improve health attitudes in the best interests of the student. But just as the hidden shape of the iceberg is a mystery when viewed from above, so also are health attitudes difficult to assess with most materials developed personally by the classroom teacher. If acceptable standards for validity and reliability are maintained, it is virtually impossible because the average teacher has neither the time nor the skills to refine his own paper and pencil attitude scales.

The difficulty teachers face in constructing their own attitude tests plus the well-established fact that attitudes are correlated with behavior has led many persons to view the one-eighth of the iceberg that is visible and to conclude that the observed behavior is derived from the complex pattern of attitudes. From this presumed relationship it is a short step to the assumption that attitude and behavior are one and the same. Right or wrong, health behavior (habits and practices) is viewed by many teachers as the meaningful, overt expression of health attitude. There are several ways by which the teacher can accurately measure behavior. Most require approximately the same time and effort by the teacher as the evaluation of health knowledge.

Measuring behavior

Successful health education is realized through the development of positive health attitudes and the establishment of favorable health behavior.

Positive behavior change, that is, behavior change which enhances the student's full physical endowment, represent the super goal of health education. Therefore, the teacher should be aware of the various settings in which behavior may be observed. The techniques of behavior evaluation considered here fall into two general categories, those that are structured and those that are unstructured. Behavior evaluation that is structured is more objective yet less valid than behavior evaluation that is unstructured.

Evaluation of structured behavior is represented most typically in checklists and rating scales. Teacher and pupil-made checklists and rating scales have proved valuable in many situations. Their use is obviously dependent upon good teacher student relationhsips, and when these conditions exist, the results are most beneficial.

Complete subject matter units will include among the specific objectives the desirable practices and habits that will contribute to the attainment of the general unit objectives (observe the resource and teaching units in Appendix A). These may be developed into a scale that seeks to determine the student's patterns of behavior and thus will guide the teaching process. For example, the following three habits might be listed as expected outcomes in a seventh grade unit on safety and first aid at home.

1. Handles cooking utensils properly.
2. Keeps sidewalks and steps free of ice.
3. Is careful when entering and leaving a bathtub.

These may be developed into items on a rating scale by either the teacher or the students, and a total score can be determined on the basis of an assigned value for the different points along the continuum. The three items just given would then appear as follows.

1. I handle cooking utensils properly.
    Always (5); often (4); sometimes (3); rarely (2); never (1)
2. I help to keep sidewalks and steps free of ice.
    Always (5); often (4); sometimes (3); rarely (2); never (1)
3. I am careful entering and leaving a bathtub.
    Always (5); often (4); sometimes (3); rarely (2); never (1)

Since the student responds by circling the appropriate alternative and the values of these are totaled, it is clear that the result is objective.

Validity is another problem in measuring behavior. Can we be certain that the student responds in terms of his actual behavior or with the alternative that *he knows to be most acceptable?* If rapport is excellent and it is clear that results are for purposes of counseling and not grade determination, *perhaps* the results approach a desirable level of validity. As rapport diminishes, so also does validity.

In unstructured or uncontrolled situations, objectivity declines but validity improves. This form of behavior evaluation is concerned with how the student

Table 17. Table of specifications for eighth grade content from area of personal health (wholesome activity and rest)

Unit objectives and content areas	% of emphasis	Test items (100)				
		Essay 20% (20)	Matching 20% (20)	Multiple-choice 25% (25)	Short answer 10% (10)	True-false 25% (25)
Relationship of wholesome activity to development of:	80	16	16	20	8	20
Skeletal system	16			4	2	4
Muscular system	16		7*	4	2	4
Circulatory system	16		7*	4	2	4
Respiratory system	16		6†	4	1‡	4
Excretory system	16			4	1‡	4
Need for sleep, rest, relaxation, and recreation:	20	4	4	5	2	5
Relief of fatigue by sleep	10	10§		2‡	1	3‡
Relief of fatigue by rest, relaxation and recreation	10	10§		3‡	1	2‡

*It was pointed out earlier that matching items should have from three to seven alternatives. Hence, these matching items are positioned in the three most suitable areas, and the weights are redistributed slightly.

†These matching items are moved to offset the shift in short essay items.

‡Since it is impossible to have a fraction of an item, adjustment is made at these points.

§Essay items cannot be used with certain subject matter, and here the essay portion of the examination must be shifted to two short essay questions, each worth 10 points, in the area of sleep, rest, relaxation, and recreation. This unbalances the original weightings, and adjustment is made in the column of matching test items.

actually responds to various stimuli in numerous life situations. The effectiveness of the several evaluation methods depends entirely upon the teacher's ability to observe, record and interpret behavior reliability. Skills of observation may be developed if the teacher is interested. Behavior evaluation of unstructured situations includes the following types.

1. *Dairy-keeping.* Although it is time-consuming and difficult for the average secondary health teacher, occasionally there are medical or other reasons to keep a diary on a particular student. When it is used in this manner, especially when more than one teacher contributes to the log, there is considerable contribution to a more complete understanding of the student in question.

2. *Anecdotal records giving an account of events that have occurred.* When significant student behavior is observed from day to day by different school observers and this behavior is made a part of the student's cumulative record, subsequent evaluation judgments are based on a more concrete foundation.

3. *Analysis of student projects which often reveal clues to the real behavior of students.* For example, a student who is intensely interested in a bacteria-culturing project with all its possible health ramifications will very likely demonstrate positive health behavior relating to communicable diseases.

4. *Case studies developed by school health service personnel* (nurse, physician, psychologists, psychiatric social worker) and by the school administration general counselors, class advisers, etc. These studies can provide valuable clues to health behavior.

Clues to real health behavior may also be derived from similar and related school activities. These include the following:

1. Student reports in class
2. Exhibits developed by students
3. Plays
4. Debates
5. Interviews with students in which the student's response to the interview itself and the discussion therein are carefully noted and recorded.

Return to the table of specifications

It was previously mentioned that a table of specifications should be included in the initial course or unit planning. It was indicated that the teacher should plan the per cent of time to be devoted to each subarea of content and that the available class time should conform to this as nearly as possible. These per cents of emphasis should be entered in the table of specifications so that later evaluation will reflect the same per cent of emphasis. In Table 17 a hypothetical situation, this decision is represented in the second column (per cent of emphasis). When this much is done prior to teaching the course or unit, the table of specifications would not need to be referred to specifically until it is time to develop the evaluation scale or test, probably toward the end of the allotted instruction time.

Before proceeding further, it should be pointed out that the teacher may wish to conduct ongoing evaluation of attitudes and behavior, using one or more of the methods that have been suggested. Also, occasional short quizzes, question periods, and other methods for determining the level of knowledge should be in constant use. Most of these latter methods are discussed in more detail in subsequent chapters since they represent method as much or more than evaluation per se. Our concern at this point is to complete the table of specifications and thus demonstrate the attainment of curricular validity.

There are two decisions which the teacher should make before he begins the actual construction of a test. First, he must decide on the number of total items or points, and, second, an almost coincidental decision, he must decide on the types of items to be included in the final test. In Table 17 it is seen that the hypothetical test will have 100 items and that these items will be distributed between the five types of test items in the per cents indicated. This decision to include five types of test items added to the earlier decision relating to distribution of content emphasis assures that the evaluation will vary not only throughout the test but also throughout each subarea. Thus, the usual student arguments that a test is unfair can be eliminated.

From this point it is an easy task to fill in the appropriate squares of the table of specification, and the teacher is ready to prepare the test items. A test which follows the suggested distribution in Table 17 is reproduced in Appendix B. Careful examination of this test in Appendix B reveals several variations of the five basic types of test items discussed earlier.

STANDARD EVALUATION MATERIALS

Brief mention has been made of ways in which a teacher can standardize his evaluation procedures. Usually, for the teacher who is also teaching a full load, standardization procedures while valuable and meaningful are time-consuming. Sufficient cases for satisfactory statistical treatment might require a study covering several years and resulting ultimately in but one test over limited material. To compensate for this and to provide the teacher with valid, reliable, and objective instruments which satisfy specific evaluation purposes, many tests and scales are available both commercially and in the professional literature. These should increase as the field expands and evaluation procedures improve.

Recently Solleder* provided an excellent review of the tests currently available for secondary school teachers. An adaptation of this report is presented here.

Published instruments

1. Adams, Georgia S., and Sexton, John A.: California Tests in Social and Related Sciences. Part III. Related sciences, Test 5, Health and safety, Monterey, Calif., 1953, California Test Bureau.
   For grades 4 through 8, this seventy-five item test is composed of true-false and multiple-

---

*Solleder, M. K.: Evaluation instruments in health education, Journal of Health, Physical Education, and Recreation **32**: Nov., 1961.

choice items designed to measure knowledge in the health and safety areas. Norms and a manual of directions are available. This test is one of a battery of subject matter tests in the sciences for the upper elementary grades.

2. Elementary health: Every pupil scholarship test, Emporia, Kan., 1959-1960, Bureau of Educational Measurements, Kansas State Teachers College.

This sixty item multiple-choice test is for grades 6 through 8. The test aims to measure the student's knowledge of rules and principles of healthful living and his health attitudes. A new form is issued each April and January, and norms are available following each testing period.

3. Health education and hygiene, Grades 7, 8, and 9, Columbus, Ohio, 1959-1960, Ohio State Department of Education (751 Northwest Blvd.)

The Ohio Scholarship Tests consist of matching, multiple-choice, and other objective type items to measure health knowledge. New test forms are available twice a year (December and April), and norms are available after each testing session. The tests may be purchased by out-of-state persons. Consult other state departments of Education for similar tests.

4. Johns, Edward B., and Juhnke, Warren L.: Health practice inventory. Stanford, Calif., 1952, Stanford University Press.

Thirteen health areas are represented in the statements included in this one hundred item inventory which appraises the health practices of senior high school students, college students, and adults. A manual of directions and norms for senior high school and college are available.

5. Kilander, H. Frederick: Information test on biological aspects of human reproduction, New York, 1958, New York University (mimeographed).

This thirty-three question multiple-choice test is for junior high school through college levels. Norms are available; single copies may be obtained free from the author.

6. Kilander, H. Frederick: Nutrition information test, ed. 4, New York, 1959, New York University (mimeographed).

This thirty-three question multiple-choice test is for junior high school through college levels. Norms are available. Single copies may be obtained free from the author.

7. Kilander, H. Frederick: Stimulants and depressants information test, ed. 2, New York 1958, New York University (mimeographed).

This thirty-three question multiple-choice test is for junior high school through college levels. Norms are available. Single copies may be obtained free from the author.

8. Kilander, H. Frederick: Tuberculosis information test, ed. 3, New York, 1957, New York University (mimeographed).

This twenty question multiple-choice test is for junior high school through college levels. Norms are available. Single copies may be obtained free from the author.

9. Kilander, H. Frederick: Kilander health knowledge test; evaluation and adjustment series, Yonkers-on-Hudson, N. Y., 1952, World Book Co.

This secondary school test measures the extent of the individual student's knowledge and understanding of health matters. Two forms are available, each consisting of seventy-five multiple-choice items. A manual of directions and norms are available.

10. Los Angeles health education evaluation instruments, Los Angeles City School District, Calif. Address inquiries to Dr. Blanche Bobbitt, Supervisor of Health Education, P.O. Box 3307, Terminal Annex, Los Angeles 54, Calif. (A number of instruments for evaluation of health knowledge, attitudes, and behaviors at the secondary levels are now available.)

11. McHugh, Gelolo: Sex knowledge inventory, Durham, N. C., 1950 and 1955, Family Life Publications, Inc.

Form Y (1955) of this inventory measures understanding of the human reproduction system and vocabulary relating to sex. It is suggested that this form could be used at high school, college, and adult levels. Form X (1950) is designed specifically for use by marriage counselors in determining sex knowledge and preparation for marriage. Instructor's manuals are available for both forms.

12. National Safety Council Tests, Chicago, Ill., National Safety Council, 425 North Michigan Ave.

These tests are included in a series of school safety lessons, issued monthly September through May, for each of four grade levels: lower elementary, upper elementary, junior high school, and senior high school.

    13. Shaw, John H., and Troyer, Maurice E.: Health education test: knowledge and application, Rockville Centre, N. Y., 1956 (Form A) and 1957 (Form B), Acorn Publishing Company, Inc.

For grades 7 through 12 and college freshmen, this 100 item test has two forms consisting of multiple-choice and true-false items. Knowledge and the application of knowledge are tested. Some physical education items are also included. Norms (based on stastistics from more than 6000 students in various sections of the United States) and a manual of directions are available.

    14. Speer, Robert K., and Smith, Samuel: Health Test, Rockville Centre, N. Y., 1957 (Form B and 1960 (Form A) Acorn Publishing Company, Inc.

This test, for grades 3 through 8, has two forms and was designed to test the student's judgment, understanding, and knowledge of health facts. Multiple-choice and problem-type questions are used. Norms and teacher's directions are available.

    15. Committee on Medicolegal Problems: Test your A.Q. (alcohol quotient), Chicago, 1959, American Medical Association.

This is a twenty question true-false test which provides a basis for a good discussion at the senior high school and college levels.

Theses and dissertations

    1. Augustin, Wilbert Raymond: The construction and standardiaztion of two alternate forms of a health knowledge test for senior high school students, doctoral dissertation, Temple University, Philadelphia, 1959.

    2. Colebank, Arthur D: Health behavior of selected junior high school pupils, doctoral dissertation, University of California, Los Angeles, 1952.

This three part 108 item test evaluates health behaviors, attitudes, and knowledges. Copies are available from Dr. Albert Colebank, Supervisor of Health Education, Ontario City Schools, Ontario, Calif.

    3. Dzenowagis, Joseph G., McPherson, Patricia V., and Irwin Leslie W.: Harmful health and safety misconceptions of a group of tenth-grade girls, Journal of School Health 24:240-245, Nov., 1954.

    4. Le Maistre, E. Harold: The development of a health behavior inventory to evaluate health education in the senior high school, doctoral dissertation, University of California, Los Angeles, 1958.

This fifty item inventory consists of a number of problem situations met by two senior high school students.

    5. Lundh, Ina Joanna: The development of an instrument for appraising dental health knowledges, attitudes, and practices of junior high school students, master's thesis, University of California, Los Angeles, 1957.

    6. Mayshark, Cyrus: A health and safety attitude scale for the seventh grade, doctoral dissertation, Indiana University, Bloomington, 1954.

Two forms consisting of sixty situation-response and multiple-choice items have been developed. Refer to Mayshark, Cyrus: A health and safety attitude scale for the seventh grade, Research Quarterly 27:52-59, March, 1956.

    7. Myers, Frank H.: A safety attitude scale for the seventh grade, doctoral dissertation, Indiana University, Bloomington, 1955.

Refer to Myers, Frank H.: Safety attitude scale for the seventh grade, Research Quarterly 29:320-32, Oct., 1958.

    8. Pellett, Elizabeth A.: Tuberculin test questionnaire.

This test is available from Mrs. Elizabeth A. Pellett, Consultant in Secondary Curriculum, Los Angeles County Schools, 808 North Spring Street, Los Angeles 12, California.

    9. Poole, Richard D.: A health knowledge test for high school, doctoral dissertation, Indiana University, Bloomington, 1959.

Two test forms each consisting of seventy-two best answer type of items were developed. Percentile and T-score norms are available. Microfilm is available from University Microfilm, Ann Arbor, Michigan.

10. Veenker, C. Harold: A health knowledge test for the seventh grade, doctoral dissertation, Indiana University, Bloomington, 1957.

Two test forms consisting of multiple-choice items were constructed. Mimeographed copies and test manual may be purchased from the author at Purdue University. Refer to Veenker, C. Harold: Health knowledge test for the seventh grade, Research Quarterly 30:338-48, Oct., 1959.

SUMMARY OF NECESSARY COMPETENCIES IN EVALUATION

This chapter has presented a full range of evaluation concepts. Yet, since a single chapter cannot cover all aspects of this problem in detail, interested persons may select specific areas of evaluation for further study.

Evaluation of learning is a vital aspect of the teaching-learning cycle, and it is expected that all teachers will develop the competencies necessary for successful evaluation. Some of these basic abilities include the following:

1. The ability to construct and use the results of objective health tests suitable for use at particular grade levels
2. The ability to select and use those standardized tests which are best adapted to local situations
3. The ability to use oral questioning in such a way that it becomes an effective means of evaluation
4. The ability to interview students through conferences and casual conversation in order to appraise learning that has accrued
5. The ability to employ the technique of observations in matters which concern student health so as to make the best possible valid estimate of growth in health attitudes and health behavior

QUESTIONS FOR DISCUSSION

1. What is the definition and purpose of evaluation as the term pertains to the school health education program?
2. What aspects of the education program may be reflected in any single evaluational judgment? Can the teacher be sure that a statistical result is measuring only one of these aspects?
3. Differentiate between general and specific health education evaluation.
4. Evaluation in health education is more difficult than in the so-called core subjects. Why?
5. Define the following terms in your own words:
   (a) Table of specifications
   (b) Mean
   (c) Median
   (d) Mode
   (e) Standard deviation
   (f) Validity
   (g) Reliability
   (h) Objectivity
6. What are the advantages of using each of the following test items?
   (a) Essay test items
   (b) Matching test items
   (c) Multiple-choice test items
   (d) Short answer and completion test items
   (e) True-false test items
   In what situations would each of these be disadvantageous?
7. Define the distinction between measures of central tendency and measures of variability.
8. Validity is a more important characteristic of a test than reliability. Why?

9. What are attitudes?
10. Is behavior a reflection of attitude?
11. Are behavior and attitude the same?
12. What does it mean to say that a test or rating scale has been standardized.

SUGGESTED CLASS ACTIVITIES

1. Discuss the interrelationship of educational material, teacher, student, and environment as seen in Fig. 6.
2. Divide the class into five groups and develop a detailed scale to evaluate a health education program using the initial breakdown on p. 136 as the starting point.
3. A table of specifications is difficult to develop in those areas in which expected outcomes are not directly and immediately derived from the necessary content. Examine the suggested content given at the end of Chapter 6 and discuss what some of these areas might be.
4. Have the entire class discuss the steps in organizing a table of specifications. Select a content area from Chapter 6 to use as a guide.
5. Divide the class into small groups, assign a type of test item to each group and have them develop a series of items which represent both strengths and weaknesses of construction. Discuss each with the entire class.
6. Analyze and criticize the suggested test given in Appendix B.
7. Have each class member draw twenty two-place numbers from a table of random numbers and compute a mean, median, and standard deviation. Interpret each of these statistical measures.
8. Have each student compute the Flanagan Index of Discrimination for the items in a short test and apply the simplified Kuder-Richardson test for reliability. The instructor may prepare for this by using material collectd from previous test results.
9. If there are psychology students in the class, ask them to study and report on the difference between the traditional approach to attitudes—a predisposition to act—and the behavioristic interpretation which states that attitudes do not exist except as they are evidenced in some form of overt behavior. References 3 and 21 may be helpful in this assignment.
10. Develop a short scale to evaluate objectively a student's lunch time behavior pattern, his safety practices in all phases of school life, and his health habits during the physical education class. Arrange to observe a student for a period of time in one of these three areas and score his performance.
11. Analyze some of the standardized health tests and rating scales that are available commercially or from private authors.

REFERENCES

1. American Association for Health, Physical Education, and Recreation: Research methods in health, physical education and recreation, ed. 2, Washington, D. C., 1959, The Association.
2. American Public Health Association, School Health Section, Committee on Evaluation of School Health Programs (Wesley P. Cushman, chairman): Evaluate your school health program, New York, 1955, The Association.
3. Bain, Reed: An attitude on attitude research, American Journal of Sociology 33: May, 1928.
4. Davis, F. B.: Item analysis data: their computation, interpretation, and use in test construction, 1946, Harvard University.
5. Ebel, R. L.: How to judge the quality of a classroom test, Technical Bulletin no. 7, Iowa City, The Examination Service of the State University of Iowa, Sept., 1955.
6. Edwards, Ralph: an approach to health attitude measurement, Journal of School Health 26: Sept., 1956.
7. Engelhart, M. S.: How teachers can improve their tests. Chicago Schools Journal 25:16, 1946.
8. Hicks, Dora: Evaluative Survey for Improvement in Health Education, Gainesville, 1953, University of Florida.
9. Jackson, C. O.: Let's rate your health education program, Educational Press Bulletin, Feb., 1956, Springfield, Ill., Superintendent of Public Instruction.

10. Jordan, A. M.: Measurement in education: an introduction, New York, 1953, McGraw-Hill Book Co., Inc.

11. Kelley, J. L.: The selection of upper and lower groups for the validation of test items, Journal of Educational Psychology, **30:** Jan., 1939.

12. Kilander, H. F.: Evaluating health teaching, Journal of Health, Physical Education, and Recreation **32:** Nov., 1961.

13. Knutson, A. L.: Evaluating progress in health education, Journal of Health, Physical Education, and Recreation **28:** May, 1957.

14. Mair, B. H.: The school health program—a self study, The Journal of School Health **25:** Dec., 1955.

15. Mayshark, C.: Critical analysis of attitude measurement in health education, Research Quarterly **29:** Oct., 1958.

16. Mosier, C. I., Myers, M. C., and Price, H. G.: Suggestions for the construction of multiple choice test items, Educational Psychological Measurement **5:** Autumn, 1945.

17. Rash, J. K.: Refining the health education test, Journal of School Health **23:** Jan., and Feb., 1953.

18. Ross, C. C., and Stanley, J. C.: Measurement in today's schools, Englewood Cliffs, N. J., 1954, Prentice-Hall, Inc.

19. Rugen, M. E., and Nyswander, D.: The measurement of understanding in health education, Forty-fifth yearbook, Part I, National Society for the Study of Education, Chicago, 1946, University of Chicago Press.

20. Shaw, J. H.: Evaluation of the school health instruction program, American Journal of Public Health **47:** May, 1957.

21. Thurstone, L. L., and Chave, E. J.: The Measurement of Attitude, Chicago, 1921, University of Chicago Press.

22. University of the State of New York, State Education Department: Evaluation of school health education, Albany, 1952, The Department.

Part III

METHODS OF TEACHING IN HEALTH EDUCATION

Chapter 8

METHODS AND CONCEPTS OF LEARNING IN HEALTH EDUCATION

WHAT IS METHOD?

Although various educational groups have severely criticized the emphasis placed on methods of teaching, nevertheless anyone who teaches in any area must employ some types or kinds of methods. In other words there can be no teaching without the use of methods of some kind. Even the nonprofessional person lacking a background in teaching methods will use some kind of method if he attempts to teach. His way of teaching may be disorganized, inefficient, and ineffective; yet the procedures he uses are his ways or methods of teaching.

The term *method* can be arbitrarily defined as an organized, orderly, and systematic way of achieving a given purpose or objective. Reduced to plain and practical terms, method is concerned with "how to do" something in order to achieve desired results.

It has been expressed previously that health education is concerned with the provision of learning experiences for the purpose of influencing knowledge, attitudes, and behavior relating to individual and group health. If the best results are to accrue, the most desirable teaching and learning situations should be provided. If one accepts the thesis that learning results in modification of behavior and that teaching is the guidance and direction of behavior which results in learning, it becomes essential that there be a full understanding of the meaning of method when applied to health education.

Applied to health education, method is concerned with how best to provide learning experiences so that the individual's behavior will be modified in the best interest of his own health and the health of others. More specifically, the teacher must be concerned with how a teaching-learning cycle can be evolved so that optimum learning and achievement can take place.

WHY ARE METHODS OF TEACHING IMPORTANT?

For the most part, methods of teaching have held an important place in the education system of the United States for many decades. The significance of method in education is clearly shown by the fact that philosophers of education in the United States have been recognized and followed largely on the basis of their contribution to methods.

Often certain types of educational methods are subjected to extensive criticism. However, this provides for a desirable situation as long as criticism is of a constructive nature and results in improved methodology. Indeed, methods in any educational endeavor are of extreme importance, and any desirable improvements which can be made should always be welcomed by persons engaged in the direction and guidance of learning.

The importance of sound methods in health education should not be minimized, and the exploration of new and better methods in this area should always be under consideration. This is particularly true because the provision of learning experiences so often has a direct influence upon the health of the individual as well as on the health of the group. Because mental, physical, and emotional health and well-being are involved, the choice of methods of teaching in health education can be considered more important than in many of the other subject matter areas.

DEVELOPMENT OF METHODS IN HEALTH EDUCATION

Educational history reveals scant mention of the study of health as an important part of the education of the child. Locke, the seventeenth century English philosopher, recommended this concept when he wrote about a "sound mind in a sound body." Later, Horace Mann, the prominent midnineteenth century American educator, gave strong emphasis to the need for the subject of health as a part of the curriculum. He was of the opinion that there should be a study of "the rules and observances by which health can be preserved and promoted." Possibly, as a result of the declaration by Mann, some schools offered courses in physiology and hygiene before 1880. For example, a law passed in California in 1866 indicated that "instruction shall be given in all grades of schools, and in all classes, during the entire school course, in manners and morals, and the laws of health."

Beginning during the period between 1880 and 1890, some states passed laws which required instruction regarding the effect of alcohol and narcotics. In that many of the state laws indicated that instruction concerning alcohol and narcotics should be part of the teaching of physiology and hygiene, this period can be considered the beginning of health and hygiene teaching in the schools. With the spread and development of health and hygiene teaching in the shools, there has been an ever-increasing need for better ways, means, and methods of teaching in this comparatively new area.

Two prevailing concepts of the time served as a basis for the methods used in imparting health knowledge to students. First, there was the idea that all that was needed was information about the structure and function of the body and, second, that the teacher was the only person who had a complete understanding of the health needs of students. As a consequence, the method of teaching was largely teacher-dominated and evolved into a procedure of having students memorize such things as the parts of the body and certain rules of hygiene which were thought best for good health. This method of memorization and repetition harkened back to medieval times, and as a result student interest was stifled, and in many cases students were turned against any kind or type of health teaching.

RECENT TRENDS IN HEALTH TEACHING METHODS

During the past few decades leaders in the field of education have placed more and more emphasis on the improvement of methods of teaching in all areas. As a consequence, teaching methods in most of the subject matter areas have undergone extensive study and revision in an attempt to assure more efficient and effective learning on the part of the student.

Although the methods used in teaching in health education are not radically different from those employed in other areas, nevertheless, teaching methods in health have not kept pace with some of the long-established subject matter areas. This is perhaps due to a number of factors. In many cases health teaching has not been given status in the school curriculum on a basis comparable to most other subject matter fields. In other words, health teaching is at a distinct traditional disadvantage. Furthermore, the responsibility for teaching in health education has been somewhat on a "selected volunteer" basis from the viewpoint of teacher assignment. In addition, the atmosphere in health and hygiene classes is not always desirable. For example, when large numbers of students are brought together in a gymnasium for so-called health instruction, it is readily understandable why so little is accomplished and why most students in such situations so thoroughly dislike it.

Perhaps another reason for the lag in teaching methods in health arises from the fact that, until very recent years, teachers in general have not been adequately prepared to teach health on a basis comparable to other courses in the curriculum. The inadequate preparation of teachers in health, however, is gradually being overcome as a majority of the colleges and universities preparing teachers are now offering better education in this area.

With health education gaining more and more the status it deserves in the school curriculum, there are evidences of departure from the early methods which consisted predominantly of learning parts of the body and committing to memory and repeating a variety of health rules. As in many of the other subject matter areas, health teaching is being considered more from the functional point of view. In other words, health knowledge as an end in itself is slowly but gradually being replaced with the idea that health knowledge is a means of helping students cope intelligently with health problems. This concept indicates that health subject matter is not an end but a tool through which desirable health learning experiences may be provided. This implies that sources of criteria for health teaching do not come from subject matter, but from man and his environment. The newer concept of method in health teaching, then, recognizes the student as a living organism capable of sharing in the solution of problems which concern his health. In other words, modern health teaching based on these changing concepts provides for numerous learning activities designed to take into account individual differences and characteristics of the learner. When this procedure is followed, emphasis upon teaching of health subject matter gives way to emphasis upon the optimum growth of students with respect to matters which influence their health. Furthermore, emphasis upon the teaching of health facts gives way to emphasis upon meanings which will function in improving living.

WHAT IMPORTANT FACTORS AFFECT METHODS IN HEALTH EDUCATION?

It is a generally accepted theory that successful teaching should be based upon the needs and interests of students. The implementation of this theory may be dependent upon a variety of factors which may affect health teaching methods. In general these factors center around school personnel and school environment. In this regard experience has shown that the following factors exert considerable influence upon methods employed in health education:

1. Differences in teachers
2. Time allotment
3. Equipment and materials
4. Classification of students

Differences in teachers. There are certain individual differences among teachers which will influence teaching methods. The fact that many teachers may have a limited amount of training and background in health teaching methods may cause them to resort to use of the textbook as the sole means of providing learning experiences.

Frequently a teacher may have much greater success with one particular method or set of methods than with others. This implies that there should be no ideal method or exact pattern of methods to follow. On the other hand, teachers should be encouraged to select and develop those methods best fitted to their individual special abilities.

Time allotment. In a majority of schools too little time is devoted to health teaching. In those schools in which health learning experiences are provided in the form of health units, there appears to be a greater opportunity to preserve continuity and to utilize a variety of activities related to problem solving. Conversely, in those situations in which health teaching is done on a haphazard or sporadic basis, it may be necessary to curtail the number of learning activities and resort to methods which do not provide for individual differences in students.

Equipment and materials. Until recent years the use of demonstration equipment and materials in health education has not been fully appreciated. This perhaps is due to the fact that the early purposes of health instruction were based on what the teacher felt the student should know about health. In other words, in the early days of health education, teachers did not feel the need for equipment and materials so acutely since the main objective was to try to teach students an abundance of health facts, many of which were wholly unrelated.

With the modern trend in health education directed toward learning activities which are close to the everyday activities in the lives of students, there has been more widespread use of certain kinds and types of health equipment and instruction materials. In the absence of suitable equipment and materials some desirable learning activities which can take place through demonstrations, visual aids, and the like may have to be dispensed with in favor of other methods of teaching which are not likely to produce the desired results.

Classification of students. The relative merits of homogeneous and heterogeneous grouping of students have been discussed by numerous educators with regard to their effectiveness in teaching-learning situations. Although it is not the purpose here to extol the merits of either of these methods of grouping, it should perhaps be conceded that classification and grouping of students will have an influence on the method of teaching. This may be particularly true when a wide range in variation of traits exists in a given classroom situation.

The problem of grouping occurs most frequently at the secondary school level in situations in which health education is alternated with physical education class activities. When physical education class scheduling degenerates into a catchall basis, it becomes inevitable that health education will fall into the same pattern if alternated with physical education classes. Consequently, faulty classification of pupils for physical education results in a duplication of faulty classification for health education. This situation amplifies the problem of method in health education in terms of providing for individual differences of students.

WHAT ARE SOME BASES FOR SELECTING METHODS?

Teachers are constantly confronted with the problem of how best to provide learning experiences in order that the most effective and efficient achievement will result. A perennial question is the following: How can we teach best those things which students should learn? The fact that there is no single simple answer to this question is readily discerned when one considers the variety of factors inherent in each specific learning situation. In other words, there is no single method which supersedes all others in every teaching-learning situation.

What sources then must we rely upon for the selection of methods? Considering the fact that progress is likely to be dependent upon the mutual action of experiential and experimental processes, there evolves two rather broad categories upon which we may draw as sources for the selection of methods in health education. The first of these is concerned with the use of our knowledge of psychology in the provision of learning experiences. The second source pertains to practices which have met with success in their application by teachers in the field.

One of the main purposes of using our knowledge of psychology as a source of teaching method lies in the fact that psychology should help us to keep from violating certain fundamental principles of learning. The paramount problem here is concerned with the application of psychology to the specific area of health education. Solution of this problem might be simplified if the teacher of health were also a specialist in psychology. In that the health teacher is not likely to be a psychologist, it may be considered entirely justifiable for teachers to rely to a certain extent upon the successful practices of others because these successful practices more than likely will have as their bases the application of fundamental psychological principles of learning.

WHAT PRINCIPLES OF LEARNING APPLY TO HEALTH EDUCATION?

There are certain fundamental facts about human nature with which educators of the present day are more fully aware than educators of other eras. These facts pertain to some basic aspects of the learning process which all good teaching should take into account.

As previously stated, the older concept of health teaching was concerned predominantly with imparting information on the parts of the body, on the evils of alcohol and narcotics, and on rules pertaining to health. The student who could commit this information to memory and then recite it to the teacher when called upon to do so was said to be receiving an education in health. In other words, students became the gramophone records upon which instructors recorded health information, and at the desired time the information was reproduced through recitation or written tests.

Present-day teaching for the most part replaces this older mode of approach with methods which are based on fundamental facts of educational psychology. Outgrowths of these facts appear in the form of principles of desirable learning procedures. The following list of principles of learning accompanied by a discussion of each is intended to portray some of the reasons why the application of the principles are essential. Learning usually is most efficient and effective when the following conditions are evident.

1. *When the student has his own purposeful goals to guide his learning activities.* To create a desirable learning situation teachers must be concerned with certain features of purposeful goals which guide learning activities. For example, the goal must seem worthwhile to the student. This involves such factors as interest, attention, and motivation. Learning a variety of health rules may not seem a worthwhile goal to some students. This is especially true if the motivating factors are extrinsic to the extent that the rules are memorized only for the purpose of reciting them to the teacher or writing them down correctly in the form of a health test.

The goal must not be too difficult to achieve. It should present a challenge to the student, but at the same time it should be within his realm of achievement. On the other hand, it should not be too easy, lest the student lose interest. The degree of difficulty of goals presents a problem in the grade placement of health learning experiences. This is substantiated by the fact that students often feel that they may be repeating the same materials over and over again from grade to grade.

A purposeful goal gives direction to activity and learning, which means that after a student has accepted the goal he has a better idea of where he is going. In health education students are more likely to accept goals which are close to real life situations, and the subject of health provides unlimited possibilities in this respect.

Finally, it is necessary for students to find and adopt or accept their own goals. This means that they do not or should not receive them directly from the teacher. If the most effective learning is to accrue, it is doubtful that one person can give another person a goal. This does not always mean that goals will not originate with the teacher. On the other hand, teachers can do a great deal to help students find their own goals. This may be accomplished by planning the classroom environment in such a way that students with different kinds of previous experiences and interests may find something which appears to be worthwhile. This can be done and can still be in keeping with the teacher's objectives. For example, health concepts may be considered the teacher's goals. However, in a desirable classroom setting the competent teacher often influences in many ways the student's mental set toward possible goals. As a consequence, in a good classroom teaching environment students may adopt the health concepts which approximate the teacher's objectives as their own goals.

2. *When the student is free to create his own responses in the situations he faces.* This principle implies that problem-solving is the way of human learning and that the individual learns largely through experience, whether direct or indirect. The validity of this principle is brought more clearly into focus when one considers experience as the interaction of the individual with his environment. In other words, the student is educated in accordance with the influence that the environment has upon him.

Another important factor to take into consideration in connection with this principle is that all students differ in one or more characteristics. While it may be true that adolescents are more alike than they are different, they will perhaps always differ in what they know and are able to do in any given class in health education.

Although the individual learns through experience, this does not mean that experience will always assure learning since it might possibly come too soon. For example, anatomy as taught at the higher grade levels is not offered in the first grade because children at that grade level are not ready for it. Conversely, experience can come too late, and this may often be in the form of repetitive experience. This may result in students' being taught the same thing in the same way in the area of health over a range of grade levels.

When the individual is free to create his own responses in the situation he faces, individual differences are being taken into consideration, and generally experience then comes at the right time for desirable learning. This situation calls for a classroom procedure which is flexible to the extent that students may achieve in relation to their individual abilities. It is evident then that one student may learn best through one specific activity, whereas another student learns best through another activity.

3. *When the student organizes his own materials in the process of satisfying his own purposeful goals.* The implication of this principle has its basis in the thesis that a purposeful goal may at first be perceived only in a partially defined form. Consequently, the goal may change in the act of problem-solving, or it may change as the student works toward it. When the individual is free to organize his own materials, complete definition of the goal is facilitated, and problem-solving is more readily accomplished.

Implementation of this principle requires freedom as a fundamental necessity in the teaching-learning process. This means that each student should be permitted as wide a range of selection as he is able to use wisely in determining how he shall go about problem-solving. It becomes essential then that in the study of a specific health topic there should be basic core learning activities for a majority of the students and also numerous optional learning activities. In this way all students should have an opportunity to express themselves through a medium of learning adaptable to their individual needs, interests, and abilities.

When it is stated that "the individual should be free to make his own organization of materials," this should not be interpreted to mean that student planning should dominate the health problem-solving situations. On the contrary, there should be maintained a proper balance between student planning and teacher planning. Moreover, a certain amount of teacher planning will have to precede student planning for best results to be attained.

4. *When the student shares cooperatively in learning experiences with his classmates under the guidance and direction of the teacher.* The point of importance here is that, although learning may always be an individual matter, it is likely to take place best in a group. In other words, students learn individually, but the social setting is advantageous. Furthermore, it should be kept in mind that the group can serve as a motivating factor for individual activity, and that individuals in the group can learn through indirect experience by capitalizing on the direct experiences of other members of the group. Moreover, sharing in group activities seems an absolute essential in educating for democracy.

In health education it should not be too difficult to maintain a happy balance between individualization and socialization. For example, a class committee studying a phase of a health problem might gather data individually and then present findings as a group to the rest of the class. This type of activity involves a pooling and sharing of experiences and provides an opportunity for direct experience for one group of students and indirect or vicarious experience for another group.

5. *When the teacher who understands the student as a growing personality acts as a guide.* This principle takes into consideration the fact that the teacher should view learning as an evolving process and not merely as instantaneous outward behavior. In that teaching may be expressed in terms of guidance and direction of behavior which results in learning, the teacher must judge when to speak and when to step aside and watch for further opportunities to guide and direct behavior.

The application of this principle precludes an approach which is teacher dominated. On the other hand, implementation of the principle is perhaps more likely to be realized in health classes which are student centered. For example, in the study of community sanitation students can accompany a public health sanitarian on a tour of inspection of restaurants. In this activity it is possible to provide a situation close to the lives of students to help them more fully realize the need and value of community sanitation protection. The students as well as the teacher are active participants, with the teacher guiding and directing behavior at times when it appears feasible to do so. In this way the teacher attempts to help students discover direct pathways to meaningful areas of experience and at the same time, contributes to the student's ability to become a self-directing individual.

6. *When the student agrees to act upon the learning which he considers of most value to him.* In most cases a majority of people accept as most valuable those things which are of greatest interest. This principle implies in part then that there should be a balance between health needs and interests of students as criteria for the selection of health course content. Although it is of utmost importance to consider the needs of students in selecting the health content, we must not lose sight of the fact that we need their interest if learning is to take place. However, neither should student interest in health be the sole criterion for selecting health content. This is substantiated by the fact that lack of interest may be synonymous with ignorance. Also, the student may have a primary interest in health matters which are not significant. Moreover, there may be an interest in some phase of health that should be delayed until a later grade.

If a student acts upon the knowledge which he feels is personally valuable to him, it seems essential that health course content be considered from the viewpoint of psychological organization as well as from logical organization. For example, psychological organization of material takes into account the fact that gaps may be left in the study of a specific health topic. These gaps are permitted because the material may be too difficult for the student to understand. Logical organization, on the other hand, which is based on an orderly sequence of material, may make it necessary for the student to try to comprehend too many things at once. Since the student is perhaps logical only within the limits of his past experience, it is unwise to insist upon a too strict logical approach.

WHAT ARE SOME GENERAL METHODS OF TEACHING HEALTH?

Methods used in teaching health are largely the same as those used in other subjects. However, there are certain specific ways in which health may be taught. Furthermore, certain intermediate methods, such as demonstration, visual aids, and field trips, have a definite type of application in the teaching of health. These specific and intermediate methods will be treated at length in subsequent chapters. The remainder of this chapter will be devoted to a discussion of certain methods used in health which may also be common to a number of subjects in the school curriculum.

All of the general methods presented here have a certain amount of value when properly applied by a teacher skilled in their use. Since certain extenuating circumstances must be taken into consideration in the use of general methods in health education, it may be safely stated that all of these methods are useful if applied in the right way at the right time by the right person. This is to say that any one general method should perhaps not be used to the entire exclusion of other methods. It should also be clearly understood that some of these general methods are very broad in scope and may require the use of a variety of submethods, procedures, or techniques. On the contrary, the lecture method, for example, could be considered an entity in itself. These factors should be kept in mind with regard to the discussion of general methods.

Lecture method. The lecture method was perhaps one of the first formal methods to be used in health education. For instance, in the early stages of the teaching of hygiene, Harvard University offered a series of six lectures to young men on "what they should know about the human body."

In recent years the chief criticism of the lecture in the teaching of health has stemmed from the fact that it is an authoritative way of setting forth health principles. The validity of the objective arises from the fact that the teacher is likely to be the only active participant when the lecture method is used in absolute form. That is, when the teacher relies entirely on the lecture in developing health concepts, there seems to be little possibility of capitalizing on real life experiences which have a wide range of application in health teaching. As a result, students are not likely to assume much of the responsibility for learning.

In that the lecture method is almost totally dependent upon listening as a medium for learning, the question arises with regard to the grade level at which this method can be used most effectively. With the short attention span characteristic of students in the lower grade levels, listening activities in the form of health lectures will be less useful than at the higher educational levels. Consequently, other factors being equal, it seems advisable that the lower the grade level taught, the less the lecture method should be used. Very limited use should be made of the straight lecture method in junior high school health classes. Senior high school health teachers may use the lecture method more, but even in high school classes it should ordinarily be somewhat limited.

The previous discussion has emphasized the use of the lecture method on an absolute basis. The next inevitable question is as follows: Can this method be used most effectively in any phase of health teaching at the secondary school levels? Certainly a reasonable amount of listening is essential if worthwhile health learning experiences are to be provided. Therefore, the lecture method in the form of oral presentation can be used successfully in introducing new material and in summarizing the main points of a health unit. If used wisely it can be a desirable way of communicating health information to students through brief explanation. However, experience has shown that health information in the form of eloquent verbosity may have little meaning and may fail to hold the interest of students. This is a particularly important consideration for those teachers who use the services of resource people to talk to health classes. Often the resource person may deliver a fine talk without appropriately gearing it to the age level of the group.

Textbook method. There are a variety of ways in which the textbook can be used in health teaching. Furthermore, there are a combination of factors which influence the way the textbook may be used. For example, in some states there are laws which require a specified number of minutes of hygiene teaching "from a textbook in the hands of the pupil."

Traditionally, teachers of most of the subject matter areas have looked upon the textbook as the foundation for any plan of teaching. The teaching of health is not an exception. Perhaps relatively few educators would advocate the elimination of the textbook as a source of study material in health teaching. However, the practice of relying on a single textbook without supplementing it with other study materials is not recommended.

It has been postulated that health textbooks are needed because it would be difficult for teachers to find sufficient time to prepare all of their own study materials. This is especially true in small secondary schools in which teachers have teaching responsibilities in many different areas of the curriculum.

In most cases health textbooks contain a suitable organization of materials for health teaching. Moreover, the textbook can be used as a common basis for all students in the teaching of health. Depending upon the resourcefulness and ingenuity of the teacher, the textbook in health can either become the unquestioned gospel of the health class, or it can be used wisely and supplemented with many other worthwhile health learning materials and experiences as seem necessary in the study of specific health topics.

Recitation method. In its early form the recitation method consisted generally of having students recite on certain sections of the text which had been previously assigned for study. Early health teaching employed this method as a means of having students commit certain health facts to memory. The recitation method in its original form has been largely abandoned as a health teaching technique on the basis that it does not distinguish between learning and memorizing health rules. It should be emphasized that as far as health teaching is concerned, the recitation method in the modern school need not be considered undemocratic. On the contrary, this method can be very useful in teaching health through the group process. The recitation method may serve as a valid means of estimating educative growth with respect to health knowledge.

Questions for recitation purposes can generally be used in all phases of a health lesson. They can be used to arouse and guide the thought process. Furthermore, questions and recitation may be important in previewing or approaching new health materials. In this way the teacher has a means of determining the current tone of the class and further identifying the needs of the class with regard to a particular health topic.

The usefulness of the recitation method in health teaching may be dependent to a large extent upon the ability of the teacher to formulate questions in such a way that worthwhile learning will result. In this connection, it will be to the advantage of the teacher to establish criteria for use in developing questions. For example, questions should be thought-provoking and not drill-type questions. Furthermore, questions should be of a problem-solving nature and should be well adapted to the specific grade level. It is important that questions be addressed to the entire group and that the teacher accept and use worthwhile answers of students even though they may not have been the exact answers that the teacher wanted.

Teachers should give time and thought to the preparation of questions. Questions should be written out in the most logical and systematical order, with sufficient latitude of flexibility.

Individual method. The rise of individualized instruction was perhaps a direct result of attempts to provide for the individual differences in intelligence of students. This method eventually developed into what is currently known as the unit method, which is discussed at greater length in Chapter 9. The individual method is briefly presented here in the interest of continuity.

The individual method is based on the idea that learning is an individualized matter and that students should be permitted to proceed at a rate commensurate with their individual intellectual capacities. One of the early noteworthy attempts at a solution to this problem was the plan devised by Helen Parkhurst. It is sometimes referred to as the contract plan but is perhaps better known as the Dalton plan. In substance this plan consisted of the student making a contract with the teacher covering a specified period of time. The student then divided his own time and did his own work with the help of the teacher.

Although it may seem that the most effective and efficient approach to the recognition of individual intellectual differences of students is through highly individualized instruction, nevertheless, it has been learned through experience that instruction can become too highly individualized. In the final stages of the development of individualized instruction it became so highly individualized that each student worked alone on his own work materials and projects entirely exclusive of other class members. It reached a point at which there was practically no intercommunication between students in the same class. Students frequently lost all interest in each other and in the progress of the class as a whole. The humanizing and socializing effects of student participation in class activities, so important and desirable in developing the democratic concept, were almost completely lost. As time went on, the small group plan was introduced and developed to offset some of the ill effects of the individual method.

Small group method. The small group plan was devised and introduced to regain some of the highly desirable experiences and outcomes in education which were lost when the individual method became too highly developed. The small group plan is applied satisfactorily in health teaching at all grade levels by dividing a class into small groups for the purpose of attempting to arrive at the solution of a health problem. Students can work together in committees and can then come together as an entire class to present their findings.

Problem-solving method. Although the problem-solving method is frequently referred to as such in education, in reality it is not a specific specialized method, for it is used in and throughout practically all methods of teaching including even the lecture method. For example, a good lecturer frequently poses questions or problems that the students must think through and solve in order to keep abreast of the lecture. One objective of the problem-solving technique is to develop the ability to do reflective thinking. The readily evident need for reflective thinking in matters pertaining to individual and group health is indicative of the important place of problem-solving in health education. Consequently, if a student has had the opportunity to engage in problem-solving situations he should be better able to cope with problems which involve his own health and the health of others.

Another reason why the problem-solving approach is so important in heatlh education is that students seem to have a natural interest in problem-solving of any type commensurate with their abilities and capacities. Therefore, problem-solving should be used as much as possible in all methods of teaching in order to gain and hold the interest of students, to provide for more meaningful learnings, and to develop the ability to do reflective thinking.

QUESTIONS FOR DISCUSSION

1. How do health teaching methods differ from teaching methods in other subject matter areas?
2. Why has it been necessary to modify health teaching methods in recent years?
3. How does the individual teacher influence health teaching methods?
4. How does student classification influence health teaching methods?
5. What are some of the sources for the selection of health teaching methods? How valid are these sources?
6. What are some of the chief disadvantages of the lecture method in health teaching?
7. What is the place of the recitation method in health teaching?
8. How can problem-solving be applied to health teaching?

SUGGESTED CLASS ACTIVITIES

1. Form a round table discussion group for the purpose of considering the importance of method in health education.
2. Write a brief summary on some of the early methods of health teaching.
3. Prepare a statement to a superintendent of schools recommending a specified time allotment for teaching health in the local high school. Justify the time allotment that you recommend.
4. Form a panel discussion group for the purpose of discussing the principles of learning which are presented in this chapter.
5. Write a brief report explaining how the lecture method can be used to advantage in health teaching.
6. Give an oral report to the class describing how you would use a textbook in both a seventh and twelfth grade health class.
7. Form a panel discussion group for the purpose of discussing the advantages and disadvantages of the individual method and the small group method in health teaching.

REFERENCES

1. Brown, M. B.: Knowing and learning, Harvard Educational Review **31**: Winter, 1961.
2. Burton, W. H.: Guidance of learning activities, ed. 2, New York, 1962, Appleton-Century-Crofts, Inc.
3. Cassel, R. N.: The psychology of instruction, Boston, 1957, Christopher Publishing House.
4. Douglass, H. R., and Miller, H. H.: Teaching in high school, New York, 1958, The Ronald Press Co.
5. Eastern States Health Education Council: Psychological dynamics of health education, New York, 1951, Columbia University Press.
6. Faunce, R. C.: Teaching and learning in the junior high school, San Francisco, 1961, Wadsworth Publishing Co.
7. Howard, B. D.: A practical approach to teaching in the secondary schools, Minneapolis, 1956, Burgess Publishing Co.
8. Kersh, B. Y.: Motivating effect of learning by directed discovery, Journal of Educational Psychology **53**: April, 1962.
9. Milton, A. W.: Science of learning and the technology of educational methods, Harvard Educational Review **29**: Spring, 1959.
10. Stiles, L. J., Corey, S. M., and Munroe, W. S.: Methods of teaching. In Encyclopedia of educational research, New York, 1950, The Macmillan Co.
11. Tyler, R. W.: Health education implications from behavioral sciences, Journal of health, Physical Education, and Recreation **31**: May-June, 1960.
12. Weaver, G. G.: Applied teaching techniques, New York, 1960, Pitman Publishing Co.

Chapter 9

THE UNIT METHOD IN HEALTH EDUCATION

WHAT IS THE UNIT METHOD?

There are perhaps few terms consistently used in education that have as many different meanings in the minds of different people as the word *unit*. A universally accepted definition of unit does not seem possible at the present time because it does not have a fixed meaning in educational terminology. The different meanings of the term *unit* become very evident in the reading of professional books and periodicals and when educators discuss it as a method of teaching.

The varying and different meanings surrounding the unit method are due in part to the fact that the unit idea in the field of education has had such widespread recognition in recent years. As a consequence, there has not been sufficient time for unit terminology to crystallize into common meaning and understanding among educators.

From the point of view of etymology the word *unit* (shortened from the word *unity*) has been derived from the Latin word *unus,* meaning one. In that the word *unit* may be used somewhat loosely in education, there may be some merit in giving thought to its original derivation. This implies that the idea of oneness should prevail. In other words, there should be a union of component related parts evolving into a systematic totality. In health education this means that the health unit will consist of a number of interrelated learnings which are concerned with a specific topic or central theme. This is to say that the health unit involves a learning situation with respect to a certain area of health. Various types of experiences as well as of areas of subject matter are drawn upon for the purpose of enriching the learning medium for all students so that desirable changes in behavior will be most likely to take place. Unity is more likely to be retained when provision is made for pupil-teacher planning and when there is a sufficiently wide range of learning activities to meet the individual needs of all pupils.

174

DEVELOPMENT OF THE UNIT METHOD

Although the unit method of teaching has received widespread acclaim in recent years, unit organization should not be regarded as an entirely new development. On the contrary, for many years educators have been making contributions to method which were the seeds that have eventually grown into what is now generally referred to as the unit method. The following discussion is intended to show that the modern unit method is by no means a recent discovery but a process of educational evolution.

The modern unit method is perhaps the product of certain changes that came about in the field of education around the turn of the century. At that time in our educational history the type of formalism which characterized the late years of the nineteenth century through the influence of Pestalozzi and Herbart began to recede in favor of the somewhat more progressive thought of such men as Dewey, Thorndike, the McMurry brothers, and others.

As a result of some of the contributions of these men, the first two decades of the present century brought about some near-phenomenal changes in educational practice. Developments in educational psychology tended to create a situation which eventually led to the submergence of the earlier philosophic idealism in favor of a more scientific approach to education. Two prevailing concepts of formalism in education in earlier years emerged in the form of beliefs which held (1) that memorization should be replaced by a problem-solving type of learning and (2) that a student should progress through school at a rate commensurate with his capacity and ability.

The implementation of the ideas of transition from memorization to learning through problem-solving and recognition of individual differences of students have not been easy matters. As a consequence, many and varied plans have been set forth in the last three or four decades in an attempt to provide desirable and acceptable learning experiences for the youth of America's schools. For example, as mentioned in a previous chapter, effort to allow for individual differences of students was carried to such extremes in some places that the important aspects of socialization were almost entirely lost. The fallacy of this practice was brought clearly into focus during the great financial depression of the early 1930's. At that time a greater need was seen for more stress on the social aspects of our society. If the public schools were to play a major role in the maintenance of democracy, then it became essential that attention be given to those factors which concerned living and getting along with others in a democratic society.

Consequently, many schools gave students an opportunity to learn to work together in groups, to share experiences, and to cooperate in problem-solving situations. At the same time individuality was retained to the extent that each member of the group engaged in learning activities in relation to his individual capacity. This practice, which emphasized individualized teaching and democracy in education, is one of the outstanding features in the modern unit method.

It becomes clearly evident that the unit method as practiced in many schools today has resulted largely from a continuous evaluation of procedures set forth by many American educators and scholars over a period of the past several decades. A few of the educators who have made significant contributions to the unit method include Dewey, the McMurry brothers, Parkhurst, Morrison, Washburne, Alberty, and Billett.

The fact that health teaching as such is a relatively new area in the school curriculum gives rise to the belief that health educators have a unique opportunity to incorporate a type of unitary teaching which could capitalize on past experience, based on advanced thinking, experimentation, and research. In other words, those persons responsible for providing the most acceptable health learning experiences for students should be in an ideal position to establish unitary teaching on a solid foundation of practices which have been improved upon through the years.

TYPES OF UNITS

Little progress has been made in standardizing the nomenclature of units. Nevertheless, there is substantial agreement with respect to terminology which describes the types of units with which teachers should be familiar. The types of units referred to here are *Resource Units* and *Teaching Units.*

Resource units. Resource units consist of collections of suggested health teaching materials and learning activities and experiences centered around specific topics. These units are to be used only as resources for teachers when teaching units are constructed. In other words, the teacher goes to the resource unit as a source of information in devising a teaching unit for a specific class.

Resource units may be devised by curriculum groups and published in courses of study or curriculum guides so that teachers may refer to them. They may also be devised in workshop groups, in study groups, and by students in preservice or graduate training. In that latter case the resource unit is generally constructed on the basis of a hypothetical situation which the inexperienced teacher tries to visualize.

It should be kept in mind that the resource unit contains suggestions only, and the teacher should consider it as such. Unfortunately, because of some existing confusion in unit terminology, some individuals have looked upon the resource unit as a teaching unit ready to be used without deviation in actual teaching. When this occurs, the purpose of the resource unit is defeated. It should be kept in mind that the resource unit is more or less an outline of a unit.

Teaching unit. The teaching unit is sometimes referred to as the *learning unit.* The latter may actually be a better term, but the term *teaching unit* seems to have more widespread usage in the literature and is used here for that reason.

The teaching unit differs from the resource unit in that it is much more detailed, and it contains those materials and learning activities to be used in a particular class. In building a teaching unit the teacher may wish to study resource units in state and local curriculum guides, taking out items of the unit which can be useful in developing a teaching unit for a particular class.

The patterns or outlines for resource units and teaching units can be essentially the same, the main difference being in scope. For example, resource units offer as many suggestions as possible for use in a variety of situations, whereas teaching units should be limited to those procedures which would provide for the best learning in a specific situation.

The first unit of Appendix A is a resource unit on alcohol education that has been developed by the Alcohol Studies and Rehabilitation Section, Mental Health Division, Oregon State Board of Control and is included here as an example of excellent materials provided by special interest groups to assist the classroom teacher. Study of this unit will reveal the depth of subject matter upon which the teacher may draw to develop the more specific teaching or learning units.

UNIT PATTERNS

A few of the terms which the framework of the unit is called include, among others, the following: outline, sequence, guidelines, and patterns. The term *unit pattern* is used here with the idea in mind that it is to be used as a framework guide or a pattern in the construction of the unit. It should be clearly understood that there is a wide variety of unit patterns. The examples that follow are submitted for the purpose of furnishing the reader with a small sampling of unit patterns. The reader should study these various patterns with a view to their similarities as well as to their differences.

Johns* suggests the following guidelines for constructing the resource and learning unit in health education.

    I. Title of unit
   II. Overview of the unit
 III. Objectives or goals
 IV. Initiation of the unit
   V. Development of the unit
      A. Content
      B. Experiences
      C. Instructional materials
 VI. Culminating procedures
VII. Evaluation
VIII. Sources

Rash† recommends seven major headings as follows.

   I. Name or title of unit
  II. Expected outcomes
 III. Content
 IV. Methods and devices
  V. Evaluation procedures
 VI. Teaching aids
VII. References

---

*Johns, E. B.: Guidelines for health education units, Journal of Health, Physical Education, and Recreation 22: June, 1951.
†Rash, J. K.: Planning the health education unit, Journal of Health, Physical Education, and Recreation 24: Nov., 1953.

Yeo* in devising a resource unit outlines it in the following way.

I. Central theme
II. Delimitation
III. Outline of content
IV. Core activities
V. Optional activities
VI. Evaluation activities
VII. Teaching aids
  A. For teachers
  B. For pupils
  C. Visual and auditory materials

Billett† refers to the unit in terms of two sequences, the unit of learning and the unit of work, as follows.

Sequence I: Unit of learning
A. General statement
B. Itemized statement or delimitation
C. List of probable indirect and incidental learning products
D. Materials and references for teacher's use only

Sequence II: Unit of work
A. Unit assignment—overall tentative preliminary plan which the teacher makes for pupil activity
B. Introductory activities
C. Core activities—all pupils engage in these at some time to some degree
D. Optional related activities—for fast learners and slow learners
E. Evaluative activities
F. General study and activity guide
G. List of materials for pupil use

The following unit patterns have been selected at random from various courses of study and curriculum guides.

I. Determination of area of health education
II. Determination of objectives
III. Pretesting
IV. Materials needed
V. Teacher's plan and procedure
VI. Pupil plan of procedure and activities common to all
VII. Optional and related activities
VIII. Evaluation
IX. References

I. Introduction
II. Objectives
III. Outline
  A. Recommended common basic content
  B. Suggested common basic activities
  C. Culminating activities
IV. Evaluation
V. Materials for teachers and pupils including references

I. Introduction
II. Objectives
III. Basic information to be acquired
IV. Suggestions for initiating the unit
V. Pupil problems and activities
VI. Evaluation of outcomes
VII. References for teachers
VIII. References for pupils

I. Introduction
II. Objectives
III. Teacher procedure
IV. Pupil activities
  A. Common to all
  B. Optional
V. Evidence of mastery

---

*Yeo, J. W.: A sample guide in educational guidance (unpublished materials)
†Billett, R. G.: Fundamentals of secondary school teaching, Boston, 1940, Houghton Mifflin Co.

A study of the various unit patterns presented here reveals that none of them are exactly alike. However, it should be noted that all of them contain certain constant features that are inherent in a valid teaching-learning cycle. These phases include (1) an introduction, (2) a provision for learning experiences, and (3) an evaluation.

UNIT CONSTRUCTION

In building either a health resource unit or a health teaching unit, the teacher should take into account two very important factors. First, there is the problem of how to organize the unit, and, second, there is the consideration of a valid teaching-learning cycle. It will be the purpose of this section of the chapter to show through discussion, illustration, and example some of the important features that the teacher should consider when attempting to construct a unit. This is supplemented by the second and third teaching units of Appendix A. The second unit is an eleventh grade unit in community health. The third unit is an eighth grade unit in personal health designated to correspond to the Table of Specifications in Chapter 7 and the objective examination of Appendix B. Examination of these units in conjunction with the study of this chapter will contribute to a more thorough understanding of the unit method in health education.

The teacher should consider some sort of unit pattern as a guide for unit construction. In this connection it should be understood that the teacher is not obligated in any way to follow any pattern to the letter. In other words, the unit pattern should serve only as a guide, and the teacher should feel free to deviate from it if necessary. As a matter of fact, the teacher should perhaps devise his own unit pattern if others do not suit him. The important factor to consider is that the pattern must include those features which make for good organization as well as the recognized phases of a valid teaching-learning cycle.

For purposes of discussion here, the pattern suggested by Rash (p. 177) and cited earlier will be used.

    I. Name or title of unit
   II. Expected outcomes
 III. Content
 IV. Methods and devices
  V. Evaluation procedures
 VI. Teaching aids
VII. References

Name or title of unit. The title of the unit should first be informational. Precise phraseology helps to inform the student as to the intent or direction of the unit. Second, it should motivate and challenge. Motivation will arise as the teacher makes wise selection of subject matter to satisfy the most immediate needs and interests of students.

Expected outcomes. The term *outcome* is used here because it emphasizes the importance of what happens within the student. By contrast, the term *objective* is often interpreted as the teacher's goal, and the emphasis on student development is diminished. For example, it is not difficult to find in many published units an objective worded similar to the following: "To teach the facts of communicable disease control." This is a teacher objective in the strictest sense and signifies little concern for the success or failure of the learning process itself. Instead, it is important that the expected outcomes be selected in light of the student's needs, interests, and abilities.

If teaching is to be based on the needs and interests and specific problems of students, then there should be some way of determining what the needs are in a given situation. Teachers for the most part are familiar with the general health needs of students. For example, the teacher need only to review the national mortality rates to learn those things that are taking the lives of the school age population. Similarly, the morbidity rates can be studied to determine the types of illnesses that threaten the health and welfare of children and youth. Although such information is of utmost importance in building a unit, nevertheless it is equally important that teachers consider needs that are closely related to the local school and community. The alert and competent teacher will be quick to discover such needs. This can be done in such ways as consulting the local school health service personnel, studying health records, and day-to-day observation of students. For example, in one school an eighth grade teacher noticed that an unusual number of students in his room appeared to have defective teeth. Several of them were absent from school or had asked to be excused because of toothaches. A unit on dental health was devised for the purpose of stimulating interest in learning how to take better care of teeth. The teacher felt that he would like to find out what the dental defects of his students were and what the class members could do to help themselves. In order to gain a better understanding of the dental problem he circulated an anonymous questionnaire among the students and received the following responses.

	Yes	*No*
1. Have you ever had a toothache?	83%	17%
2. Have you ever been to a dentist?	94%	6%
3. Have you had or are you having your teeth straightened?	18%	82%
4. Do you often have inflamed or bleeding gums?	40%	60%
5. Would you like to find some of the causes of defective teeth?	90%	10%

6. How often do you brush your teeth?	Once a day	70%
	Twice a day	24%
	Never	6%
7. How many of your teeth do you think you have had filled?	Total for class	17
8. How many teeth have you had pulled in the last five years?	Total for class	9

Because of this information and the fact that 90% of the class wanted to find some of the causes of defective teeth, the teacher and students set out to study the problem.

The expected outcomes should be worded in terms of the habits, attitudes, and knowledge that the student is expected to acquire. Examples of these are taken from the eighth grade unit in Appendix A and are restated here.

Habit outcome—*Practices* appropriate physical activity
Attitude outcome—*Appreciates* the function of the body as a whole organism
Knowledge outcome—*Understands* the interrelationship of all body systems

When outcomes of the unit are being formulated, it is usually advisable for teachers to devise criteria for evaluating the outcomes. When this is done, the teacher should be in a better position to determine whether the outcomes are suitable for the particular group. The following list of suggested evaluative criteria are submitted.

1. Are the outcomes adapted to the specific grade level?
2. Does the teacher understand the outcomes?
3. Are the outcomes measurable so that suitable evaluation can be made?
4. Do the outcomes contribute to the educational needs of students?
5. Is it possible to achieve the outcomes through the health learning activities and experiences in which the students will engage?
6. Will there be sufficient time to achieve the outcomes?

Content. The content section of the teaching unit is a topical outline of the subject matter thought necessary to attain the expected outcomes. For instance, the general knowledge outcome just given has a corresponding content item in the teaching unit under the circulatory system which appears as the following: How the skeletal system serves as a functional element in activity. Related content items are seen in the other subsections of the unit.

It is a recognized teaching principle that not all students will react similarly to the same stimulus. Because of this, each expected outcome should have two or more content areas provided for it if the teacher hopes to help all students reach some degree of achievement. In developing each of these areas, however, the teacher must be sure that the content is related to the specified outcome and that both content and outcomes are appropriate to the grade level for which the material is designed.

Methods and devices. This part of the unit includes the methods and devices considered best in helping students learn and achieve. In order to provide for differences in students, a variety of learning experiences should be developed. For example, there are various media through which desirable learning can take place such as reading, observing, demonstrating, experimenting, constructing, creating, playing, singing, dramatizing, drawing, exploring, writing, and listening. Some of these media include reading materials, demonstrations, experiments, audiovisual aids, dramatizations, field trips, and panel discussions.

Although the teacher should list many and varied learning activities and experiences, students should also be given a part in planning the experiences. That is, they should be given an opportunity to decide some of the things they might try to find out and some of the ways in which the problems of the unit might be solved.

In order to be reasonably sure that the methods and devices have a sufficient degree of validity, it is recommended that the teacher subject them to critical evaluation. In other words, there should be certain standards that the methods and devices should meet so that the teacher will be reasonably certain that the most desirable learning activities and experiences have been selected for a specific situation. The following list of suggested evaluative criteria is submitted as a guide for teachers.

1. Has sufficient provision been made for problem-solving experiences?
2. Has economy of student time and energy been taken into consideration?
3. Is further teacher-student planning needed?
4. Do the activities and experiences provide for integration through use of school and community resources?
5. Are there possibilities for integration in relation to the student's life aims, other subject matter areas and courses, extraclass activities, and out-of-school activities?
6. Has provision been made for differences in students through choice in required work, optional activities, and encouragement of student suggestions?

Evaluation procedures. A detailed analysis of the problems involved in the appraisal and evaluation of learning in health education was presented in Chapter 7. The discussion here should aid the reader in gaining an insight into the need and purpose of evaluation as it concerns unitary teaching.

There are a number of valid techniques which may be used for estimating the educative growth of students. Some of these include objective tests, observations, behavior records, anecdotal records, and case study outlines. In that health is concerned with attitudes and behavior as well as with knowledge, the teacher is cautioned not to rely entirely on health knowledge tests as a means of measuring learning. The health knowledge test merely indicates the amount of knowledge that has been acquired, but it gives no indication that the knowledge has been put into practice. For this reason it is highly recommended that teachers give consideration to other evaluation techniques which indicate behavior changes.

Teaching aids. It is essential that the teacher have clearly in mind all of the materials that will be needed for a specific health unit. The possibilities of health learning experiences are so varied and extensive that the scope of possible materials is almost without limitations. The teachers should recognize that he must stay within the limits of materials and resources that are accessible in a given situation. However, in order to make use of available materials, all of the resources of the school system and community should be explored.

As the teacher lists the learning experiences of the unit, he should have clearly in mind the materials that will be necessary to carry out the unit successfully. However, during the process of student-teacher planning some students may wish to engage in activities for which there are insufficient materials available. If the desired materials cannot be obtained, the teacher may recommend alternate activities of a similar kind. In some cases students have devised their own materials in carrying out activities. This is a commendable practice that should be encouraged in that it provides creative learning experiences.

References. It is desirable that there be two separate lists of references—one for use of the teacher and one for students. If the teacher wishes, he may give the exact page numbers in listing references. This is a good procedure if mimeographed study guides are provided for students. The teacher then has sufficient specific references for study questions. Although students should perhaps be furnished with some specific references, this practice should be limited to some extent in the upper grades so that these students may have the experience of finding information through exploration of general reference material.

The following is a suggested form for a unit plan.

SUGGESTED FORM FOR UNIT PLAN*

Name of unit_____Grade_____

Expected outcomes†	Content	Methods and devices	Evaluation procedures	Teaching aids	References
In terms of practices, attitudes, and knowledges	Activities, subject matter, and/or situations designed to develop expected outcomes	Ways, means, instruments, and approaches in teaching the subject matter in order to achieve the expected outcomes	Ways, means, and devices for measuring results of teaching	Instruments, materials, and aids of different kinds	Books, magazines, pamphlets, etc., to be used in implementing expected outcomes

*From Rash, J. K.: Planning the health education unit, Journal of Health, Physical Education, and Recreation **24:** Nov., 1953.
†Selected in light of the needs, interests, abilities, and ability to do for one's self.

LENGTH OF UNITS

The following question is often asked: What is the ideal length of a health unit? When one considers the many factors surrounding unitary teaching in health, it becomes readily apparent that there can be no ideal standard in terms of a specified time allotment for a unit. For this reason the time allotted for teaching a unit should be considered in approximate terms. This is absolutely essential in order to assure the flexibility that is so necessary in unitary teaching.

For learning to be effective, sufficient time should be spent on the unit to allow for acquisition of knowledge that will form the basis of immediate or eventual improvement in health attitudes and behavior. The nature, scope, and content of the unit will govern to a certain extent the amount of time spent on it. In addition, the length of the unit should give consideration to the characteristics of the students for whom it is intended. For example, experience has shown that shorter units are more advisable when slower learners have been grouped together.

LESSON PLANNING

Regardless of the length of a health teaching unit, most teachers make some provision for daily lesson planning. In other words, it is essential that the unit be broken down on a day-to-day basis. This does not imply that a lesson will cover only one class period. It is possible that a lesson will cover less than one class period or extend into more than one class period. The important consideration to keep in mind is that the continuity preserved from one class period to another should be such that the objectives of the health teaching unit are realized. This implies that in daily lesson planning the teacher should have a clear perspective of the total learning that is expected

---

DAILY LESSON PLAN

Teacher   John Reed   School   Mt. View JHS

Date   12/6/63
Time   10:40-11:35
Grade   8

Lesson objectives: Introduce topic of first aid and prepare students for material to come

Unit title: First aid and safety education

Content (problems-outline)	Time	Activities (methods)	Resources-materials
I. Roll	3	Seating chart	
II. Introduction of unit	18	Show film *First Aid on the Spot*	State health department
III. Discussion of film	20	Ask leading questions of students on what they thought of film	
IV. Discussion of personal experiences	10	Draw out students willing to discuss situations in their experience in which first aid was or could have been helpful.	
V. Give definition of first aid	2	Write on chalkboard: "—immediate temporary care given in case of accident or sudden illness until medical attention is secured"	
VI. Read announcements and give next assignment	2		

from the unit. In this respect it becomes necessary for the teacher to determine whether procedures in daily lesson planning are such that they are related to the inclusive teaching unit. With these factors in mind the following criteria are suggested.

Does lesson planning:

1. Ensure definite objectives for the lesson?
2. Ensure proper continuity of one lesson with another?
3. Ensure proper selection and organization of learning activities?
4. Give attention to the most desirable teaching procedures?
5. Ensure provision for individual differences of students?
6. Provide for sufficient flexibility with regard to the total teaching unit?
7. Provide for suitable evaluation of the outcome of teaching?

QUESTIONS FOR DISCUSSION

1. How can the unit method of teaching provide for varied learning experiences in health?
2. In what way is integration adaptable to the unit method of teaching?
3. What is the place of teacher planning in the unit method of teaching?
4. What is the difference between a health resource unit and a health teaching unit?
5. What are some valid techniques for unit evaluation?
6. What are some of the factors that influence the time allotted for a health teaching unit?
7. Why should there be a variety of methods, devices, and activities in each unit?
8. Why should there be more methods, devices, and activities than any one teacher would have time to develop in each unit?

SUGGESTED CLASS ACTIVITIES

1. Write a brief summary on the development of the unit method.
2. With a group of class members prepare a health resource unit for the ninth grade level. Select one subject matter area from the suggested ninth grade content given in Chapter 6.
3. With a group of class members prepare a health resource unit for the twelfth grade level. Select one subject matter area from the suggested twelfth grade content given in Chapter 6.
4. Develop a health teaching unit for a specific subject matter area in the seventh grade. Use the suggested seventh grade content given in Chapter 6 as a guide.
5. Develop a health teaching unit for a specific subject matter area in the tenth grade. Use the suggested tenth grade content given in Chapter 6 as a guide.
6. Prepare a lesson plan from the unit you constructed and teach a demonstration lesson to the other class members.
7. Develop an alternative unit pattern that you believe is equally satisfactory to those suggested in this chapter and make a report on it to the class.
8. Debate the following statement: Educators are overly concerned with method and unconcerned with content.

REFERENCES

1. Alberty, H. B.: Reorganizing the high school curriculum, New York, 1947, The Macmillan Co.
2. American Educational Research Association, Committee on Curriculum: Curriculum planning and development, Review of Educational Research **30:** June, 1960.
3. Anderson, V. E.: Principles and procedures of curriculum improvement, New York, 1956, The Ronald Press Co.
4. Association for Supervision and Curriculum Development: Research for curriculum improvement, 1957 yearbook, Washington, D. C., 1957, National Education Association.
5. Bennett, R. A.: Unit Ideas for the new school year, English Journal **49:** Sept., 1960.
6. Bresvinick, S. L.: Effective daily lesson plans, Clearing House **34:** March, 1960.

7. Brubacher, J. S.: A history of the problems of education, New York, 1947, McGraw-Hill Book Co., Inc.
8. Butts, R. F.: A cultural history of education, New York, 1947, McGraw-Hill Book Co., Inc.
9. Cyphert, F. R.: Freedom of method: boon or bane of teaching, High School Journal **45:** Oct., 1961.
10. Friedman, K. C.: Using curriculum guides, Education, **82:** Dec., 1961.
11. Grambs, J. D., and Iverson, W. J.: Modern methods in secondary education, revised, New York, 1958, The Dryden Press.
12. Hansen, K. H.: High school teaching, Englewood Cliffs, N. J., 1957. Prentice-Hall, Inc.
13. Leonard, J. P.: Developing the secondary school curriculum, revised, New York, 1953, Rinehart & Co., Inc.
14. Mass, B. S.: How to teach a unit, Instructor **70:** Sept., 1960.
15. New York City Board of Education: Curriculum resource materials for meeting school retention and pre-employment needs, New York City Board of Education Curriculum Bulletin, no. 8, 1960-61.
16. Ogorodnikov, I. T.: Problem of improving the effectiveness of the lesson, Soviet Education **4:** May, 1962.
17. Oliger, L. K., and Convery, H. J.: A unit of work on foods, Journal of School Health **25:** April, 1955.
18. Saylor, J. G., and Alexander, W. M.: Curriculum planning for better teaching and learning, New York, 1954, Rinehart & Co., Inc.
19. Schneider, R. E.: Methods and materials in health education, Philadelphia, 1958, W. B. Saunders Co.
20. Wagner, G. W.: What schools are doing, Education **80:** April, 1960.

Chapter 10

EFFECTIVE PRESENTATIONS
IN HEALTH EDUCATION

Even though many and varied teaching aids and procedures are used, oral presentation remains one of the most fundamental and basic approaches to teaching.

The reaction against lecturing as a method of teaching in recent years has created a tendency among educators to overlook the very basic role that oral presentation plays in teaching. Although the lecture method as such has an important place in teaching at the college level and with advanced high school students who are capable of handling the abstractions of language, it becomes increasingly ineffective at successively lower grade levels. However, oral presentation within the context of the present discussion bears little relationship to the lecture method ordinarily used at the college level. Rather, oral presentation refers to that type of verbal communication by which the teacher guides the students into and through learning experiences. Thus, it is a tool of major importance, for it is one of the most successful means whereby thought is stimulated and tested, ideas are shared, and appreciation of the thinking of others is developed. Actually, no instructional device or teaching aid reduces the importance of oral presentation. As a matter of fact, it may be said that the relationship of student to teacher and student to student rests to a considerable extent upon oral communication. It has been said that man lives in a speaking world; thus it is important that close attention be given to the role of oral presentation in the teaching-learning situation.

EFFECTIVE USE OF ORAL PRESENTATIONS

Exclusive of lecturing, oral presentation usually takes the form of (1) brief statements or exposition by the teacher, (2) question and answer sessions, (3) student presentations, and (4) one or another type of group discussion.

187

In practice, oral presentation is commonly employed in the following ways.

1. As an introductory activity used by the teacher to do such things as introduce new units of instruction and audiovisual aids and to plan field trips and classroom experiments. When oral presentations are used in these ways, emphasis should be upon orientation of thought, relating old material and experience to new and rousing interest by relating the new material to the life interest of the students. Oral presentation of this kind should be as brief as possible and usually should be supplemented by other forms of introductory activities such as demonstration and films.

2. As a means of determining the present level of knowledge of a class. Before actual teaching begins, it is sometimes desirable to ask a series of questions which will reveal not only what the students already know about the new unit but also how their thinking is organized in relation to their existing knowledge and what application and implications they see in what they know. In the process of determining the extent of knowledge the students have about a new unit, the teacher can also find out what they want to know as well as what they think they need to know. If this is the case, specific questions may be asked in order to determine needs and interests of students.

3. As a means of clarification and illustration.

4. As a means of evaluating progress during the course of a unit. Again, by means of class discussion and questions, it is possible for the teacher to determine the extent and effectiveness of learning. When oral presentation is used in this way, it becomes to some extent an evaluative procedure in that it reveals achievement on the part of students and it also measures the effectiveness of teaching. Other results of oral presentation of this kind are that it may indicate the need for more audiovisual aids and more question and answer sessions to clarify health concepts, and it may help to identify students in the group who are learning and progressing very rapidly and need extra work and assignments. Also, the slow learning students who may need extra assistance can be identified through oral presentations.

5. As a means of encouraging student participation. This may take several forms, including individual student reports, class discussions, presentation of demonstrations, panel discussions, and the like. It may also take the form of students responding to questions posed by the teacher with the intention of drawing the class out on subjects about which they have some awareness.

QUESTIONS AND ANSWERS

The question and answer technique is one of the oldest of pedagogical procedures. It was highly developed by Socrates in the fifth century B.C. as a means of leading his students to higher levels of thought. It should be used ordinarily as a device for discovering, enlarging upon, and integrating what is known rather than what is *not* known, although in some cases its use in finding out what is not known can be justified. Skillful use of questions and answers is an excellent way to develop and maintain good teacher-student and student-student relationships in addition to stimulating desirable verbal exchange among the students.

Some advantages of question and answer technique. Some of the advantages of the question and answer technique are the following.

1. Misunderstandings and vagueness can be corrected immediately to avoid the formation of misconceptions.
2. Vocabulary can be clarified immediately.
3. The thinking of students can be stimulated, guided, and challenged.
4. Known areas of knowledge can be quickly differentiated from unknown areas.
5. Questions and answers can be utilized to good advantage at all stages of the lesson or unit.

Experience in the use of the question and answer technique shows that the best results are obtained when careful thought, planning, and organization are given to building and constructing sets of questions. The haphazard, inspirational types of questions frequently used by some teachers, especially when they are not properly prepared for the daily lesson, are usually inefficient and ineffective. As a general rule question and answer periods and sessions should be planned in detail and in advance as carefully as any other teaching procedure. Moreover, it is well to improve upon questions immediately after they have been used and to keep them for future use.

Some considerations in developing and utilizing questions. Questions should be clear and challenging, and they should be carefully adapted to the grade level of the group. When utilizing a series of questions, the teacher should take care that their unity be evident—that is, that one question and answer builds upon or is related to another for some definite purpose. A constant stream of questions and counter questions is unlikely to be effective, although it may seem so, particularly to an inexperienced teacher.

A series of questions and answers may be framed in such a way that they constitute a problem-solving device. A specific problem may be posed (questions may also be used to define the basic problem in itself) and may be solved by the group, as in the illustration entitled *A typical class discussion* which appears later in this chapter and which has to do with solving problems related to the spread of diseases. However, care must be taken that question and answer sessions of this type not be permitted to become time-consuming beyond their importance.

It is important for teachers to learn how to deal with the responses that students make to questions. Such a question as the following—Now let us review what should be done if a companion is badly hurt while on a trip with you some distance away from home—may elicit a variety of responses ranging from the proper and best answers to excited accounts of accidents that individual students have observed. The teacher's task is to keep the attention of the students directed to the purpose of the discussion so that it will constitute a learning experience, but it is also important that students not be discouraged or embarrassed because of irrelevant responses. A personal account may be interrupted in such a way by the teacher's saying, "Tell us about your experience after we have reviewed these basic ideas, and then we'll see how well the accident you saw was handled." Thus, instead of rebuffing the student, allowance is made for his contribution, and instead of his story being merely an exciting episode, it is made a desirable part of the discussion.

The teacher should avoid letting some students monopolize the question and answer sessions, and he must do this courteously and without stifling initiative and interest. Quiet and less aggressive individuals should be encouraged to contribute their share of responses. Also, all students should be made conscious of the need to deliberate before answering and to make well-thought-out and well-stated responses.

ORAL PRESENTATION AS AN INTRODUCTORY ACTIVITY

Regardless of the age level involved, in principle the introductory activity entails setting the stage for what is to follow. This is usually done by means of recalling known related experiences, materials, or problems before venturing into the unknown. For example, a unit on grooming at the seventh grade level might begin in something like the following manner.

Teacher: "You remember in our animal feeding experiment that when the rat did not get the proper food a number of things happened to him. What were some of those things?" (The class enumerates the symptoms.)

Teacher resumes: "Isn't it interesting that so many things having to do with the rat's appearance had to do with the kinds of food that he ate? Do we have any reason to believe that what is true of animals and their food might also be true of human beings?"

Thus from such a starting point related to work that has gone before, the teacher is in a position to develop the various concepts of grooming and personal appearance.

It should be emphasized that, regardless of the grade level of the class, introductory activity is most successful which goes directly to the life interests of the particular students involved and moves on from there to new concepts. It is for this reason that many successful teachers of health explore the numerous leisure time interests of young people as a point of departure for many units of teaching. These interests include nature, camping trips, games and sports, dating, and plans for the future.

One tenth grade teacher, whose athletic days are still not far behind, likes to introduce the subject of the effect of wholesome activity on the systems of the body by describing some of his personal experiences. Thus, he is able to cite the increase in performance through growth, development, and training. Invariably this sort of an introduction will draw out the boys, and their participation encourages the girls to take part also. It is a short step then to relate activity to world record performance and to contrast this with the results of inactivity as seen in certain diseases.

Having aroused interest in this way, this teacher finds it a comparatively simple matter to launch the unit on activity and rest. This teacher has great success with his approach and rarely fails to make his students more activity conscious and more receptive to learning about the importance of planned, regular activity accompanied by sufficient rest.

ORAL PRESENTATIONS BY STUDENTS

Some commonly noted advantages of student presentations are (1) that students ordinarily present and describe experiences with which others of their age and grade level are familiar, (2) that, usually, the illustrations and examples students give are of interest to the group, and (3) that the vocabulary used by students tends to be on a level with and understandable by the other students.

Some common disadvantages of student presentations are (1) that they may select extreme illustrations, (2) that they may select examples which are not entirely pertinent to the subject under consideration, (3) that their information may not be entirely accurate, and (4) that their presentations may not contribute materially to the learning of the group. It is readily apparent that the disadvantages do not necessarily invalidate student presentations but merely underscore the need for the teacher to exert some guidance and control over them.

Discussions among the students as well as between teachers and students can be a very desirable means of sharing experiences and expanding knowledge in health.

When group discussions, panels, forums, and the like are employed, they should be preceded by periods of study on the subject under consideration. Otherwise, the discussions are likely to degenerate into a pooling of ignorance and a random intermixing of truth, half-truth, and untruth which in the areas of health and safety can be very harmful. Discussions not preceded by study are likely to be of value only if the teacher is using them as a means of (1) showing how fruitless and frustrating the exchange of uninformed opinion on any subject is likely to be, (2) as a means of dramatizing the need for facts and understanding if value is to be derived from discussion, or (3) as a means of showing the limits of present knowledge and of making plans for extending it.

Discussions or panels may also be used as culminating activities which engage all students in the process of outlining and appraising the status of their knowledge and of making applications of their knowledge. In this way the students are in the position of having to defend their ideas, and they are under pressure to marshal their facts and clarify their thinking. Emphasis is thus upon getting at the facts and their meaning rather than upon pleasing the teacher or just meeting specified requirements.

Discussion leader. A few considerations relative to discussion-leading should be noted. Certainly, before turning the duties of discussion leader over to the students, the teacher should prepare them for the task if they have not had such training. Essentially, the leader's role is to make the discussion as fruitful as possible. The leader's first responsibility is to orient the group as to the direction and scope of the discussion.

Ordinarily, he states any rules which seem necessary, such as limiting individual contributions to a specified amount of time, particularly when verbal exchanges become heated and not particularly productive.

Usually, the leader should not take too active a part in the discussion. Rather, his job is to get a maximum amount of thoughtful and orderly participation from the group. If there is any doubt as to a contributor's meaning, the leader may restate that point of view briefly as he understood it and ask the speaker whether that was as he had intended it, or he may ask the speaker to restate his own position briefly for clarification purposes. In either event, he should avoid seeming partial in any argument. He reacts quickly to any speaker's tendency to become diverted from the agreed upon subject, but in doing so he remains tactful. Finally, the leader is responsible either to summarize the ground covered and conclusions reached in the discussion or else to appoint a summarizer to assume responsibility for the task.

Typical class discussion. The following illustrates a tenth grade class discussion in progress.

Teacher: "Let us see how we can use our knowledge about the spread of disease in deciding some things of importance with regard to community health. The state health department has recently reported the capture of four rabid bats in Spring County. What should we point out about rabies before we consider community health precautions?"

Student 1: "I have read that the infecting agent is a virus."

Teacher: "That's true. What is the source of infection for man?"

Student 1: "I thought that it was dogs."

Student 2: "But I know a girl who had to be treated when a field cat that she was trying to catch bit her."

Teacher: "Both cats and dogs are involved and, as I indicated, bats also. Can we make a generalization?"

Student 3: "Well, all three of the animals mentioned are mammals. Is it correct to say that the bites of any warm-blooded mammal are suspect?"

Teacher: "Good. That is what we want. Now, why is the bite of concern, and yet we don't worry at all when our pet dog licks our hand?"

Student 4: "Perhaps the virus is able to travel in the circulatory system. This is possible from the bite but not from the hand-licking."

Teacher: "That's correct. Can you say anything more about a biting dog?"

Student 4: "Yes. If the rabies virus infects a dog, he becomes vicious and is inclined to bite. When he bites, he deposits the virus in the blood stream of his victim. The house pet who only licks the hand most likely is uninfected."

Teacher: "Fine. Now remember that the same thing may result from the bite of a bat. In October of 1961 an 11-year-old boy in Idaho died from rabies inflicted by a bat that bit him while he slept. Now, John, I asked you to read about the symptoms of rabies. Can you tell us of these?" (John recounts the symptoms that develop both in the animal and in man.)

Teacher: "Thank you. Your description indicates that there is severe neural involvement. This is described as acute encephalitis and death will result from respiratory paralysis. Once even the early symptoms of paralysis occur, such as in spasm on drinking, the infecting agent has reached the central nervous system and will be fatal. With this in mind, what steps do you believe a community should follow in protecting itself against this dread disease?"

The class then proceeds to discuss the steps a community might follow to avert a severe rabies epidemic. Perhaps a local health officer is finally invited in to check their plans and to give them ideas from his own experience and from his knowledge of actual epidemics that demanded similar control measures.

THE LECTURE

The limitations of straight lecturing as a teaching procedure are so well known that it is not necessary to elaborate on them. Regardless of the grade level in question, the basic problem seems to be that in the lecture method active participation is centered in one person.

Although the lecture method is relatively ineffective below the advanced grades in the secondary school, it is widely used in the upper high school grades and in colleges. Therefore, as students progress throughout the junior high school grades, they should gradually develop the ability to profit from the lecture method.

ORAL COMPREHENSION

As the student matures, certain of the oral presentations which precede and follow the various learning activities may be gradually extended. In this way, the student's ability to comprehend sustained oral presentation may be increased in a manner that is comparable to his increased ability to learn during periods of uninterrupted reading. For example, in time, students should become able to listen to speeches and round table discussions by experts on various health subjects with real comprehension of the information and points of view presented.

Critical listening. Just as it is esesntial that students learn to read critically, they should also be taught to listen critically as well. We know that communication is an active two-way process, and that it is important to develop the ability to listen intelligently as well as to speak effectively.

In the field of health all manner of claims are made by advertisers. Some of these claims are factual and responsible. Others are concerned solely with selling a product. Most claims are probably relatively harmless, but some are quite misleading and harmful. The teacher of health should, of course, help students to become cautious in their acceptance of advertising and other claims, whether they are by printed or spoken word. Specific instruction on this subject seems essential. However, excellent practical experience can be acquired by means of listening critically to class presentations. For the most part, of course, lectures should be devoted to the development of concepts that are based on the established facts in the field. On the other hand, on some occasions the class may be forewarned to be alert for misleading or false statements. The teacher may sometimes deliberately include false statements in oral presentations in order to test the ability of the students to detect them. After long years of being urged to accept and obey authoritative statements and commands at home and at school, it often comes as somewhat of a shock to students to realize that authority can actually be trying to trip them. In the present day perhaps even more than in the past, a doubting and skeptical attitude toward authoritative statements, particularly those dealing with health, seems desirable.

The teacher should have little difficulty in locating misleading and false statements, arguments, and misconceptions. For example, a miraculous cancer-curing machine was recently used to cheat hundreds of desperate people of their money. The teacher could report the machine as a new weapon in the fight against cancer in the same terms used by its inventor, telling just enough about it to cast doubt on its authenticity. In challenging the value of the machine the students can be led to state what they would need to know about such a thing before putting their faith in it.

EVALUATION

Whatever instructional technique is employed, whether discussion, film, demonstration, or lecture, it is essential that suitable evaluation take place. In many instances this may take written form, but more commonly it is in the form of oral exchanges which are calculated to take the experience apart for its meaning and uses. The evaluation may include a summary of major points usually by one or more students and interpretation and application of the concepts involved. Since thought is primarily in terms of verbal symbols, and since the communication of ideas is based upon verbal symbols, oral evaluation of educational experiences may be regarded as a most essential phase of health education in terms of both (1) checking the effectiveness of the teaching-learning experience and (2) cultivating in the learner the habit of systematically evaluating his experiences for their significance. Thus, for example, students may not only grow in their ability to grasp the content of oral presentation of health concepts, but they may also form the habit of evaluating what they hear in terms of sound criteria.

QUESTIONS FOR DISCUSSION

1. What are some important relationships between the capacity for oral communication and the mental development of students?
2. What are some major uses of oral presentation in health education?
3. What are some advantages and limitations of the lecture method?
4. How can pupils be active participants in oral communication? Discuss a number of ways.
5. What are some important considerations to be taken into account in preparing questions for class discussions?
6. In what ways is oral presentation important in relation to teaching aids?
7. What is meant by critical listening? Of what importance is critical listening when information on health is presented by way of the popular media of communication?

SUGGESTED CLASS ACTIVITIES

1. Prepare a talk on a health topic which is designed to challenge the critical thinking of the group.
2. Outline ways in which students at specific grade levels may be participants in oral presentation of health subjects.
3. Prepare a sequence of questions for use in a question and answer session on some phase of health. Specify the grade level for which the questions are intended and specify where and why they should be used.
4. Prepare a list of visitations, field trips, and other activities which can form the basis of oral presentation by students.
5. For a week, collect examples of advertising which are concerned with health. As a class activity, analyze each in terms of its likely influence upon the health concepts of the persons who see it.

REFERENCES

1. Carr, R. W.: Lecture method in the junior high school, Social Studies **53**: Jan., 1962.
2. Crabtree, Peter: Socrates in the seventh grade. National Education Association Journal **51**: March, 1962.
3. Duker, Samuel: In an age of communication, are we listening? Educational Forum **18**: May, 1954.

4. Koess, W. A.: Reliability, sex differences, and validity in the leaderless group discussion technique, Journal of Applied Psychology **45:** Oct., 1961.
5. Ross, J. A.: Group discussion in high school needed, Ohio Schools **39:** Nov., 1961.
6. Smith, P. G.: Art of asking questions, Reading Teacher **15:** Sept., 1961.
7. Taylor, H. O.: Comparison of the effectiveness of a lecture method and a small-group discussion method of teaching high school biology, Science Education **43:** Dec., 1959.
8. Watkins, L. I.: Some problems and solutions in teaching group discussion, Speech Teacher **10:** Sept., 1961.

Chapter 11

EXPERIMENTS IN HEALTH EDUCATION

Discussion in previous chapters indicated that strong emphasis is currently being placed on upgrading the entire school curriculum. The teaching of health science is certainly involved in this upgrading process, and nowhere is this quite so evident as in the increased use of experiments as a teaching method. This chapter reveals some of the possibilities that experiments provide in the teaching of secondary school health.

Although the use of experiments is one of the most valuable of teaching aids which may be employed in health education, it remains a vast untapped potential. Some reasons for the limited use of experiments include (1) little or no understanding of the scientific method on the part of many teachers responsible for health instruction (see the discussion on teacher preparation in Chapter 19), (2) poor demonstration facilities in the health classroom (see Chapter 17), (3) insufficient funds to purchase the needed experimental items, and (4) lack of understanding regarding the purpose of experiments as a health teaching method.

PURPOSE OF EXPERIMENTS

Perhaps the most frequent use of experiments is to illustrate something that has already been presented in some other way. As an example, the teacher might first introduce the topic respiration with a lecturette, supplemented by a large chart of the respiratory system. A follow-up lesson might include the bell jar experiment, the equipment for which is shown on the teacher's desk in Fig. 8, and is explained in the experiment description entitled *Mechanics of Breathing*. Finally, an experiment using a beef lung will convincingly demonstrate the resiliency of lung tissue and its relationship to circulation (Fig. 7). Progression of this sort is interesting and challenging to students.

A less frequent but equally valuable purpose of the experiment is to intro-

196

duce new units of instruction. When used at the start of a unit, an experiment should set the stage for later material and should focus student attention on the objectives of the material to be presented. The corollary in stage craft is the drama that opens with a rapid-fire, traumatic event to catch and focus the audience's attention. The health teacher who possesses a flair for the dramatic will find the experimental method particularly helpful. For instance, the beef lung experiment just mentioned could well be placed in the opening scene for the purpose of directing and fixing attention on the respiratory system.

EXPERIMENTS BY THE TEACHER

The teacher should keep in mind certain principles which apply regardless of where or how the experiment is used in the teaching-learning situation. Some major considerations are the following.

1. The experiment should work; obviously, if it does not, students tend to lose confidence as well as interest.
2. Adequate preparation should be made. The experiment should be rehearsed before the class arrives.
3. If possible, all equipment should be arranged on the demonstration table before rather than after the class arrives.
4. Equipment should be large enough and the experiment on a large enough scale to be easily seen by all students.
5. Experiments should be as simple and speedy as possible.
6. Equipment should be stored away intact until it is to be used again.

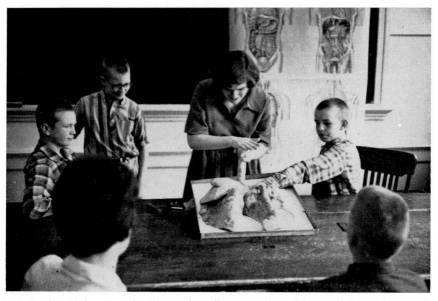

Fig. 7. A junior high school health teacher discusses the resiliency of lung tissue. The left lobe of this beef lung had been pierced at the packing house, and the student is holding it closed as the teacher fills the right lobe with air.

7. Students should be prepared ahead of time for the experiment. Perhaps problems and other materials may be mimeographed and distributed for use following the experiment.

It should be kept in mind that experimentation in health education is not to replace a basic science class in the curriculum. To teach the scientific method, as such, is not the purpose of experimentation in health instruction. Rather, experiments are used to emphasize a particular aspect of the teaching unit. Therefore, they should ordinarily be short and simple rather than complicated and involved. Also, they should require small amounts of relatively inexpensive equipment. Most of the experiments which are included in this chapter are of this sort. Exceptions to this are sometimes desirable depending upon the capabilities of the teacher and students and the facilities and equipment available.

The following are some common errors frequently made by teachers in utilizing experiments:

1. Failure to show how the experiment fits into the health unit being studied
2. Failure to direct the student's attention to the important health facts of the experiment
3. Failure to allow students time to record data
4. Failure to stimulate students to ask questions
5. Failure to emphasize major health and hygiene facts over minor ones
6. Failure to require students to make generalizations and reach conclusions concerning health and healthful living
7. Failure to encourage students to suspend their judgment until adequate data on the problem have been accumulated

It is impossible to indicate the multitude of experiments that the teacher can draw from to assist in the presentation of a unit. By way of example, however, and within the context of the eighth grade unit so extensively developed already, the experiments which follow are a few that have been used successfully by secondary health teachers.

Experiment 1—osmosis
Purpose:

To show students the action of osmosis

Procedure:

1. Remove a small piece of shell from the large end of a raw egg.
2. Make a small hole through both the shell and the lining in the small end of the egg.
3. Insert a small glass tube through the hole in the small end. Seal around the hole with sealing wax.
4. Place the egg, large end down, in the top of a milk bottle filled with enough water to cover the large end of the egg.
5. Observe the results the next day.

Results:

Through the process of osmosis, the water in the bottle passes through the membrane of the egg which was exposed in the large end. The pressure of the additional liquid in the egg causes the displacement of liquid up into the glass tube.

Experiment 2—diffusion of molasses through the intestine of a frog

Purposes:

1. To show students the major principles of diffusion
2. To show students the rapidity with which foods are absorbed through the intestinal wall

Materials:

Intestine of frog, Ringer's solution (to keep intestine moist and to wash preparation), molasses, string, beaker, and Benedict's solution

Procedure:

Begin this experiment with a freshly dissected intestine from a frog. Keep the intestine moist with Ringer's solution to keep the tissue alive. To do this moisten the specimen repeatedly. Tie off one end of the intestine with a small piece of thread. Make sure the intestine is clean and free of all foreign material by washing it thoroughly with Ringer's solution. Pour a solution of molasses or sugar and water (syrup) into the open end of the intestine (make sure there are no punctures in the intestine). Tie off the open end and tie both ends to a stick long enuogh to reach well beyond both edges of a 200 ml. beaker. Place the intestine in the beaker and fill the beaker with water so that it just covers the part of the intestine containing the molasses.

Results:

Allow 30 minutes before checking water with Benedict's solution to see if there is any sugar present outside the intestine.

Experiment 3—cilia and how they work

Purpose:

To give the pupils a chance to see how cork is moved in the digestive system by cilia

Materials:

Pithed frog, pins, cutting knife, piece of cork, frog board, paper towels, Ringer's solution, and eyedropper.

Procedure:

Stretch the pithed frog on the frog board. Cut through the lower jaw in the midline and continue the cut back to the stomach. Draw back the flaps of the lower jaw and pin out the esophagus to form a flat surface. Keep the frog moist with Ringer's solution. Lay a piece of bread on the exposed mucous membrane. Have the students note the direction it moves. Tilt it so food has to move upward to reach the stomach.

Results:

Cilia are located in the respiratory tract, eustachian tube, tear duct and sac, cavities of the brain and spinal cord, and certain parts of the reproductive organs. By contractility, the cilia sway back and forth. During forward movement the cilia are rigid and during backward movement they become limp. In the body, dust and mucous are in this manner moved upward in the respiratory tract. The function of cilia is to move fluid and suspended matter bathing the epithelium.

Experiment 4—mechanics of breathing

Purpose:

To demonstrate the passive function of the lungs as they respond to pressure differences

Materials:

Glass Y-tube, hole stopper, bell jar, two balloons, rubber sheeting (large enough to cover the bottom of the bell jar) (see **Fig. 8**)

Procedure:

The bell jar represents the chest cavity, the Y-tube the treachea and bronchioles, the balloons the lungs, and the rubber sheeting the diaphragm.

Results:

Since the area within the bell jar is increased by pulling down the "diaphragm," there is less pressure on the "lungs." Thus atmospheric pressure pushes outside air into the lungs or balloons in this case. When the sheeting is puhed inward, the air pressure in the interior of the bell jar is increased, and the air in the lungs is forced out. Then the balloon "lungs" collapse.

Experiment 5—observing red corpuscles in a living fish
Purpose:

To examine the path of blood through the three kinds of blood vessels in the tail of a goldfish

Procedure:

Wrap a small goldfish in wet absorbent cotton so that its gills are kept wet. Leave only the tail exposed. Lay the fish in a Petri dish and then place a glass slide over the tail to hold it flat. Examine under low-power objective of the microscope. Should the fish flip its tail and wet the lens, which is likely, add water to the cotton, dry off the lens of the microscope, and examine again under low power.

Results:

Find the circulatory pattern under the high-power objective. Look for red corpuscles in the blood as it circulates. Observe the blood moving rapidly, in spurts almost, in one blood vessel, and moving slowly in the opposite direction in another large blood vessel. Return the fish to water within 15 minutes.

Experiment 6—how smoking affects the body
Purpose:

To show students the effect of tobacco on the body

Materials:

Cigarette, vacuum pump, gallon jug, glass tubes, two hole cork, and rubber hose (see Fig. 8)

Procedure:

Fill the glass jug half full of water. Connect the glass tube with the cigarette in one opening in the rubber cork. Connect the pump with the rubber hose in the other opening of the cork. Light the cigarette by drawing up on the pump handle. Continue pumping action. Each upward stroke of the pump represents one puff on the cigarette.

Results:

The dark oily material in the water is a mixture of tars from the burning tobacco. The odor is mainly from these tars. The water also contains nicotine, a powerful poison sometimes used in insecticides. It is colorless. Another poison, carbon monoxide, is also present in the tobacco smoke. From this experiment, it should be clear that smoking does not help you to stay healthy.

Experiment 7—detection of glucose in urine
Purpose:

To show how glucose is detected in the urine of a diabetic person

Materials:

Test tube, Bunsen burner, test tube holder, Benedict's solution, freshly voided urine, and Tes-Tape

Fig. 8. Senior high school experiment to show the properties of tobacco smoke. Note the bell jar with simulated lungs (use of this device is explained in the text in the discussion of the experiment on the mechanics of breathing).

Procedure:

1. Tear off 1½ inches of Tes-Tape, dip it in urine, remove it immediately, and let stand for 1 minute; if the color changes, let it stand longer.
2. In a test tube boil 5 ml. of Benedict's solution. Add 7 or 8 drops of urine (no more) and boil for 2 minutes; allow to cool normally.

Results:

1. With the Tes-Tape, the tape will begin to turn colors if there is any glucose present. Yellow will indicate the absence of glucose. Green is indicative of its presence; the darker the color, the higher is the percentage of glucose. (The Tes-Tape can be checked to determine whether it is still effective by dipping it in Coca-Cola.)
2. With the Benedict's solution, a greenish, yellow or red precipitate is formed if a reducing sugar is present. If no precipitate appears immediately, let the tube stand for several minutes.

Experiment 8—heart under strenuous exercise

Purpose:

To show the pulse rate and blood pressure results taken in three different positions, one of which is an exercise movement and to also show that the results are different between males and females (as these experiments are taking place, the teacher can explain these differing results)

Materials:

Table, blanket (to cover table), sphygmomanometer, stethoscope, and stopwatch (to use in counting the pulse rate for 1 minute)

Fig. 9. Using a beef heart, two junior high school students consider the effects of exercise on the musculature of the human heart.

Procedure:

1. Place a student on the table; take his pulse rate and blood pressure.
2. Have the student stand and repeat the taking of the pulse rate and blood pressure; note the difference in the results between lying down and standing.
3. Have the student run around the block or a field outside or have him run up and down a flight of stairs four or five times. Immediately, within a minute, take the pulse rate and blood pressure. Comment on the big difference in pulse rate and blood pressure after strenuous exercise.
4. Repeat procedure with a member of the opposite sex.

EXPERIMENTS BY THE STUDENTS

The preparation and conduction of experiments in health education provide students with an excellent opportunity to learn by doing. When facilities and equipment are adequate, groups of students can work through an experiment together and can demonstrate the results to the rest of the class. For example, in a ninth grade class which was studying community hygiene, one group visited a dairy, another a water purification plant, and another a sewage disposal plant. Each group was responsible for giving a full description of the operation of these plants to the entire class, and each developed an experiment as part of its presentation.

Dairy experiments. Several simple experiments were suggested by members of the group. These had to do with separating cream from milk, the principle of homogenization, and heating as in pasteurization. The teacher asked whether it would be possible to show the class what actually happened to the milk as a result of the heating. This question lead to microscopic examination of the milk before and after pasteurization and the development of bacteriological cultures. Two especially interested boys eventually stained some slides. Also included was a sample of contaminated milk for microscopic examination in order to show the effects of careless handling.

Water purification. The second group studied water purification and visited the city water works. For a demonstration they considered two possibilities: a mechanical filtering system and chemical treatment of the water to destroy bacteria. They decided on the filtering system, and following the design of the large filters, they filled a metal box with layers of sand, gravel, and rock. The demonstration then consisted of pouring dirty water into the filter and observing the clear water which flowed from an outlet pipe at the bottom.

Sewage disposal plant. This group decided upon an experiment having to do with destroying bacteria by chemical means. During the presentation, the class had an opportunity to examine some swamp water under a microscope and a second sample of this same water after it had been treated with chlorine. This experiment was used as the basis for describing how it is possible to make sewage safe for use as fertilizer after it has been treated by various means to kill the mocroorganisms in it.

Nutrition. Experiments designed to augment a junior high teaching unit in nutrition in which all students can participate might include the following:

Experiment 1—detecting proteins

Purpose:

To test for proteins in foods

Materials:

Meat (raw), egg white (cooked), American cheese, sugar, cornstarch, flour, milk (dry), skim milk (dry), whey (dry), dissecting needle or forceps, Bunsen burner or other flame, tripod, and asbestos sheeting or sheet iron

Procedure:

1. Using either the dissecting needle or the forceps, burn a small piece of meat in the flame. Notice whether there is an odor of burned feathers.
2. Burn small pieces of cooked egg white and American cheese in the same way. Rest the piece of asbestos sheeting or sheet iron on the tripod. Now burn each of the other foods by placing about $\frac{1}{2}$ teaspoonful of each on the asbestos sheeting or the sheet iron. Notice in each case whether there is an odor of burned feathers.

Results:

A simple test for protein is to burn the food. If an odor of burning feathers is given off, the food contains protein. Meat, egg white, American cheese, cottage cheese, flour, and milk (whole or skim) give off such an odor. Sugar and cornstarch do not; they do not contain protein.

Experiment 2—detecting starch

Purpose:

To test for starch in foods

Materials:

Cornstarch, baking soda, milk (dry), sugar, potato, hard cooked egg, knife, test tubes, iodine, dropper, test tube holders (optional), and test tube rack (optional)

Procedure:

Place about ½ teaspoon of cornstarch in a test tube. Fill the test tube one-half full of water. Add a drop of iodine. Note what happens. Make the same test with baking soda. Does the same thing happen? Try each of the other foods suggested under *Materials*. In all cases soften the food thoroughly with water as is suggested for the cornstarch. In the case of potato and other solid foods it is best to use scrapings. Look for any change in color in the water or on the bits of food.

Results:

When a blue color is formed with iodine, starch is present. Other foods may be brought from home to test such as bread, oatmeal, cornmeal, ripe bananas, apple, meat. The test shows best on solid foods. Omit dark-colored foods, since the test is a color test.

Experiment 3—detecting fat

Purpose:

To test for fat in foods

Materials:

Butter, milk, cream, American cheese, peanut butter, sugar, white flour, olive oil, suet, knife, and several sheets of ordinary notebook paper or brown paper

Procedure:

Spread a small amount of butter on a sheet of paper in three small areas. Then scrape it off. Observe what happens to the paper. Put small amounts of the other foods suggested on paper of the same kind. Place the papers on the radiator or in some warm place for a few minutes. Liquid milk must be left on the paper and allowed to dry. Examine the different papers. Observe what happens to the paper in each case.

Results:

Fat in food can be identified with a grease spot left when the food is placed on paper under conditions described in the experiment. Butter, milk, cream, cheese, suet, peanut butter, and olive oil make a grease spot. Sugar and white flour do not. They do not contain fat. Foods with considerable amounts of fat give more clear-cut results with this test. The grease spot from whole milk will be fainter than that from butter and cream.

Experiment 4—action of rennin on milk

Purpose:

To show that the enzyme rennin is necessary to digest milk

Procedure:

1. Crush a junket table and add it to a test tube of milk. Warm the milk but avoid boiling it. Keep accurate records with a stop watch.
   (a) What happens to the milk?
2. As a control experiment follow the same procedure only do not put any rennin in the milk.
   (a) Observe both experiments and compare the results.

Results:

The milk in the test tube containing the junket (rennin) will curdle. The milk in the control tube will not curdle.

Experiment 5—testing for acids
Purpose:

To show that acid is a significant component of food

Procedure:

Place a piece of blue litmus paper in contact with the following: vinegar, grapefruit juice, lemon juice, and sour milk

Results:

The change of color of the blue litmus paper to red indicates the presence of an acid.

Community health problems. A senior high school health unit on community health problems can be made more effective if the students, individually or by groups, complete one or more of the following four experiments.

Experiment 1—growing flys
Purpose:

To show how rapidly flys can multiply

Materials:

A jar with a lid, a live fly, raw meat, and a few drops of water

Procedure:

Punch a number of very small holes in the jar lid or cover the jar with a cloth because the fly must breathe. Place a live young fly in the jar with the meat. Young flies will be very small.

Results:

Keep the jar with the eggs at room temperature. Have the students keep a record of how many days it will take for the eggs, seen as small white specks, to hatch. This may vary, depending on the type of fly and the temperature.

Experiment 2—growth of microorganisms
Purpose:

To show how fast microorganisms can grow

Materials:

Package of yeast and teaspoon of sugar

Procedure:

Mix the yeast and sugar in a large test tube with warm water.

Results:

The yeast will grow rapidly. If a rubber stopper with a glass tube is put in the test tube, tests can be made to show whether oxygen or carbon dioxide is being produced. Direct the gas at a flame or pass it through limewater.

Experiment 3—growing bacteria
Purpose:

To show the rapid growth of bacteria

Materials:

Petri dishes, agar, and nutritive broth

Procedure:

Prepare a sterile nutritive broth, add some liquid agar to it, and pour it into a Petri dish. Mix a small amount of sputum with the solution and cover. Other student groups may wish to follow a similar procedure with a drop of blood, feces, or other materials.

Results:

A single bacterium cannot be seen without using a microscope, but when many bacteria grow together, they form a colony which can easily be seen by the naked eye. The agar in this experiment hardens and fixes the bacterial colonies. Different bacteria form colonies of different shapes, outlines, texture, and color, and they can be identified.

Experiment 4—disease control
Purpose:

To demonstrate the public menace of uncontrolled water areas

Materials:

Two jars of stagnant water containing mosquito larvae, and lubricating oil

Procedure:

1. Observe the mosquito larvae in the water. Note that they come to the surface for air. Observe their growth.
2. In one jar place enough oil on the water so that the water is completely covered with oil.
3. Observe the effect of the oil on the mosquito larvae.

Results:

The larvae are destroyed when they cannot breathe, thus indicating the need to control open water areas and thereby prevent mosquito reproduction. Indicate that various insecticides are equally effective as oil.

ANIMAL EXPERIMENTS

Some of the most successful experiments reported in health education are those involving animals. White rats, guinea pigs, mice, and hamsters are the most commonly used animals. In one situation, for the last several years students have been taken to the biological laboratory of a nearby college to observe the results of feeding experiments conducted for their benefit. Numerous other teachers provide their own experiments by raising animals, usually rats or mice but sometimes guinea pigs or hamsters, in the classroom.

Cage. A number of satisfactory designs for inexpensive animal cages are available. The most important consideration in selecting a design is whether the cage can be readily cleaned. The greatest single objection to raising animals in schools or homes is that they sometimes create an odor which is noticeable in distant parts of the building. This unpleasantness is, of course, unnecessary if the cages are properly made and maintained. The animals will keep themselves clean if given the opportunity. It is recommended that not only should droppings and urine be removed each day (a simple matter if the floor of the cage consists of $1/4$ inch wire screen and is constructed so that a newspaper can be easily inserted under it to catch the droppings), but also the screen and wood of the cage should be washed with soap and water each week.

Sample animal experiments

Studies of inheritance. A variety of inheritance experiments may be performed which will help to supplement and clarify class studies of the subject. Black rats may be crossed with white in order to observe the coloring of the resulting young. Of course, the color ratios of the young are highly unlikely to follow those indicated by mendelian ratios, but some of the basic points, including the variability of white and black proportions, may be made. Experiments of this kind may be used to show that acquired knowledge and injuries of the parents are not transmitted to the young. Injuries may take the form of small clippings on the ears. Demonstrations of this kind are valuable in helping to teach the kinds of things that are inherited and the kinds that are not inherited.

Feeding experiments. Animal experiments have been found suitable for demonstrating the effects of good and poor diets upon growth and health. These can be a highly effective means of clarifying basic concepts related to food values.

Experiments can be developed in which established optimum diets can be used and varied with careful measurements of different foods in very much the same way in which scientific experiments on the subject are conducted. With guidance, perhaps sometimes by university scientists, interested high school students can employ scientific methods and help to bring such techniques into the classroom in a highly interesting way. Thus, an experiment on something in the field of health can also be a demonstration of the functioning of the scientific method. For example, some people find it difficult to understand a controlled experiment when it is expressed to them as an abstract concept. However, it is much more likely to be comprehensible when it is explained in the setting of, say, an animal experiment. We can "see" the meaning of controls when it is explained why litter mates are used for comparative studies (to guarantee equal age and at least some similarity of genetic background) and why the animals must be treated and fed in exactly the same way except for the one factor under study, such as a vitamin or mineral food which is included in one diet and excluded from the other.

Of course, many teachers prefer not to *tell* their students the answers in relation to how to do experiments. Instead, they consider it important to encourage the class to think out many of the answers for themselves by means of skillful questioning. For example, the teacher may ask, "But how can we make sure that one rat isn't bigger to start with or older or growing more rapidly because of age?" Or, "If we use just one rat, how will we be able to tell what a properly fed rat would like after a few weeks? Don't we need a basis for comparison?"

The effects of vitamin deficiencies upon growth can be demonstrated strikingly by carefully controlling the feeding of animals. Diets deficient in vitamins A, B, C, and D soon result in stunted or disturbed growth and thus illustrate the need to include all of these vitamins in a good diet. Two young guinea pigs or rats may be placed on identical vitamin C-free diets except that one is given a small amount of orange juice each day. Within a few weeks the animal which did not receive the vitamin C (orange juice) will be found to have had its growth stunted.

Two cull chicks may be obtained to demonstrate the effects of sunlight (which causes the body to generate vitamin D) upon growth. If both are placed on identical vitamin D-deficient diets and only one is exposed to sunlight, the one deprived of both the vitamin D foods and the sunlight will undergo marked growth failure. By a similar technique it may be shown that if vitamin D-poor food is exposed to sunlight or other ultraviolet source, the resulting irridation will compensate for that lack of D vitamin and will prevent growth failure.

One of the most dramatic phenomena to be seen and stressed in animal feeding experiments is the usual speed of recovery of animals when the missing essential food is restored to the diet.

ASSIGNING EXPERIMENTS

Some teachers prefer to regard experiments by students as voluntary assignments of the nature of the optional related activities included in some unit plans. This point of view is usually based upon the idea that such work must be well done if it is to be effective as a teaching device; consequently, some teachers feel that only the exceptional students are qualified to design and develop experiments. Of course, it is recognized that sometimes students who are not considered exceptional will take a keen interest in some phase of the work and because of special knowledge or manual skill will produce quite satisfactory experiments.

On the other hand, the use of experiments may be considered too important a part of health teaching to be left to the chance interests and talents of class members. In such cases the teacher may assume full responsibility for the experiments, or he may assign them to superior individuals as regular class responsibilities in order to assure satisfactory presentations of those experiments deemed essential.

A third possibility, and one that seems to deserve serious consideration, involves requiring the preparation and presentation of experiments by all students, but doing so primarily on the basis of their interests, insofar as possible. Some aspect of the health education curriculum may be counted upon to interest virtually every student if a skillful job of teaching is done. Considering the range of the subject, extending as it does from a study of nutrition, exercise, and rest to disease, mental health, human reproduction, personal grooming, and the like, there should be no great difficulty in helping each student to find a health subject upon which to concentrate special effort, either as an individual or as a member of a small group.

PRESENTATION OF EXPERIMENTS

The presentation of experiments, like the showing of films, should not be regarded as single events in themselves, but as a sequence of related events. In the first place, if at all possible the presentation of an experiment should be appropriate to the subject matter content. Thus, for example, an experiment which demonstrates adjustment of the lens of the eye should be planned to fit into a unit on vision. Yet, it frequently happens that experiments, especially those prepared by students, are not completed until a considerable period of time after the units to which they pertain have been completed. However, even in such circumstances experiments can be used to advantage for review as well as for further expansion or clarification.

Special attention should be given to (1) introducing the experiment, (2) presenting it, and (3) doing proper follow-up. If students are to present the experiment, they should be carefully coached on how to present and follow up the demonstration.

Introducing the experiment. The class should be properly oriented regarding the purpose of the experiment. Significant related information should be provided. For example, historical background of the thing to be presented or of the experiment itself may need to be given. The demonstrator should describe the principle of the experiment to be shown in order to encourage the students to give their undivided thought and attention to it. Also, students should be told specific things to watch for.

Presenting the experiment. It was previously mentioned that teachers should pretest their own experiments and that informal rehearsals are desirable if students are to be expected to be effective in presenting experiments. The experiment rehearsal is proposed not only to assure that the experiment will work as expected, but also to coach students in the principles of effective presentation. In practice, the teacher may accomplish his coaching by simply asking a student a series of questions, such as the following: Now what do you intend to say about your experiment? and How will you show it without obstructing vision? The student's language, voice, posture, and possible distracting mannerisms should be considered by the teacher. These observations should be made and mention should be made of them in such a way that the student will not become self-conscious and unable to concentrate his attention on his experiment. Having constructed the equipment alone or having spent considerable time studying the subject individually, the student is likely to consider it simple and the details obvious; consequently, it may be necessary to remind him to give a full account and to proceed deliberately. The class should feel free to raise questions when details are not made clear.

Follow-up. The follow-up should include a review of the experiment by way of clinching significant understandings. The class may be asked questions informally or perhaps in examination form in order to determine the extent in which the principles and applications of the experiment are understood. The students may be asked to make constructive criticisms for improving the experiment or the presentation. It sometimes happens that suggestions will be made and assistance offered which lead to major improvements. Almost invariably one good experiment can be used to stimulate thought and to lead to other good experiments. Moreover, when the evaluation is completed, each student should have a better idea of a good experiment. Thus, improved ability to express ideas can be achieved and imaginations can be stimulated for further creative work.

The follow-up phase of the experiment provides an invaluable opportunity for both teacher and class to relate the experiment to its various applications. For one of many possible examples, one junior high school teacher followed the presentation of an animal feeding experiment with a brief discussion of the role of animals in scientific and medical research.

QUESTIONS FOR DISCUSSION

1. Of what value are experiments in health education?
2. For what specific purposes can experiments be used in a health teaching unit?
3. How can students participate in the preparation and presentation of experiments?
4. What advantages are there in encouraging a maximum of student participation in experimentation?
5. How would you evaluate individual laboratory work in health in the ordinary school situation? Compare the possibilities of experiments and individual laboratory work in your own school or in a school with which you are familiar.
6. Of what value are animal experiments?
7. How can animal feeding experiments be modified to be suitable for junior or senior high students? Give specific examples.
8. Of what three phases is the presentation of an experiment composed? Discuss each.

SUGGESTED CLASS ACTIVITIES

1. List several experiments which might be used with each major unit in health education. Working in small groups develop a card index of experiments by culling the literature and selecting those that are appropriate for the secondary health education class. Consider the important characteristics of a good health experiment discussed earlier.
2. Draw up complete plans describing how a specific experiment can be (1) introduced, (2) presented, and (3) followed up.
3. Write to a number of organizations and agencies for materials on animal feeding experiments. Make detailed plans for conducting such experiments. Take into account such factors as obtaining or building cages, obtaining animals, care of the cages and the animals, and details of the experiment to be conducted.
4. Working in committees, prepare a number of experiments. Present them to the entire class.

REFERENCES

1. Animal feeding demonstrations for the classroom, National Dairy Council, Chicago, 1958.
2. Creswell, W. H.: Helping pupils to learn about sanitation, Education 82: Nov., 1961.
3. Davies, E. M.: Introducing the inductive method, Science Teacher 29: Dec., 1962.
4. Elmore, C. W., Keeslar, Oreon, and Parrish, C. E.: Why not try the problem solving approach, Science Teacher 28: Dec., 1961.
5. Foster, R. A., and Koski, Arthur: Experiments to illustrate concepts in junior and senior high school health education, prepared for the Oregon Association for Health, Physical Education and Recreation and available from the authors, Oregon State University, Corvallis, Ore., 1963.
6. Grant, Madeleine: Microbiology and human progress, New York, 1953, Rinehart & Co., Inc.
7. Haag, J. H.: Health content of the future, Journal of School Health 32: April, 1962.
8. Henrici, A. J., and Ordal, E. J.: The biology of the bacteria, Boston, 1948, D. C. Heath & Co.
9. How to conduct a rat-feeding experiment, Wheat Flour Institute, 309 W. Jackson Blvd., Chicago 6, Ill.
10. Humphrey, J. H.: The place of the demonstration in health education, Science Teacher 19: Oct., 1952.
11. Meier, F. A.: Opportunities in general science for health instruction, Research Quarterly 22: Dec., 1951.

12. Milgaard, K. G.: Science for human beings, Educational Leadership **20:** Jan., 1963.
13. Montgomery, Herbert: Don't tell, teach, Instructor **72:** Feb., 1963.
14. Munch, J. W., and Stansell, William: Animal engineering, Instructor **71:** Sept., 1961.
15. Nutrition experiment, General Biology Supply House, Inc., 761 East 69th Place, Chicago 7, Ill.
16. Thurber, W. A., and Collette, A. J.: Teaching science in today's secondary schools, Boston, 1959, Allyn & Bacon, Inc.
17. Vrana, R. S.: Laboratory work, grades seven and eight, Science Teacher **28:** Nov., 1961.
18. Wagner, Victoria: Crisis in education: science and human values, Science Education **46:** March, 1962.
19. Wilson, E. A.: Structure and function of the human body, Education **82:** Nov., 1961.

Chapter 12

HEALTH EDUCATION
BEYOND THE CLASSROOM

I t is frequently said that the community outside the classroom can serve as a worthwhile laboratory for enriching the study of students. This holds particularly true for the health sciences.

Health education that occurs outside the classroom but under the auspices and direction of the school is designed to provide sensory experiences with school and community health and safety projects, programs, and phenomena which cannot be brought into the classroom. Such education, often described as field trips, involves detailed planning and transporting of students to places and locations where the subject matter of health and safety may be observed and studied in its normal setting. The field trip is a way of teaching employed outside of the classroom and usually in the community. In most cases it is the most practical and certainly the most real of all teaching methods because it brings students into direct contact with existing health and safety conditions as they affect the lives of the people within the community, state, or nation.

Although field trips, tours, excursions, or journeys have been used to some extent in all phases of education in the schools, they have perhaps as yet not been fully capitalized upon as an effective means of teaching. Even though the possibilities of field trips have not as yet been fully developed in the area of general education, they are used even less in the teaching of health. Experience in the use of trips in teaching health in secondary school shows that they are far more effective in teaching certain parts of health and safety than virtually any technique of classroom teaching.

There are a number of reasons why field trips have not been fully developed in the teaching of health. First, there has been a lack of experience. In order for the school health and safety trip to be most effective there must be careful planning and organization; otherwise, the visit is likely to result in wasted time from an educational viewpoint. There is need for the development of a body of knowledge in this area which is based upon experimentation and research as well as upon the experiences of many teachers and schools in the actual conduct of school health trips.

A second reason why trips in health education are not widely used is that many schools are slow to discard the rigid lines of formal education marked by inflexible programs and time schedules. Also, the feeling of both school personnel and laymen has been to some extent that education can take place most effectively only in the classroom. There has been a failure on the part of some people to recognize the values and potentialities of the community and surrounding area as a laboratory-type setting in the educational process. In chapter 13 the trend in recent years toward flexible scheduling that should provide the opportunities for student health education beyond the classroom is considered.

Another reason why the school health education trip remains undeveloped is that health, as it is recognized today, is comparatively new in the school program. A majority of the schools in the United States do not as yet have highly organized and acceptable health and safety education programs. Furthermore, in many of the schools that attempt to conduct organized health education programs, many of the teachers lack the proper background and training in health and safety education which is fundamental to the most successful teaching regardless of methods used. Lack of training, background, and experience on the part of teachers is particularly handicapping in the organization and conduct of trips in health education. Nevertheless, it is often easier for the inexperienced teacher to plan and conduct trips in teaching certain parts of health than it is for him to attempt to impart the same information and knowledge through classroom procedures. In those schools in which a definite allotment of time has not been given to health teaching in the program and in which health is taught more or less incidentally and haphazardly, the effective use of field trips is practically nil because the teachers have insufficient time to plan, organize, and conduct the visits.

Because the success and value of health trips, the same as of all school trips, depends upon the attitude of the teachers, it is highly essential that the faculty as a whole, as well as the individual teachers, give their full support to this phase of the program. Some teachers in a school may not be directly involved. Others will have to plan, organize, and conduct the trips. All teachers in the school, however, will be affected either directly or indirectly. An example of this is that in which a high school class may go on an all-day trip. The students making the trip miss their regularly scheduled classes in other school subjects as well as in health education. It is then necessary for all teachers to arrange and plan their work for the students in accordance with the program of field trips arranged by the school.

The community must be educated to accept school health trips as a recognized, desirable, and acceptable means of education. The attitude that education takes place only in the classroom and that time is being wasted if students are on trips during school hours must be changed if laboratory study through trips is to be most successful. The public can be enlightened as to the value of health trips the same as to other school trips through various means, including Parent-Teacher Associations, civic organizations, and newspapers, and through the students.

It is also important to develop the proper attitude toward health trips on the part of the students. In those schools in which they are a common occurrence, the students are likely to have the proper attitude whether or not the trips have been made for the expressed purpose of studying health. In schools in which trips are rare, it is usually advisable to educate the students concerning the value of trips and what is expected of them. This is also highly important from the viewpoint of reaching and educating parents through the students. In the high school, the students can be enlightened concerning the proper attitude toward trips through teachers of the various academic subjects, school newspapers, homerooms, assembly programs, and posters.

PURPOSES AND VALUES OF SCHOOL HEALTH TRIPS

One main purpose of field trips in health education is to use the community and surrounding area as a laboratory. Teaching through the use of the community as a practical and working laboratory helps to create interest and provides a medium whereby students can actively participate in the instructional program.

A substantial part of health education in the schools, just as in other areas, is to a certain extent unrelated to the practical existing conditions within the community. A considerable part of the usual curricular work in the schools remains more or less formal and academic, following the rigid pattterns upon which education in the United States was originally founded. Through trips and visitations the opportunity is provided for the subject matter of instruction to become real and meaningful to the student. Study and exploration of existing health and safety conditions outside the classroom tend to blend the school program with that of the outside world. Interest in health education as it affects society as a whole is created and stimulated.

The usual type of classroom instruction in health and safety, based largely upon the use of textbooks, printed materials, and class discussions, frequently results in boredom and a lack of interest on the part of the student because the reality of the situation is more or less remote from the oral and printed descriptions. For example, the use and production of milk and milk products are included in the health teaching program at various grade levels. Textbooks in health as well as supplementary reading and study materials may give detailed descriptions and enthusiastic accounts of modern methods of sanitation and hygiene that are applied in the production and distribution of milk. These descriptions are often accompanied by drawings, pictures, and illustrations which are for the purpose of clarifying the descriptive material and embellishing the printed material in general. Experience in the use of textbooks and other printed and study materials of this type indicates that students frequently have the greatest interest in the pictures and illustrations seemingly because they are the nearest thing to reality in the abstract learning situation in which they are placed. This should not be interpreted to imply that textbooks and study materials are unnecessary or undesirable in the teaching of health and hygiene, for certainly they have a highly important place. The main point to be made is that the instruction phase is only partially completed if no effort is made to expand and fortify the learning process by real and existing conditions whenever it is possible to do so. When a class is studying the problems of milk and milk production, for example, it is far more interesting and meaningful to the student to visit, observe, and study the dairy and milk distribution plant. The process of milk pasteurization, for example, may mean very little to a student as studied from descriptions in textbooks or other printed materials or even after watching a laboratory demonstration; yet after a visit to a milk distributing plant or a modern dairy where the process of pasteurization can actually be observed, studied, and understood in all of its ramifications, the process is more likely to become real and meaningful to the student.

One of the modern trends in education is to give students the opportunity to help in planning their work on the basis of their interests. Planning health trips may be made a joint cooperative enterprise in which teachers, students, and community groups participate. Planning of visits can be done largely by the students, with the teacher assuming the role of counselor and guide. The teacher can remain in the background; yet he can stimulate initiative and self-dependence on the part of the students. In this way the school health and safety education field trip can be organized and conducted on a project and problem-solving basis which is readily adaptable to the most modern and acceptable methods and procedures in teaching.

It cannot be emphasized too strongly that health education beyond the classroom should be carefully planned, organized, and conducted if it is to be most effective and serve the purpose of interpreting, enriching, and properly supplementing classroom instruction. Many teachers are often somewhat reluctant to share the responsibility for planning with the students. There is no question but that the teacher alone can plan a field trip with the greatest efficiency; yet it deprives students of a rich educational experience if they do not have the opportunity to participate in the plans. Teacher-student cooperative planning of health trips seems the best approach, then, since it capitalizes upon the interest and natural experience in direct connection with the classroom instruction program.

The main purposes of the health trips may be summed up as follows:

1. As introductory activities for health units
2. As a teaching device for developing keen and accurate observation on the part of students
3. As a means of creating and developing interest in individual and community health and safety
4. As a means of securing definite and firsthand information concerning health and healthful living
5. As a means of securing definite and firsthand information concerning safety and accident prevention
6. As a means of verifying, supplementing, and enriching information gained through the usual classroom procedures

7. As a means of giving students actual practice in cooperative group planning in health and healthful living and in safety and accident prevention

KINDS OF SCHOOL HEALTH AND SAFETY TRIPS

School health and safety trips can well begin within the school plant and facilities. There are many phases of health and safety education that can be studied and surveyed in the usual facilities used by the schools. Furthermore, a study of the school plant and facilities from the viewpoint of health and safety helps to create and develop interest in the total school program. The students are more likely to regard field observation, as well as the total health and safety program, as something real and meaningful in that it directly affects their daily lives. Examples of things in and about the school that may be studied are the heating and ventilating systems, school lighting, the water supply system, safety and potential hazards in the school buildings including shops, laboratories, halls, stairs, and classrooms, school building construction from the viewpoint of acoustics and hearing, school building construction from the viewpoint of fire safety, hygiene and sanitation in the cafeteria and lunchrooms, hygiene and sanitation in the swimming pool including water purification, care, and testing of the water, sanitation and general care of the buildings, nutrition as reflected through plans and provisions in the school cafeteria and lunchrooms, and safety hazards on the athletic fields.

Trips to study health and safety within the confines of the school have many advantages for a number of reasons. First, they can be more readily arranged than community trips. Second, they do not necessarily need to consume more than one class period in most cases. Third, it is relatively easy to arrange for any number of repeat visits if the study is not completed on the first trip. Fourth, surveys, experiments, and continued and extended studies of existing condition can more readily be carried out on a visitation plan within the school building and facilities. The fact that visits within the school plant have certain advantages largely because of accessibility and comparative ease of making arrangements does not exclude the necessity for trips within the community and surrounding areas. Although the school facilities ordinarily provide a highly important source and laboratory for studying certain phases of health, hygiene, and safety, they alone are far too limited and narrow to be considered sufficient.

The trip to some point within the community or surrounding area is the usual type of field trip. A trip to the community water purification plant or to a modern dairy are examples of the usual kinds of community field trips. The community field trip usually requires more specific and detailed arrangements. It ordinarily consumes more than one class period. Often it requires a half day and sometimes a full day or more. Occasionally the community field trip is arranged and taken on Saturdays and holidays.

In addition to the trip in which groups of students participates, there are those in which a student makes a trip alone. In such instances the student may be given some particular assignment in connection with a health or safety lesson or unit, or the trip is made to pursue a special interest in some phase of the program being studied or investigated. As a result of the trip, the student may give a class report on the basis of his study and observations, or he may submit a written report. Regardless of the uses made by a student and class of the results of individual visitations in the study of health and safety, perhaps the greatest value is to the individual student in learning to accept responsibility in the pursuit of knowledge.

Even though students are eager to make individual trips in the study of health and safety, the teacher must necessarily give considerable supervision and direction in making arrangements. As a general rule persons outside the school prefer to have contact with and the approval of the teacher before permitting the students to visit. Junior and senior high school students are mature enough in most cases to take considerable responsibility in organizing and arranging for individual health trips. Sometimes, though, it is necessary for the teacher to give considerable assistance even to those more mature students.

Another type of trip is the school tour or journey. Two distinguishing characteristics between the field trip and the tour is that the tour usually takes several days, a month, or even a longer period of time, and it is usually made to more distant points than in the case of community trips. An example of this type of trip is that in which a group of students make a tour to another part of the country, to a state capital, or to the national capital. The school tour or journey seems to be growing in popularity in the schools. The development of rapid and safe means of transportation and the ease of travel have given impetus to the growth of school tours for large numbers of students.

School tours are seldom if ever made for the sole purpose of studying health and safety. The aims are ordinarily much broader than the subject matter lines drawn in the classroom. It is to be expected and recommended that there be correlation and integration of subject matter materials on extended trips. Therefore, some time and attention should be given to a study of health and safety the same as to other phases of the curriculum. When tours or journeys are being planned for students, teachers in health and safety education should cooperate with other teachers in the school in planning the total program of study for the trip.

CORRELATION AND INTEGRATION THROUGH SCHOOL TRIPS

The aims of the community trip, just as for tours or journeys, may be made much broader than the usual subject matter areas. A class may visit some objective within the community with a number of purposes in mind, one of which is the study of health and safety. The correlation and integration of subject matter through field trips is recommended when the object of study is to view the situation in its entirety and in proper relationship to other factors involved. A main criticism of the trip with broader aims and purposes in which many phases of the school curriculum are to be studied is that it may result in only general observation on the part of the students, without a thorough understanding of all phases. Too often on trips of this kind the health and safety phases are almost completely ignored or at best so little attention is given to them that the students fail to gain the proper understanding because of a lack of time to observe and properly study existing conditions. There is perhaps less justification for attempting to rigidly correlate and integrate health and safety with other school subjects on community trips than on tours and journeys, largely because in the case of community trips any number of repeat visits can usually be made as needed to give thorough study and attention to the problems under investigation. If the study of some phase of a health or safety problem is not completed on the first trip, it is relatively easy to arrange other trips to the same point. This does not usually hold true for the tour or journey which may last several days and entail considerable expense. Nevertheless, there are times and situations when the more generalized field trip is recommended. An example of this might be that in which a science class makes a trip to some objective largely for the purpose of studying science. Yet, because some phases of health and safety are closely related to or dependent upon science knowledge to be gained on the trip, it may be the most opportune time for the study and observation of the health and safety phases. Another example might be that in which a class in social studies is making a study of the community. As a part of the activities of the study, a series of trips may be planned to study and observe firsthand the various phases of community life. Certainly, a complete picture of community life could not be gained without study and understanding of means, methods, and steps taken to control and safeguard the health and safety of the people.

ORGANIZATION FOR SCHOOL HEALTH TRIPS

There are a number of important factors to be considered preliminary to the immediate planning of specific trips. The teacher should survey the community to learn the extent of the possibilities for health and safety trips which will be helpful in teaching the materials to be presented to the students in the classroom. After places and objectives for the trips are located, contact should be made with the persons in charge to learn whether permission can be gained for the students to visit the objectives. Ordinarily the school administrator should make the original contact. In some cases he may wish to delegate this responsibility to supervisors or teachers. In this way general plans for visits can be made ahead of time, which may be helpful to the teacher and students in planning units of study.

The value and success of the health or safety trip depends materially upon the efficiency of teachers and students in planning and carrying out the many details. Those experienced in the conduct of health and safety trips are far more likely to make the trips successful. This holds especially true for the longer and more complicated trips. It is usually thought advisable for teachers with limited experience in the conduct of health and safety trips to plan short and less complicated visits at the beginning. As experience is gained, the longer and more complicated trips can be added, with far greater chances of success. A logical beginning for those inexperienced in this area is in planning and conducting visits and surveys in and about the school plant and facilities.

Teachers of health education should give consideration to the total yearly school program of field trips. As a matter of fact, it is highly recommended that the total school program of trips be considered by the entire faculty. It would perhaps be best for all faculty members within the school to participate in working out and drawing up plans for trips for an entire school year. In addition to stimulating interest in general, it would help to prevent overlapping and perhaps broaden the study horizon for many of the visits. Because schools in general have not fully recognized the potential values of the field trip as an instrument of education, it is likely to be a number of years before complete faculty cooperation can be gained in most schools in planning a yearly program for the entire school. Until the faculty as a whole plans the total yearly field trip program, those teachers who recognize the value of health and safety should proceed with whatever cooperation they can get from administrators, supervisors, and other teachers who may be interested.

It is sometimes advisable for the teacher to make a preliminary visit to become familiar with the objective of the health or safety trip. This is highly recommended especially if the teacher has not previously visited the objective. If the teacher has taken students on the same trip at other times, it may not be necessary for him to make the preliminary visit. In some cases the teacher may think it advisable to send a committee of students to make the preliminary visit. In any case, one of the main objectives in the preliminary visit is to facilitate the planning, particularly from the point of view of students gaining the most in the way of understanding. The information gained on the preliminary visit is helpful in preparing the group for the visit.

PLANS, PROCEDURES, AND ARRANGEMENTS FOR SCHOOL HEALTH TRIPS

Final plans should be made a short time before the trip is to be taken. The teacher or committee should attempt to visualize and think through the details in the process of making arrangements.

Although details and arrangements to be made will likely vary from one trip to another, the following points are suggestive of those that should be given consideration in most instances:

1. Consent of the school administrators and other school personnel involved.
2. Final arrangement with the owners or those in charge of the objective of the trip. These arrangements should be made by the school administrator or by the person to whom he has delegated the responsibility.
2. Estimation of the amount of time necessary for the total trip with all other arrangements made accordingly.
4. Determination of the number of students to make the trip.
5. Permission of the parents of each student making the trip. Follow the policy of the school in securing parents' permission.
6. Arrangements for transportation. These arrangements should be cleared through the school administrative officers. Many schools have formulated a definite policy concerning the transportation of students. Ordinarily the transportation of students should be by bonded carriers. In some cases school buses may be available for field trips.
7. Determine the expense involved. If there are expenses involving the school, they should be approved by the administrative officers. If there

are expenses involving the students, they should be approved by students and their parents. It is usually best if the trips can be managed without cost to the students.

8. Determination of the amount of supervision needed. It is often necessary for the teacher to have assistance in supervising the trip. The matter of additional supervisors should be discussed with and arranged through the administrative officers. Sometimes parents can be enlisted to help supervise.

9. Plan the route of the trip. Take into account the possibilities for observing interesting and educational phenomena along the route.

10. Determine the equipment needed by both supervisors and students and make certain it is ready. In most cases the students will need nothing more than pencils and notebooks.

11. Advise the students concerning the kinds of clothing to wear.

12. Be certain the students are prepared to profit most by the trip. Discussion of problems to be solved and things to look for help in making the trip most profitable to the students. It is sometimes advisable to have mimeographed materials of questions and problems to be answered and solved for the students to study before the trip is taken.

13. Discuss the standards of conduct, safety, and behavior expected of the students on the trip.

EVALUATION AND APPRAISAL OF SCHOOL HEALTH TRIPS

One of the most important questions to be answered is the extent to which the trip served the purpose for which it was intended. In other words, did the students profit from the trip sufficiently for it to be considered successful? The teacher can judge the value of the trip somewhat by the reaction of the students in terms of attitude, interest, questions, and knowledge gained. The knowledge gained can be measured to some extent through written and oral tests prepared to cover the things studied and observed and through written and oral reports of the trip.

A second important question to be answered concerning the trip is whether it was justifiable on the basis of time, expense, and effort required. Determination of the worth of the trip from the viewpoint of time, expense, and effort depends greatly upon the degree to which the trip served the purpose for which it was intended. The teacher must finally decide whether it would have been possible to have used other methods less involved than trips to reach the ends desired. It is always best to consider the health or safety trip, before it is taken, from the viewpoint of time, effort, and expense involved. Yet, it is often impossible to determine exactly whether the trip should be taken. After a trip is once taken and it does not prove its worth in terms of time, effort, and expense, it can be eliminated from the list of trips to be taken in future years.

Other points and questions to be considered in evaluating, appraising and improving health trips are the following.

1. Was the supervision adequate?
2. Were undue safety or health hazards involved?

3. Were the arrangements satisfactory with the owners or persons in charge of the objective?
4. Was the transportation adequate and managed satisfactorily?
5. Were the plans for study and observation carried out efficiently and with a minimum of wasted time?
6. Were cordial relations developed and maintained with guides, managers, and other persons involved in the trip?
7. Was discipline and management of students satisfactory from the viewpoint of the teacher, the school, and the persons in charge of the objective?
8. Were there too many students on the trip from the viewpoint of efficiency of study and observation?

HEALTH AND SAFETY LEARNING OPPORTUNITIES OUTSIDE THE CLASSROOM

Although the possibilities and resources for health and safety trips vary greatly from one community to another, there are many objectives in any community that can be visited and studied with profit year after year. The following list of possible objectives is not intended to be complete. It is included for the purpose of suggestion and for stimulating thought in developing a program of school health and safety trips.

Health and safety learning opportunities within the school

1. Lunchrooms and cafeterias to study hygiene, sanitation, and care of foods
2. Acoustics in classrooms, auditoriums, swimming pools and other rooms and areas
3. Water supply system
4. Heating system
5. Ventilating system
6. Lighting in classrooms, laboratories, shops, and other rooms
7. Color schemes throughout the school including classrooms, auditoriums, gymnasiums, laboratories, offices, and halls
8. School lunchrooms, to study the lunch hour from the viewpoint of time, serving, crowding, and noise
9. Swimming pool, to study sanitation, hygiene, care, and testing of water
10. School building, to study from the viewpoint of sanitation and hygienic care of lavatories and washrooms
11. Building survey to determine the location of first aid supplies in places such as shops, laboratories, home economics rooms, etc.
12. School nurses' quarters
13. Medical examination center
14. Equipment used in maintaining proper sanitary and hygienic conditions of the buildings and facilities
15. Survey of housekeeping throughout the school
16. Equipment and procedures for waste disposal
17. Safety hazards in school shops
18. Safety hazards in laboratories
19. Safety hazards in classrooms, halls, and corridors
20. Safety hazards in gymnasiums and swimming pools
21. Building construction from the viewpoint of fire safety
22. Potential fire hazards
23. Electrical wiring throughout the school from the viewpoint of fire safety
24. Safety hazards on play areas and athletic fields

25. Traffic hazards surrounding the school
26. Safety in pupil transportation and school busses
27. Survey of fire fighting equipment such as extinguishers and their locations in shops, laboratories, basements, engine room, and halls.

Health and safety learning opportunities in the community and surrounding area

1. Modern dairy, to study sanitary and hygienic methods employed in the production, care, and handling of milk
2. Milk distribution plant, to study sanitary and hygienic methods employed and the pasteurization of milk
3. Health museums
4. Museums with special health exhibits
5. Ice cream manufacturing plant, to study such phases as sanitary means employed
6. Health centers
7. Health clinics, to study and observe phases related to health education
8. Hospitals
9. First aid stations
10. Food plants, to observe and study modern methods of caring for and handling foods
11. Packing plants
12. Canning factories
13. Frozen foods plants
14. Food storage plants
15. Municipal vegetable markets
16. Food plants preparing dairy products
17. Food plants preparing breakfast foods
18. Pharmaceutical manufacturing and supply houses
19. Municipal water filtration and purification plant
20. Municipal health department
21. Municipal sewage disposal plant
22. Physicians, to study work and methods of physicians
23. Dentists, to study work and methods of dentists
24. Pharmacy, to observe work and methods of pharmacists, patent medicines, etc.
25. Restaurant, to observe and study care, preparation, and handling of foods
26. City departments of health
27. State departments of health
28. Truck farms
29. Veterinaries and animal doctors
30. Health laboratories
31. Public organizations assisting in health work
32. Private organizations assisting in health work
33. Water storage plants
34. Plants that manufacture waste disposal equipment
35. Manufacturers of heating, lighting, and ventilating equipment
36. Factories and plants, to study and observe health measures for employees
37. State testing laboratories
38. County health departments
39. Housing projects, to observe and study from viewpoint of health and hygienic conditions
40. Special health exhibits in department stores
41. Survey and study of traffic conditions
42. Survey and study of traffic control methods
43. Municipal safety bureaus
44. State safety bureaus
45. Safety procedures, equipment, and devices in all types of factories

46. Safety equipment on all types of motor vehicles
47. Fire prevention equipment and measures used in factories and plants
48. Fire prevention equipment and measures used in large buildings
49. Manufacture of safety devices and equipment
50. Study and survey of hazards on public playgrounds
51. Study and survey of safety hazards of municipal swimming facilities and public beaches
52. Study and survey of safety conditions and hazards in both public and private recreational facilities
53. Observation of safety condition in homes
54. Traffic courts
55. City and state officials responsible for safety
56. Traffic control divisions and emergency units of police stations
57. Sanatoriums of some types
58. Police stations, to study their responsibilities concerning health and safety in the community

QUESTIONS FOR DISCUSSION

1. What are some major advantages of school health and safety trips in contrast with other health education methods?
2. Why have health and safety trips not been widely used in school health education?
3. What are some important considerations to be taken into account when planning and organizing a health trip?
4. Why is it recommended that the school and community be surveyed for possible health field trips?
5. Why is it important that the public be taught the value of field trips in health education?
6. What are the roles of introductory activities and of follow-up activities in relation to health trips? Give an illustration in relation to a specific trip.

SUGGESTED CLASS ACTIVITIES

1. Make a list of the possible health trips in a school with which you are familiar.
2. Make a list of the possible health trips in a community with which you are familiar.
3. Prepare an outline showing how a health trip might be used effectively as an introductory activity for a unit on foods and nutrition, community health services, water purification, and health and safety organizations in the community.
4. Draw up detailed plans for a health trip for a group of eleventh grade students.
5. Take an individual health trip and prepare a study guide which might make the trip most profitable for students taking the trip at some later date.
6. Make a list of tours or journeys which might be planned for students in health classes.

REFERENCES

1. Davis, P. F., and Thomas, F. C.: What are recent developments in planning, conducting and evaluating extended school trips, National Association of Secondary School Principals Bulletin 41: April, 1957.
2. Dexter, R. W.: Early movements to promote field study in the public schools, Science Education 42: Oct., 1958.
3. Durrill, John: Student seminar at public health center, Science Teacher 25: Sept., 1958.
4. Hillson, J. S., Wylie, A. A., and Wolfensberger, W. P.: Field trip as a supplement to teaching: an experimental study, Journal of Educational Research 53: Sept., 1959.
5. McNair, C. B., et al.: Organizing and conducting field trips, School Activities 29: April, 1958.
6. Ruth, F. S.: Field trips: why and how, American Biology Teacher 24: Jan., 1962.
7. Sassman, E. H.: Classroom methods: do laboratory and field experiences change behavior, Phi Delta Kappan 39: March, 1959.
8. School Administrators Opinion Poll Findings: Administrators reverse opinion on class trips, Nation's Schools 69: April, 1962.

9. Sommers, N. L.: Nature hikes for more than fun, School Activities **34:** Nov., 1962.
10. Toporowski, J. J.: Our school trips are educationally profitable because . . . . School Activities **32:** Jan., 1961.
11. Travis, J. L.: Field trip extraordinary, Clearing House **33:** April, 1959.

Chapter 13

NEW APPROACHES TO HEALTH TEACHING

Since World War II, particularly since October, 1957, when the first sputnik was launched, the field of education has ceased to be complacent except perhaps in the most remote areas. The educator today is under constant pressure to improve his teaching methods for the purpose of teaching more subject matter in a shorter period of time—and more effectively—than was expected of him only a few years ago. This pressure has done for education what Pearl Harbor did for national defense. Education at all levels is constantly in a fluid state in which new ideas are being generated and striking changes are being made in the educational profile of the United States.

A few of the recently developed teaching approaches are presented in this chapter. Each of these has been applied to one or more areas of health instruction, but because of the recency of these methods, the preponderance of their application has been in the more traditional subjects. Nonetheless, health education must explore and possibly make extensive use of these and future methods if it is to improve its effectivness of presentation.

The discussion which follows is concerned with programed instruction, teaching machines, team teaching, and flexible scheduling.

PROGRAMED INSTRUCTION

Advocates of programed instruction, under constant criticism by many educators, maintain that this is not really a new teaching method. One writer compares it to the socratic dialogue as follows: "It is clear that programed instruction is similar to the socratic dialogue, but in its differences lies the potential for widespread and enduring changes in the educational enterprise."*

Although Socrates may have demonstrated a kind of programed instruction,

---

*From Cohen, I. S.: Programed learning and socratic dialogue, American Psychologist **17**: Nov., 1962.

the current approach has seemingly been an attempt to develop a truly new science and technology. Thus, the art of teaching is being transformed into the science of learning through the development of programed instruction. Carried to extremes, and some persons who are less secure in the teaching profession are inclined to do this, the implication is that teachers will become obsolete. Nothing could be further from the minds of even those persons who paint the most glowing future for the automation of learning.

Programed instruction, or as some educators call it, self-instruction, possesses the following characteristics.

1. A question or problem is presented to the student either on a printed card in a ringed notebook, on a printed sheet seen through a window of some kind of automated box, or by a film projected on a reading screen.
2. The student records his answer. He may be asked to select a response from a number of alternative answers, or he may be asked to write out an answer without suggested alternatives.
3. As soon as he has written his answer, the student receives a check on the accuracy of his answer.
4. The student proceeds at his own pace since he controls the rate at which each frame is presented.

Psychological approaches to programed instruction. Two distinct schools of thought exist today concerning the most effective manner in which educational material should be programed. One is known as the linear theory and dates from a well-known article by B. F. Skinner, that appeared in 1954.* The other is known as the intrinsic theory, a form of programing that dates back to pioneer research in teaching machines by S. L. Pressey at Ohio State University in the 1920's. Today the leading intrinsic theorist is N. A. Crowder, whereas Skinner retains the position of spokesman for linear theory.

The linear theory holds that a desired change in behavior, defined as learning, can best be accomplished by inducing and then rewarding the correct behavior. Programed linear materials are designed to cause the student to respond with the desired behavior as the subject matter is presented, piece by piece. Each response is immediately rewarded and therefore reinforced when the student is immediately informed that his response is correct. The student's response is considered an integral part of the learning process; the response is elicited so that it may be rewarded and learning may occur. With linear materials, it is assumed that conditioning is the essence of learning, and the techniques used derive from this assumption.

Although the programing itself is difficult, the format of linear materials, once produced, is quite simple. The student is presented small segments of information on a card or within a window. He is required to make a response, usually the writing of one or two words. Immediately he is able to compare his response with the correct response; if his response is similar, he is rewarded, and the segment of information is learned. The stimulus

---

*Skinner, B. F.: The science of learning and the art of teaching, Harvard Educational Review **24**: Spring, 1954.

and response together are contained within what is most usually referred to as a frame.

When properly programed, linear materials should result in a correct response 90 to 95% of the time. The theory is that error, then, is so insignificant that when one occurs the program has at best wasted the student's time; at worst it has caused the student to practice an incorrect response. Errors may be neglected, and when they do occur, they should be considered a fault of the program and not a fault of the student.

Example of programing. Although programed instruction is being used in many areas of the school curriculum, it has been slow to develop in health education. Nevertheless, a few attempts are being made to program some areas of health content. The following is an example of programed material in first aid.

EXAMPLE OF PROGRAMING IN FIRST AID

IDENTIFICATION AND TREATMENT OF TRAUMATIC SHOCK*

Population   grade 11

Time   two 30-minute study periods
        one 30-minute laboratory period

Erma F. Wyman, Programer

Note: Use of this unit or any portion of the unit without permission of the author is prohibited.

*This material represents the preface, objectives, and first nine frames taken from a larger body of material currently in preparation. This program, designed to teach the standard American Red Cross First Aid Course, was prepared by Mrs. Erma F. Wyman of Corvallis, Oregon, in cooperation with the American Red Cross and Teaching Research Center, Oregon State System of Higher Education.

It is important to point out that the frames shown here are purely experimental. Although the author states that she faces a long task of refining, testing, further refining, and final testing before this program will satisfy her, she has kindly permitted this limited inclusion in this book so that the reader may see an actual attempt to program in health education.

The program presented here is patterned after the linear theory and makes extensive use of the concept of fading.

PREFACE

This is a first aid program which defines shock. It describes the various types of shock and gives the causes and dangers of shock. The signs and symptoms of each type and the first aid for them are developed so that the student should be able to recognize and treat a victim of traumatic shock when he has completed this program.

This method of learning allows a student to progress at his own rate. He is not held back by slower progress of classmates nor is he embarrassed by superior students. The instruction moves forward step by step in which the learner has the immediate satisfaction of success or is alerted to his errors so that he can make a correction before continuing. The student alone knows of the error and is not frustrated by it but is encouraged to try again.

Results are immediate; there is no waiting for a busy teacher to correct the paper and return it later.

Upon completion of the program a student should be able to:
1. Define traumatic shock as given in the American Red Cross First Aid text book.
2. Explain the elementary physiology involved in traumatic shock.
3. Correctly select from a list of symptoms those associated with traumatic shock.
4. Correctly select from a list of symptoms those associated with shock other than traumatic shock.
5. Recognize the shock symptoms present in a sketch or picture of an accident.
6. List the appropriate first aid procedures involving shock when given a written description of an accident.
7. Correctly identify victims who are suffering from shock when given brief case histories of accidents.

Panel I
THE STUDENT SHOULD REFER TO THIS WHEN NECESSARY
AS HE PROGRESSES THROUGH THE FOLLOWING FRAMES

We were sitting in a first aid class when a sudden crash in the street brought all of us to our feet.

Upon rushing to the scene, we found a station wagon and a smaller car which had collided and injured persons lying in and about the wreckage.

Number 1 victim, a young male driver of the car, was vomiting blood; beads of perspiration stood out on his forehead and lips. His skin was cold, and his pulse was rapid and weak.

Number 2 victim, driver of the station wagon, an older man who received a deep gash on his scalp, was calling for water incessantly. This victim was too weak to stand.

Number 3 victim, a young lady with the driver of the first car, was thrown clear of the wreck, at first appeared quite normal, then became confused, staggered dizzily, and collapsed.

Number 4 victim was a very pale older lady who sat in the station wagon holding her right shoulder and staring from lackluster eyes, the pupils of which were very large.

Number 5 victim, a teen-age girl lying crumpled between the front and rear seats of the station wagon, was gasping for air with rapid, shallow breaths and an occasional deep one. She shook with chills.

SHOCK

	1. There are many signs or symptoms of shock. One common sign is a weak rapid pulse. Victim Number 1 had a weak, rapid pulse, which is a sign that he suffered from_____.
1. Shock	2. Whenever we observe _____, rapid pulse in an accident victim, we suspect that he is suffering from _____.
2. Weak Shock	3. If we wanted to determine if a victim were suffering from shock, we might take his pulse. If it were _____ and _____, it would indicate that he was suffering from shock.
3. Weak Rapid	4. A cold moist skin is also an indication of the presence of shock. In taking a person's pulse, the temperature of a victim's skin is readily observed. Another indication that Number 1 victim was suffering shock was a _____ skin.
4. Cold	5. The beads of perspiration on the·victim's forehead and lips would indicate a _____ skin also.

SHOCK—cont'd

5. Moist	6. Nausea is another symptom of shock. Victim Number 1 was vomiting blood. He was suffering from n_____, a sign that he was in s_____.
6. (N)ausea (S)hock	7. Victim Number 1 displayed several symptoms indicating that he was in the state of _____.
7. Shock	8. The symptoms indicating that victim Number 1 suffered shock were _____, _____ pulse: _____ and _____skin and _____.

8. Rapid, weak or
   Weak, rapid
   Cold, moist or
   Moist, cold
   Nausea
	9. A _____, _____ skin _____, _____ pulse, and _____ are all symptoms of _____.

9. Cold, moist
   Rapid, weak
   Nausea
   Shock	

Intrinsic theory, so its advocates believe, makes no claim as to how education should be conducted. In fact, the intrinsic theorist is not committed to a specific theory of learning, and the distinguishing feature of his theory is the diagnostic question accompanied by remedial material for the students who fail to select the correct answer.

The format for intrinsic programing is patterned after the multiple-choice question. The student is presented with the first unit of information and the first multiple-choice question on page one. Each of the alternatives to the question is identified by a different page number. The student selects what he believes to be the correct answer and turns to the indicated page. His selection is discussed on the page to which he is referred. If his choice is correct, a new problem is posed incorporating the learned material. If his choice is incorrect, he reads the additional information and is referred back to the original question to select the correct answer. The good student continues through the programed material with few errors; the poor student proceeds more slowly but with an increasing fund of knowledge. The items and answers are not placed consecutively in the book; therefore, the student is unable to skim through the pages for the correct answers. Thus, the student proceeds through the program, whatever his ability, by eventually choosing the right answer to each question.

The contention for both programing theories is that learning should be close to 100%. Since the student proceeds at his own speed, programed instruction by either theory results in a normal distribution curve which reflects the amounts of time that students take to learn the material, instead of in the normal distribution curve which reflects success or failure to learn. The linear theorist claims to teach both slow and fast learners effectively, since all students move through the material at their individual speeds and the step by step in-

Fig. 10. O.K., Son, a few whacks of this stuff and your education will be off to a new start. (Courtesy Stewart Fisher.)

tervals are so slight that errors are few. The intrinsic theorist claims to reach both groups, since wrong responses are supplemented by additional information to assist in making the correct response; the student who makes the correct response to multiple alternatives does not need additional information and so completes the program before the slower learner.

Disadvantages of programed self-instruction. We should be cautioned against unreserved acceptance of programed self-instruction. It has significant disadvantages. Very little is known at present about what constitutes a satisfactory programed item; once a teaching device is selected, the range of materials that can be presented is limited, and the assumption that any device or sequence of items is optimally satisfactory for all students may well be incorrect. In regard to production, programing requires large amounts of time and money and the concentration of highly diverse skills, and, most important to the success of the method, the programer is faced with great difficulty in determining the specific body of knowledge to be programed.

Future of programing. Mention has already been made of the fact that programing has the potential to change an art of teaching into a science of learning. In Chapter 7 emphasis was placed on the need to define objectives for any unit or course in health education and on the belief that a table of specifications would help assure this. As valuable as it can be, few teachers take the time to develop such a table. On the other hand, a programer cannot develop a single frame until he has determined the objectives to be attained. Having done this, he must keep them constantly in mind as frame is built upon frame to the unit's conclusion. This careful attention to predetermined objectives against which the actual outcomes are validated can only result in greater success and acceptance for the total education process. Also, self-instruction techniques will conserve teacher time since they can be adjusted to individual abilities, and they encourage independent student work because all students receive incentive and realize success.

Although the use of programed self-instruction materials is still in its infancy, especially so in health education, it should increase with time. In 1962 more than 2000 school were using commercially prepared programs and teaching machines; this figure is very likely to increase rapidly in the next decade. Although programed learning seeems to be gaining a place in education, there are likely to be many changes from its present form. To some degree as yet unknown, programed instruction is likely to help determine the extent of health knowledge as well as of habits, attitudes, and practices of secondary school students in the future.

TEACHING MACHINES

There has been a strong revival of interest in teaching machines and devices during the past few years. The revived interest has developed so rapidly that there is much confusion and misunderstanding concerning them.

What is a teaching machine? The term *teaching machine* is perhaps an unfortunate expression that connotes an inhuman, mechanical contrivance. Consequently, there have been attempts to substitute terms such as *self-instructional devices** and *auto-instructional devices†* for the term teaching machines. These attempts have not been particularly successful to date.

Unfortunate or not, the fact is that the term *teaching machine* is to the point, is meaningful, and most important, is popular, especially in the press and other noneducational literature. In all likelihood it will be with us as long as the machines continue to be developed and used.

It is difficult to define the term *teaching machine*. The literature is replete with attempts to develop a succinct definition. Three are included here.

"A self-instructional device or teaching machine is any device which can present systematically programed materials while making efficient use of the principles of reinforcement."‡

"A teaching machine is defined here as a mechanism that presents information to a student and controls his behavior in a predetermined interacting relationship."§

---

*Lumsdaine, A. A.: Teaching machines and self-instructional materials, Audio-Visual Communication Review 7: Summer, 1959.
†Lumsdaine, A. A., and Klaus, D. J.: What's in a name? A problem of terminology, Audio-Visual Communication Review, 9: July-August, 1961.
‡From Foltz, C. I.: The world of teaching machines, Washington, D. C., 1961, Electronic Teaching Laboratories.
§From Stulurow, L. M.: Teaching by machine, Washington, D. C., 1961, U. S. Office of Education.

". . . auto-instructional methods provide for the controlled presentation of material, the elicitation of appropriate responses, guidance with respect to the critical aspects of the subject matter, and control of the way in which learning proceeds (through use of proper sequencing, related features which seem to be demonstrably important for effective learning)."*

A different and seemingly more satisfactory approach has been adopted by two researchers in a recent publication.† In this very thorough study, teaching machines were defined in terms of functions, and the authors included in their study machines that could perform any five of seven basic functions. Thus, five out of the seven basic functions became the criteria for defining a teaching machine. These seven basic functions are as follows.

1. Used for individual instruction.
2. Contains and presents program content in steps.
3. Provides a means whereby the student may respond to the program.
4. Provides the student with immediate information of some kind concerning his response that can act as a psychological reinforcer.
5. Presents the frames of the program individually.
6. Presents the program in a predetermined sequence.
7. Is cheat-proof.

Controversy concerning teaching machines. Can learning take place more rapidly and efficiently through some method other than the time-honored approach to teaching? Some educators who are working in the field of teaching machines at the present time believe that it can; others seriously doubt that the machine adds anything to the learning situation. Certainly, as discussed earlier, programed instruction is here to stay although its form is likely to change. The machine, however, is only in early stages, and if it is to remain, many changes will have to be made before schools will spend large sums of money for a teaching machine.

Those who support the use of teaching machines in the presentation of programed material do so on the basis of five contentions. They believe that the machine, as differentiated from a programed textbook or other medium, is most satisfactory because (1) it can be made cheat-proof, (2) it provides for active, overt participation through questions, blanks to be filled, or responses to be selected, (3) it provides for small, step-by-step sequential learning, (4) it incorporates feedback for the student, and (5) it offers the best opportunity for reinforcement of learning.

While research to validate the superiority of teaching machines is still limited, that which has been done does not substantiate the points just given. The interested reader may wish to refer to several studies included in the references for this chapter regarding this issue of teaching machines versus other forms of instructional presentation. At the present stage in their development and considering the cost of teaching machines, especially the cost of se-

---

*From Lumsdaine, A. A., and Klaus, D. J.: What's in a name? A problem of terminology, Audio-Visual Communication Review **9:** July-August, 1961.
†Finn, J. D., and Perrin, D. G.: Teaching machines and programed learning: a survey of the industry, 1962, Washington, D. C., 1962, U. S. Office of Education.

lected response machines, existing evidence seems to indicate that schools are not usually justified in purchasing these machines. What the future will hold is unknown, and continuing research in use of the machines will most likely result in reduced costs and improved teaching. As things stand now, the teaching machine represents a teaching method that will be costly and experimental for some time to come.

Endorsement should be made again, however, for the use of programed instructional materials. Programing can be a superior learning method, and whether or not it should be used is no longer in question. Selection of the medium is the major issue. In the absence of evidence showing superiority of one medium over another, health educators must select the medium on the basis of cost.

TEAM TEACHING

Team teaching as a method may be defined as a group of teachers of the same or related subjects working together to instruct large and small groups of students. More precisely, it is the planned organization of several teachers into a team, with mutual responsibility for planning, developing, and evaluating the educational program for a relatively large number of students. The premise behind this approach is that through pooling the resources and talents of two or more teachers in joint planning and in varied approaches to the lesson the students are provided with a more effective learning environment. For example, four secondary school health educators might work with from 100 to 200 students. The four teachers would possess differing but complimentary teaching specialties and interests, and each would make contributions primarily in his area of specialization or interest. One member of this team would serve as leader; this responsibility could be rotated.

To teach a subject by means of a team implies that there are aspects of a subject that necessitate almost a direct student-teacher relationship; there are other aspects in which learning occurs best in small groups of five, ten, or fifteen students, and there are some aspects that may be taught by lecture, television, or demonstration to a very large number of students. This last assumption, content appropriate for presentation to large groups via the lecture method, is basic to the whole concept of team teaching because it releases the teacher time that makes small and individual group instruction possible.

In one sense, of course, team teaching is not new. Elementary school teachers have shared competencies since the day of the two-room school building, and for almost as long a period of time doctoral candidates, assisting in large lecture courses, have taken over small seminar sections for discussion on a regular basis. Other examples could be cited on the grade levels between these extremes. Yet, there is a great deal of difference in the present-day approach to team teaching. As long as it does not become an end in itself, team teaching can be very effective in the educational process. Many educators believe that it is the greatest single stimulus to curriculum planning on the local level. Certainly it encourages greater exchange of ideas between teachers, young and old, experienced and new, and it helps to lower barriers that may develop between subject matter areas. In addition, team teaching suggests that individualized instruction is still possible without a machine, even in this era of mass education.

Two high school health education teachers commenting on their experiences with team teaching have made the following observations.

"1. Team teaching requires much more thorough preparation and organization. We need to anticipate where and what questions may arise. We cannot rely on any other aids except the overhead projection when in the large group. Class discussions are limited for students who are hesitant with questions.

"2. The material presented does get across to the student. Attitudes and habits that we consider important can be altered as a result of the predominantly lecture type method of presentation, just as they can in the traditional small group.

"3. Discipline in the large group is not a serious problem.

"4. Those who are not teaching can use some time to observe, and since we do meet in small groups, too, we are likely to find those problems that need attention.

"5. Team teaching and large group classes indicate that more students can receive instructions without increasing the number of teachers.

"6. We, the teachers involved, are able to explore more deeply those areas of individual interest and develop others of new interest which enable us to present a stimulating and worthwhile lesson."*

To summarize this all too brief discussion of team teaching, the advantages of this teaching method appear to be these: (1) it provides variety and flexibility for both teacher and student, (2) it provides for more efficient and effective preparation by the teacher, and (3) it provides for evaluation of teachers by their peers. However, lest it be implied that team teaching is a panacea, some very real disadvantages also exist: (1) some teachers are reluctant to give up any part of their sovereignty, (2) teacher personalities do conflict, (3) individual teacher prestige must be suppressed, (4) administrators are sometimes reluctant to provide sufficient time for planning by the teachers concerned, and (5) the glamor of large lecture situations with overhead projectors, television, and other aids may cause the equally important small group sessions, in which valuable skills should also be learned, to appear insignificant.

A balance must be achieved in the use of team teaching in relation to the many other methods that may be used.

FLEXIBLE SCHEDULING

A brief discussion of flexible scheduling is included here because of the attention given to it in late years by secondary school teachers and administrators. While not a teaching method as such, the concept and practice of flexible scheduling become more and more necessary as the newer direct teaching methods become established. For example, team teaching is ineffective unless it is combined with some form of schedule adjustment which permits a break from the traditional secondary school six-period day.

There are several ways in which the high school student's schedule may be reapportioned, depending upon the subject matter being taught, the number of

---

*From Elliott, R. D., and Gamble, E. P.: Evanston, Illinois, Township High School adds to its program; health education with team teaching, National Association of Secondary School Principals Bulletin 46: Jan., 1962.

students involved, the facilities available, and the experience and skills of the teachers. Types of flexible schedules currently in vogue include the following.*

1. Organization of the school day into block or modules 15 to 30 minutes in length, providing, for example, as many as eighteen class periods throughout the day.
2. Scheduling classes for 2 hours one day, 1 hour the next day, and 2 hours the third day.
3. The use of a "floating" period to provide the student with longer class periods for certain subjects.
4. Setting Wednesday aside for field trips, greater amounts of laboratory time, library research, special interest groups, and other nonscheduled activities.
5. Organizing students into groups only 18 hours each week, reorganizing instruction, and changing staffing patterns.

Resistance to flexible scheduling is strong. Especially, is this true in long-standing programs in which a well-formed routine has been established. Many administrators and teachers, however, are trying to bring about changes. The greatest proportionate swing toward flexible scheduling is seen in new schools that are opening for the first time. In these situations tradition is not a barrier.

In new or old schools, however, certain conditions need to be determined before the construction of a flexible schedule can take place. Such things must be considered as (1) the number of courses to be offered, (2) the portion of time each course must be assigned in the school day, (3) the number of students to be involved in each course, and (4) the provision for a sufficient number of classes beginning at any given time to provide for all students leaving class at that time. This last point is of concern when all classes do not begin and end at the same time.

A prominent school superintendent, experienced in most aspects of flexible scheduling, has offered the following endorsement for the program.

"Administrators in the system feel that the ferment created by attempting new forms of flexibility has complicated their jobs and made their lives more difficult. At the same time, they are quite certain that this ferment in the area of school organization has caused their educational pot to overflow, resulting in new activity in curriculum content, in methodology, and particularly in the alertness and creativeness of teaching staff."†

In summary of this and the previous section it should be clearly seen that team teaching and flexible scheduling are not just clever devices to be employed without regard for integral parts of the curriculum. Their successful utilization demands that the entire high school program, of which health education is only a part, be taken into consideration. There is no doubt that secondary school health education will benefit from the use of team teaching and flexible scheduling. All secondary school health teachers should accept the mandate to

---

*Adapted from Trump, J. L.: Images of the future: a new approach to the secondary school, Urbana, Ill., 1959, National Association of Secondary School Principals, Experimental Study of the Utilization of the Staff in the Secondary School, The Commission.

†From Howe, Harold: Experimentation at Newton, California Journal of Secondary Education **35:** Jan., 1960.

investigate their possibilities and to determine how they will improve teaching efficiency.

IS A SYSTEMS APPROACH TO HEALTH TEACHING NEEDED?

As far as it is possible to separate *methods* from *materials,* this chapter terminates the discussion of teaching methods in health education. The next area for consideration involves health education materials. At this point, however, it seems appropriate to attempt to crystallize the total field of teaching methods in a philosophy for the future that all prospective teachers of health science might keep in mind.

Many students and teachers may be inclined to believe that the information in this chapter is far from applicable to most present-day secondary school classrooms. Yet, nothing presented in this chapter is pure theory. All methods and techniques discussed are real and at least in trial operation somewhere. All educators, particularly younger teachers-to-be, should maintain open, unbiased viewpoints concerning what they believe to be effective methods. In addition, when opportunities arise, they should be willing to experiment, often unfamiliarly, with new methods.

The question is often asked as to why new methods should be emphasized. At present, perhaps more than ever before, school administrators and teachers are under extreme pressure. The groups that exert this pressure are many. They include individual parents, special interest groups such as Parent-Teacher Associations, and the colleges and universities that continually raise their entrance requirements. Furthermore, the pressure is two pronged. First, there is the pressure to crowd more and more into the required curriculum. Every subject matter interest group is seeking to hold or enlarge upon its position in the daily schedule, and new subject matter has the habit of usurping time as well. An example of this is the necessary inclusion of driver education and training in the curriculum of most high schools, a trend created by the technological advances of the past thirty years. Second, there is the biological pressure which tells us that we dare not extent secondary school education further than it already is. Still, we must contend with the social discord that lengthening of secondary school education would only compound. And so the answer, if there is one, is to increase the effectiveness of our educational methods. We need to identify new methods, or, more appropriately, we need to identify those combinations of old and new methods that will contribute most to a particular learning situation— hence, the need for a systems approach to teaching in health education.

The analogy to a weapons system has been drawn by at least three educators.*†‡ In national defense, especially with reference to air defense, the time

---

*Tucker, J. A.: The job as a medium for training. In Finch, Glen, editor: Education and training media, Washington, D. C., 1960, National Academy of Sciences–National Research Council.

†Horton, R. E.: It's time for the systems approach to learning, Phi Delta Kappan **44:** March, 1963.

‡McPherson, J. J.: Let's look at the systems concept of educational planning, The High School Journal **44:** Nov., 1960.

is long past when we could rely on independent groups of specialists for training, communication, building, staffing, and the like. In order for a weapons system to be effective today there must be total and complete integration of every aspect of the total strategic problem. The manned space craft is only as good as its pilot; a well-trained pilot is worthless in a faulty spacecraft.

As with national defense and exploration into space, the health educator should adopt a systems approach in his classroom methods. Thus, a systems approach in health education must consider all the stimuli that reach the student and the probable effect of each. Desired health learnings will most likely take place as the student's several senses are brought in contact with effective combinations of words and writings by the instructor, sights and sounds from audiovisual aids, stimuli from programed material, books in the library, field experiences, appropriate demonstrations and experiments, and any other suitable stimuli.

Coordinated application of these methods without undue emphasis on any one and with vision to try and accept new methods that may come in the future is the philosophy that all secondary health educators must develop. The teacher who holds such a philosophy has taken a giant step in the continuing campaign to educate more youth with greater efficiency in an increasingly complex world.

QUESTIONS FOR DISCUSSION

1. What do educators mean by programed self-instruction?
2. In what areas of health content would programed instruction be most effective? In what areas would it be least effective? Why?
3. What is the difference between linear theory and intrinsic theory?
4. What are the positive and negative features of programed instruction?
5. Is a book a teaching machine?
6. Why is the term *teaching machine* a misnomer?
7. Will teaching machines replace teachers?
8. What effect will teaching machines have on the teaching profession in the future?
9. Define team teaching in your own words.
10. Is team teaching a fad that will soon disappear? What is its potential?
11. What does team teaching require of the health teacher that is different from individual teaching?
12. Define flexible scheduling in your own words.
13. Why must team teaching and flexible scheduling be combined if each is to contribute to improved learning?
14. Why do some secondary school administrators resist flexible scheduling?

SUGGESTED CLASS ACTIVITIES

1. Ask two students to compare the socratic dialogues with programed instruction.
2. Have half the class study the case for linear theory as supported by Skinner and the second half study the intrinsic theory of Crowder and others. Consider how these might apply to the programing of health materials. Debate the effectiveness of each.
3. Have members of the class continue to develop a few frames of the first aid program that was cited in this chapter.
4. Suggest as a term project the programing of a short unit in some health area.
5. Collect pictures of as many teaching machines as possible (the Finn and Perrin reference cited on p. 232 is excellent in this regard).
6. Discuss the strengths and weaknesses of teacher versus machine.
7. Discuss how team teaching may be applied to health education in the junior high school. In the senior high school.

8. Read in the literature about team teaching in health education and discuss it in class.
9. Plan a flexible schedule for senior high school health education that would permit field trips, extra reading, and opportunities for special interest groups to study independently.

REFERENCES

1. Anderson, K. E., and Edwards, A. J.: Educational process and programed instruction, Journal of Educational Research **55:** July-Aug., 1962.
2. Baynham, Dorsey: School of the future in operation, Phi Delta Kappan **42:** May, 1961.
3. Casmir, F. L.: Human teacher is still best, California Teachers Association Journal **56:** Sept., 1960.
4. Crowder, N. A.: On the differences between linear and intrinsic programing, Phi Delta Kappan **44:** March, 1963.
5. Dempster, J. J. B.: America explores team teaching, Times (London) Educational Supplement **2449-2455:** April 27; May 4, 11, 25; June 8, 1962.
6. Divesta, F. J.: Balance in teaching methods and learning processes, Association for Supervision and Curriculum Yearbook, Chicago, 1961.
7. Fusco, G. C.: Programed self-instruction: possibilities and limitations, High School Journal **44:** Nov., 1960.
8. Galanter, Eugene: The mechanization of teaching, National Association of Secondary School Principals Bulletin **44:** April, 1960.
9. Glaser, Robert, and Schaefer, H. H.: Programed teaching, Journal of Teacher Education **12:** March, 1961.
10. Goldstein, L. S., and Gotkin, L. G.: Review of research: teaching machines versus programed textbooks as presentation modes, New York, 1961, Center for Programed Instruction.
11. Hough, J. B.: An analysis of the efficiency and effectiveness of selected aspects of machine instruction, Journal of Educational Research **55:** July-Aug., 1962.
12. Johnson, R. U., and Shutes, R. E.: Biology and team teaching, American Biology Teacher **24:** April, 1962.
13. Komoski, P. K.: Programed Materials, Nation's Schools **67:** Feb., 1961.
14. Lawson, C. A., et al.: Developing a scrambled book and measuring its effectiveness as an aid to learning natural sciences, Science Education **44:** Dec., 1960.
15. Lumsdaine, A. A., and Glaser, Robert (editors): Teaching machines and programed learning: a source book, Washington, D. C., 1960, Department of Audio-Visual Instruction, National Education Association.
16. Menackez, Julius: Inter-departmental team teaching in the high school, Chicago Schools Journal **44:** Dec., 1960.
17. Nimnicht, G. P.: Second look at team teaching, National Association of Secondary School Principals Bulletin **46:** Dec., 1962.
18. Porter, Douglas: Teaching machines, Harvard Graduate School of Education Bulletin **3:** March, 1958.
19. Programed instruction; mechanics of it, Times Educational (London) Supplement **2471:** Sept. 28, 1962.
20. Schlaadt, Richard, Grant, Richard, and Sundholm, Conrad: Health team teaching, Centennial High School, a course of study, Gresham, Oregon, 1963.
21. Skinner, B. F.: Teaching machines, Science **128:** Oct., 1958.
22. Smith, M. D.: Points of view on programed instruction, Science Eduction **46:** Oct., 1962.
23. Symposium: new designs for the secondary school schedule, California Journal of Secondary Education **35:** Feb., 1960.
24. Symposium: new opportunities for expertness: team teaching and flexible scheduling, California Journal of Secondary Education **37:** Oct., 1962.
25. Wagner, G. W.: Team teaching, Education **81:** May, 1961.
26. Wagner, Victoria, and Gilbert, L. J.: Team guidance in a school, Education **81:** March, 1961.
27. Weiss, J. M., and Morris, M. S.: Critique of the team approach, Education Forum **24:** Jan., 1960.
28. Wittich, W. A.: Teaching machines: practical and probable, Nation's Schools **66:** Aug., 1960.

Part IV

TEACHING AIDS IN SECONDARY SCHOOL HEALTH EDUCATION

Chapter 14

AUDIOVISUAL MATERIALS
IN HEALTH EDUCATION

A high school teacher who took pride in having an exceptionally thorough knowledge of the subject matter in his field was recently rather rudely awakened to the fact that his teaching procedures and presentations were markedly ineffective. Over a period of several weeks he had been puzzled by a girl who seldom gave attention, asked that questions be repeated, and did poorly on tests. Suspecting that part of the girl's difficulty might be due to his way of teaching, he decided to try to stimulate her and other class members in a discussion about their responsibilities as learners and his responsibilities as teacher. The results were very revealing to him. They form the basis for the remainder of this chapter.

DETERRENTS TO LEARNING IN HEALTH EDUCATION

Critical self-analysis by the high school students mentioned above indicated several deterrents to effective understanding. These have been generalized for further discussion and consideration because they are equally valid for other age groups and subject matter other than health.

Daydreaming. A daydream may be described as a reverie filled with pleasing, often illusory, visions or anticipations. Everyone will daydream to a degree. When practiced to excess in the school setting, it is a sign of a sluggish, inattentive mind or boredom or a combination of both.

All students are likely to daydream on occasion. For some it serves as a momentary respite from the mental fatigue of schoolwork. The health teacher who understands his students accepts short moments of daydreaming as a common part of the learning process.

When one or more students daydream to excess, there is serious cause for concern. Student problems including daydreaming that pointed to the need for individual counseling and guidance were discussed in Chapter 3. It is equally true that excessive daydreaming by students may result from improper teaching methods involving inappropriate or insufficient audiovisual materials. When a teacher becomes aware of excessive daydreaming, he should first be more concerned for his teaching procedures than for the health of the daydreamers.

Disinterest. The secondary school health teacher should maintain a constant vigilance for signs of disinterest. Teen-agers are in general not particularly interested in their health unless they are ill. They tend to view deviations from the health norm as occurring to everyone but themselves. A shortened life span has little meaning for them if the person lives beyond the age of 40 years since "that's old age anyway." Health instruction must be made interesting to prove its worth to a group of resisting students.

Misinterpretation. Man is said to have risen rapidly above the primitive level of other animals when he developed the capacity to communicate with his fellow men by means of the spoken word.

Growth and progress of society have subjected the spoken word to individual interpretation, and specific words may have different meanings for different people. For example, a tuberculin shot is much different than the four-pronged subdermal needle (Tine test), but the term *shot* will continue to be used and will be accompanied by very real fears on the part of many persons.

Another example of frequent misinterpretation has to do with fluoridation of water supplies. It is frequently stated that the addition of one part per million of sodium fluoride to a municipal water supply will *prevent* dental caries. This concept cannot be viewed in the absolute sense as some persons are inclined to do but rather in the statistical sense. Because of a number of factors such as age and individual differences the fluoridation of water supplies will prevent roughly 60% of the dental caries among the members of certain age groups rather than 100%.

When so much of health learning depends upon correct interpretation of data, it is important that students learn to interpret correctly as well as critically. This requires that the teacher present specifics and interpret them correctly. A teacher cannot teach in generalities and expect correct interpretation on the part of students.

Physical discomfort. The deterrent of physical discomfort should be given serious consideration. Many health classrooms are crowded, noisy, unwanted space, many are kept too warm or too cold, and still others are too dark or are filled with unpleasant glare.

The movement to improve classrooms and the school environment will eventually help to overcome the deterrent of physical discomfort to learning. During the interim, health teachers should try to eliminate or compensate for as many physical discomforts that retard learning as possible.

Verbal frustration. Psychologists speak of a reading frustration level or the point at which a person can read a given body of material and yet not understand the meaning. Teachers must be aware also of a verbal frustration level— the point at which a given class, or part of a class, hears what is said and yet comprehends very little or nothing. Health science is especially vulnerable to verbal frustration since it is expanding rapidly and new words are being coined almost daily.

Students are often reluctant to ask what a word or phrase means for fear of inviting ridicule. If all are reluctant as well as unkowing, the objectives of a particular health unit are not likely to be attained. The teacher should be particularly careful to avoid verbal frustration on the part of students.

Verablism. Finally, and perhaps most insidious of all, is the constant outflow of words which undoutedly gives rise to the previously discussed deterrents to health understanding. Certainly verbalism is a forerunner to daydreaming and disinterest, and it contributes to misinterpretation and verbal frustration.

Almost everyone has been a victim of and a purveyor of verbalism many times in his educational life. Teachers sometimes disguise their uncertainty or lack of accurate knowledge with words, others sometimes bluff through a poorly prepared lesson with words, and still others teach with words alone because they do not know or cannot carry out the change of pace that audiovisual materials provide.

An effective health class contains a proper combination of words by the teacher and well-selected audiovisual materials.

CONTRIBUTION OF AUDIOVISUAL MATERIALS TO HEALTH UNDERSTANDING

The importance of gaining and holding the attention of students has been thoroughly established.

Gaining and holding attention. Experience in the use of audiovisual materials with students of all ages shows that these materials gain and hold attention. In the first place, they provide variety in the program which is highly essential to gaining and holding attention. Also, they help in breaking the monotony of the usual more or less formal schoolroom routine. Visual aids are usually easier to understand because they are concrete, although specially prepared health programs on radio are usually adapted to the indicated age level and are thus more concrete than other verbal sources. With the exception of some radio programs, a verbal description of an object, process, or thing may be highly uninteresting and difficult to understand, especially if the student lacks the related background with which to associate the description. An object or demonstration to accompany the verbal description provides firsthand experience which promotes interest, understanding, and possible mastery. An example of this is that in which an instructor may be teaching the use of the reef or square knot in bandaging in first aid. The students would gain practically nothing from a mere verbal description a teacher might give of the way the knot is tied. Also, they would likely lose all interest immediately because of the intangible features of the description, regardless of the skill of the teacher in presenting materials. If the teacher gives the verbal description step by step as he demonstrates the tying of the knot with a triangular bandage, the students are far more likely to be attentive and interested, and certainly they will learn far more from the presentation. This example may be carried further to illustrate another factor involved. There is a natural tendency for students to manipulate. This tendency seems to be more or less a part of the original nature of the student. The opportunity to touch, manipulate, and handle gives an added interest and appeal. When the teacher announces in advance that following the description and demonstration, sufficient triangular bandages will be provided for the students to actually practice and learn to tie the square knot, the interest and appeal of the lesson are much greater.

Providing equal experience for all students. In any high school health class there are students with a wide background of experience and travel as well as those with limited experience and travel. When properly selected audiovisual materials are used, these differences can be equated to a great extent, thereby encouraging interest and discussion from most of the students and not of just a few. For example, a lecturette and discussion about health careers will involve some of the students, most likely those who come from medically oriented families or who have had work experience in a related area. If, however, the teacher asks a committee to prepare a bulletin board display in advance, has two students interview three of four people working in health and report their conversations back to the class, arranges for the class to participate in a health careers visitation day, and shows the film *Health Careers* in class, all of the students will be on a more equal experience basis for discussion.

Extending the classroom. A classroom as large as 28 × 40 feet is still a confining structure if its full potential is not developed. Audiovisual materials make a world of the classroom and provide for interaction of the students with the realities of their social and physical environments. Certainly, any high school discussion concerning present-day nutrition problems would be limited if it did not include worldwide nutrition problems and the efforts of the World Health Organization to improve nutrition throughout the world. Useful audiovisual materials would include organizational charts of the World Health Organization and the Food and Agriculture Organization of the United Nations, one or more films on improving agricultural programs in foreign lands, related maps, slides of economic and agricultural conditions in a less developed country, and perhaps a discussion led by a food expert and a foreign student.

Correcting false impressions and concepts. From the ancient medicine man to the modern medical quack there has always been a plethora of health misinformation to confound an uneducated and unsuspecting public. The study of misconceptions cited earlier in the text is an isolated example of the several attempts made in recent years to describe the extent of health misinformation. On a broader plane, the recent action by the California legislature to make the practice of medicine by cancer quacks in that state illegal will provide a beacon for similar action by other states in the future and is certainly a sign of an awakening among responsible citizens.

The secondary school health teacher who teaches in specifics rather than in generalities will employ multiple audiovisual materials to increase knowledge and improve attitudes in those areas in which health misinformation is most prevalent. A wide variety of materials are available, for example, in safety education and particularly in automobile safety. We need only to turn to insurance statistics to understand the significant reduction in accidents and fatalities that has been achieved among persons who take a driving education course. A similar though not statistical response is offered by those high school students who participate in a well-presented unit on family life and sex education.

Integrating instruction. Health instruction must necessarily be abstract to a certain extent. Audiovisual materials, however, permit the instructor to integrate the concrete with the abstract and thus give a maximum of meaning to the desired health outcomes. Abstract concepts such as the transmission of characteristics from parent to offspring may be made less abstract through the use of flat pictures of the chromosome, only recently possible with the development of electronic photography, of a reproduction of the Watson-Crick double helix model, and of films offered by the Education Division of the National Foundation, Inc., on hereditary disorders that affect health.

Teachers must continually remind themselves that what is concrete to one student is abstract to another. A variety of audiovisual materials selected from several points on the concrete-abstract continuum may be necessary before a desired health outcome is attained among all members of a class. This is what the high school teacher referred to at the beginning of this chapter learned through the discussion of the responsibilities of the learner and the teacher. His subsequent classes proved more popular as he developed an expanding

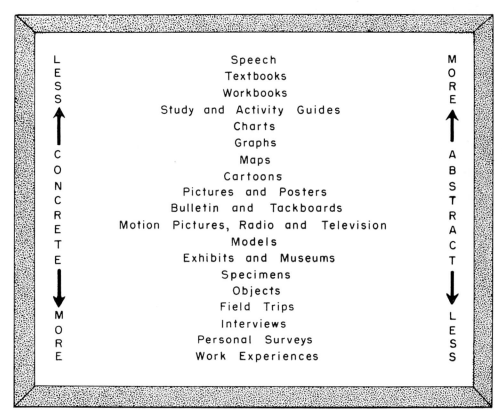

UNDERSTANDING in HEALTH

Fig. 11. Conceptual framework for understanding in health that will help determine what audiovisual materials to use for attainment of a specific learning objective.

variety of audiovisual materials selected from all points on the concrete-abstract continuum.

A CONCEPTUAL FRAMEWORK

The message contained in this chapter is two fold. For the reasons cited, and others equally important but not included, understanding in health will be enhanced if the audiovisual materials employed have *variety* and are in the correct *concrete-abstract balance.* Fig. 11 represents a model which health teachers should frequently consult.

QUESTIONS FOR DISCUSSION

1. What are some other deterrents to health understanding in addition to those listed in this chapter? Describe each in one or two paragraphs and give examples.
2. It is argued by some persons that audiovisual materials reduce the importance of the teacher in the learning process. Is this true or false? Why?
3. What are some of the implications of audiovisual materials for more efficient learning?
4. What are some factors which should influence the choice of audiovisual materials?
5. Why should the teacher assume major responsibility for determining the kinds and number of audiovisual materials to be used?
6. What does this chapter say about the need to include the students in the evaluation of methods and materials?

SUGGESTED CLASS ACTIVITIES

1. Prepare a list of major sources of audiovisual materials which are commonly available to schools.
2. Assemble a variety of audiovisual materials. Discuss each in relation to its most suitable uses in health education.
3. Prepare a list of criteria to be used in evaluating audiovisual materials.
4. Devise a checklist which might be used as an objective means of evaluating audiovisual materials.
5. Describe the audiovisual materials program of a school with which you are familiar.
6. Discuss the concrete-abstract continuum as it pertains to audiovisual materials.

REFERENCES

1. American Educational Research Association: Instructional materials: educational media and technology, Review of Educational Research **32:** April, 1962.
2. Barnes, F. P.: Using the materials of learning, National Education Association Journal **50:** Sept., 1961.
3. Brown, J. W., Lewis, R. B., and Harcleroad, F. F.: A-V instruction materials and methods, New York, 1959, McGraw-Hill Book Co., Inc.
4. Bennell, F. B.: Audio-visual aids in health education, Journal of School Health **27:** Jan., 1957.
5. Cypher, I. F., et al.: Big audio-visual issues and you, Instructor **71:** June, 1962.
6. Fisher, R. T.: Rousseau, a proponent of A. V., Educational Screen and Audio-Visual Guide **41:** Feb., 1962.
7. Gumm, B. L.: San Diego: treasure chest of audio-visuals, Educational Screen and Audio-Visual Guide **41:** Oct., 1962.
8. Kearney, William: Value of audio-visual materials, Instructor **71:** June, 1962.
9. Olivero, J. L.: Multimedia: their value in instruction, Educational Screen and Audio-Visual Guide **41:** May, 1962.
10. Palmer, Richard: Experience, information, and the mass media, In Bereday, G. Z. F., and Lauwerys, J. A., editors: Year book of education, Tarrytown-on-Hudson, 1960, World Book Co.

11. Sands, L. B.: Audio-visual procedures in teaching, New York, 1956, The Ronald Press Co.
12. Technology hits the classroom, Texas Outlook **46:** May, 1962.
13. Willey, R. D.: Teaching health through audio-visual materials, Journal of Health, Physical Education, and Recreation **26:** May-June, 1955.
14. Williams, D. G.: Audio-Visual coordinator's role, Instructor **71:** June, 1962.

Chapter 15

MATERIAL AIDS
TO
TEACHING

Anything and everything in the student's environment which contributes in any way to the learning process may be considered an aid to teaching. Thus, in the broadest sense one writer considers the school building itself to be the largest and most expensive teaching aid; if it is a good school building it says in no uncertain terms: "I have a job to do. I do it well. I stimulate learning, not deter it.— I work for the students and their educating process. I provide a pleasant, inspirational environment for study. I am a machine for learning."* Too, the classroom must be considered an aid to teaching for the same reason.

Although the concept of the term *material aids* is as broad as the concept of the school building itself, it has come to have a much more restricting meaning to most teachers. Material aids are those aids which the teacher is able to physically manipulate, show, or point to that contribute to the spoken word and thus enhance learning. Thus, it is a matter of record that the first chalkboard was considered by "professional teachers" a crutch to be used only by those who were incompetent. Today, the chalkboard is accepted, along with desks, chairs, paper, and pencils, as a very necessary material aid.

In this chapter material aids will be considered to be specific types of aids to teaching which may be used in addition to the standard traditional equipment found in almost every classroom. Consequently, such things as pencils, paper, chalk, chalkboards, desks, chairs, and textbooks, while in reality material aids, will not be considered here. The purpose at this point will be to consider the use of certain specific aids to health teaching not commonly found in all classrooms.

---

*From Caudill, W. W.: False economics in school house construction, Saturday Review, May 18, 1963.

These will be considered alphabetically except for those material aids broad enough in scope to necessitate a more detailed discussion in later chapters. It should be pointed out that the material aids to teaching presented in this chapter consist of a combination of various sensory materials used by students. They do not cover the field as far as health teaching is concerned, and they are included here only as a sampling of the numerous possibiilties.

NATURE, PURPOSE, AND USE OF MATERIAL AIDS

Life in our dynamic society presents many complex problems for the growing individual, not the least of which are the problems which influence his health. In teaching for health, all possible measures should be taken to help students learn about the principles of health which will influence their present and future well-being. Since health teaching is concerned with an accumulation of knowledge that will favorably influence attitudes and behavior, it is apparent that desirable outcomes will be difficult to accomplish if the teacher relies on limited material aids. Therefore, a variety of those aids to teaching which will help students gain a more complete understanding of abstract health principles should be used regularly.

Elsewhere it has been pointed out that health teaching has not kept pace with other subject matter areas in respect to method. The reason for this is due to the uncertain status that health has had in the school curriculum and to the fact that relatively few teachers receive sufficient actual preservice training in health teaching. As a result, many teachers who have been assigned to teach health classes have made the textbook practically the only material aid, and they have restorted to reading from it as their prime method. Undoubtedly, many of these teachers have been unaware of the contribution of other material aids.

There are various kinds of material aids in health education, and each serves a more or less general purpose. One type is designed primarily for the development and improvement of the basic tools of learning such as reading and writing. Practice materials such as health workbooks and health study and activity guides are included in this category.

A second type is one which serves the purpose of furnishing students with direct experience through use of material aids. That is, the material may appeal directly to one or more of the senses. The study of the products of tobacco smoke, a visual experiment described in Chapter 11, provides direct experience for the student.

A third classification of teaching aids is the type that is used for the purpose of having students receive an indirect experience. This type is generally used when those materials which give direct experience are not available. An example of this may be seen in the film *Is Smoking Worth It?* of the American Cancer Society.

As with methods, the secondary health teacher needs to be familiar with sufficient material aids so that his teaching has variety and appeal to the several senses. The students in any one health class represent many backgrounds, and each will respond in an individual manner to a specific material aid. Some will grasp the health meaning immediately and incorporate it into their repertoire of accomplishment. Other students will need a second and perhaps a third differently conceived material aid to gain the same point. Regardless of the range of capacity among students in a class, the variety of material aids in health instruction are such that some type of aid is available to make the specific health topic more meaningful to all students. The health teacher must discover and use the appropriate types to be most successful.

When material aids are used, certain basic procedures should be taken into consideration if the best results are to be obtained. The following suggestions may be helpful in guiding the teacher in the proper use of material aids.

1. Material aids should be readily accessible. It is very disconcerting for students to have to wait for the teacher to locate materials that have been misplaced. When this occurs, continuity and interest in the lesson are often lost.

2. It is important to remember that material aids are to be *used* and not just shown. The teacher must know just how a particular aid to learning fits into a specific situation. The material aids themselves will not do the teaching for the teacher. They should be used as tools in such a way that they make a lesson more meaningful.

3. If there are a number of different material aids to be used, it is usually best to use them one at a time in sequence. When it becomes necessary to show relationships with graphs or charts, it is then feasible that more than one be displayed at a time.

4. Material aids, when used in a logical sequence, should be such that they complement each other. In other words, the teacher can use a psychological approach within the logical limits of the class.

BULLETIN OR TACK BOARDS

The secondary school health classroom should have at least 16 linear feet of bulletin or tack board space. This will permit a great variety of materials such as pictures, charts, maps, specimens, and news clippings to be on display during the study of a specific health unit. Such materials serve as a desirable supplement and keep the current subject in the attention of the students.

One valuable purpose which the bulletin or tack board can serve is to introduce a health unit. For example, an eleventh grade unit on disease (Appendix A) may be introduced by having a suitable bulletin board display of pictures or photographs of bacterial types, viruses, and other pathogens. These will stimulate interest and questions to the extent that the initial and frequently difficult stage of unit introduction is bridged.

An important concern is the organization, arrangement, and selection of bulletin and tack board materials. Care should be exercised to keep the available space from becoming a repository for unorganized, unattractive, unrelated, and nonessential displays.

Careful attention should be given to the length of time materials are left on the bulletin board. Ordinarily two or three days are the limit for most materials.

Fig. 12. Well-designed bulletin board will focus interest on the subject matter of a health unit. Note the presence of a permanent screen for projection of audiovisual material.

Otherwise, students seeing the same things displayed day after day become bored with them. Usually it is better to leave a bulletin board blank than to leave materials displayed on it past the psychological limit of attention-holding. However, in cases in which students make and prepare materials for display, the material need not be changed as frequently.

An additional feature of bulletin or tack boards is the mobile. Three-dimensional objects suspended in front of the bulletin or tack board create depth to the display, catch the eye more readily, and, therefore, can be a more valuable aid to teaching than the one-dimensional object.

CARTOONS

In the past, cartoons have not ordinarily been used most effectively as material aids to teaching; yet when used properly, cartoons can be an excellent medium for conveying health concepts to students.* The possibility of failure in the use of cartoons arises from the fact that they may be associated with entertainment rather than with learning. This possibility, however, if recognized can also be a virtue. A well-trained teacher will balance that which is popular with the point he wishes to convey and thus will capitalize on a medium that has the advantage of being interesting to a majority of students.

In using cartoons in health instruction the teacher should always consider the need for critical appraisal and evaluation of the material. The

---

*Refer to the following sources for examples of cartoon use: Kilander, H. F.: Health for modern living, Englewood Cliffs, N. J., 1957, and Prentice-Hall Inc.; The Travelers annual book of street and highway accident data, The Travelers Insurance Companies, Hartford, Conn.

Fig. 13. Example of a safety cartoon. "I have extrasensory perception for this sort of thing."

following standards may be helpful in appraising and evaluating health cartoons.

1. Will the students fully understand the implication for health that the cartoon is supposed to portray?
2. Does the cartoon present an accurate treatment of a health concept, or is it exaggerated to the point at which the idea may be lost?
3. Does the cartoon present the health concept in such a way that the students can react intellectually toward it?
4. Does the cartoon emphasize humor over and above the health concept, or is a proper balance maintained?
5. Is the cartoon unique, appealing, and easily understood?

The guiding principle in the use of cartoons is to select those cartoons which are appealing to students and which at the same time make a contribution to their learning. Many of the voluntary agencies and commercial organizations listed in Chapter 18 have developed educationally acceptable cartoons. This is especially true in the area of safety education. Also, health cartoons constructed by those secondary school students with a flair for art can provide an effective learning experience in health.

CHARTS

An excellent way to show large amounts of data in brief is through the use of charts. Among the kinds of charts that have found application in health education are the diagrammatic chart, flow chart, genealogical chart, and summary chart.

Diagrammatic chart. The diagrammatic chart may be used in either the teaching or testing situation. In teaching family life and sex education to a class of girls, one eleventh grade teacher uses mimeographed charts of the female and male reproductive systems. The charts are labeled during the teaching of the unit. One aspect of the test over this unit is the use of unlabeled charts on which the students must indicate the several parts.

Flow chart. The flow chart is useful in depicting the functional relationships of an organization or program. This type of chart is valuable in the study of local health department structure, local and state nursing programs, and voluntary agency personnel relationships. An example of the flow chart is the one shown in Chapter 2 which describes the school health program.

Genealogical chart. Most secondary school students are interested in heredity. Aspects of the health curriculum that include teaching of the transmission of normal and abnormal conditions from parent to offspring will hold the student's attention. The genealogical chart provides a means whereby involved information of genetic influences on individual traits and characteristics can be clearly shown. Examples of these would be the normal transmission of traits for eye color, body size, sex-linked characteristics, and skin color. Abnormal conditions

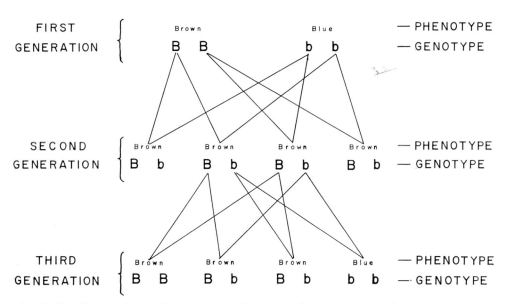

Fig. 14. Heredity in color of the eyes. In the first generation there are two homozygous parents, one for brown eyes and the other for blue eyes. Since brown is dominant, all offspring would be heterozygous for brown eyes in the second generation. When two heterozygous people marry, the mathematical possibilities are those shown in the third generation.

that the secondary school health class very likely will consider include diabetes, certain nerve disorders, feeblemindedness, and albinism.

Summary chart. The summary chart is used more often than the others. This type of chart is excellent for presenting large quantities of data in a brief, well-ordered manner. For example, one twelfth grade teacher was concerned with the immunization record of his seniors. He surveyed their health records to obtain the necessary information. He developed the accompanying chart and presented it with a short talk on the importance of individual responsibility and the fact that high school seniors will soon be on their own in this regard.

IMMUNIZATION INFORMATION CHART

A record of last protection against specific disease or test to indicate positive or negative status

Student	Smallpox	DPT	Poliomyelitis	Tuberculosis
R. Adams	2/58	6/60	6/63	6/63
A. Smithers	12/62	4/52	none	4/52

EXHIBITS

By definition, to exhibit is to "present to view . . . especially in order to attract notice as to what is interesting or instructive . . . ." Exhibits are in such common use as a means of "attracting notice" to organizations, localities, and products that every reader is likely familiar with their wide range of uses and applications. Health teachers as well as other teachers should be aware of and familiar with the uses to which exhibits may be put in health education.

Exhibits are an organization of subjects and materials in such a way that they convey a specific meaning, idea, or set of ideas. Ordinarily, exhibits appeal to the sense of sight, as, for example, an exhibit displaying the various models and demonstrations prepared by a class during a health teaching unit. On the other hand, they may be composed of objects which can be picked up, examined, and operated. However, the various elements in the exhibit should all contribute to the basic idea with which it is concerned. Thus, for example, if the point of an exhibit is to show the work of a class during a semester, all of the students' models, demonstrations, and other work may be displayed together, regardless of their application, merely to show what has been done. But if the purpose is to make a specific point regarding health or safety, only those items which contribute to the making of that point should be exhibited. For example, in conveying the idea of modern public health methods such things as a demonstration of a water purification plant, a picture of a modern sewage disposal plant, a model of a country privy and a country well, and a chart showing various bacteria which are transmitted by way of polluted water may be organized in an exhibit in such a way as to emphasize the importance of modern sanitary methods.

It is essential that exhibits be displayed in accessible locations and that they have eye appeal. Art teachers can play an important role in helping to design and locate good exhibits. Moreover, since we know that the best of exhibits in any field soon become uninteresting and boresome, as a general rule it is also essential that they be displayed for not more than a few days at a time.

There are three major ways in which health teachers may utilize exhibits: first, as a means of conveying important health knowledge to the general student body of the school; second, as a way of calling the attention of parents and other school visitors to specific health matters; third, as a tool of health education to be used in the classroom by teachers.

Conveying health knowledge to the student body. There are certain basic areas of health, including such phases as nutrition, diet, rest, exercise, cleanliness, safety, and first aid, which should be common knowledge to all educated people. Many of the vital concepts involved in these and other areas can be taught, reviewed, and re-emphasized by way of well-prepared exhibits displayed in prominent places in various parts of the school.

One of the functions of a school health council or committee might well be to plan a sequence of exhibits to be displayed throughout the school year. Individual teachers might accept responsibility for preparing and displaying exhibits on given health topics, ranging from balanced diets to exercise and mental and emotional health. Health classes can do excellent work of this kind in the form of class projects. If there are health specialists in the school, they can assist in preparing sequences of health exhibits. Also, art and science teachers can assist very materially in the planning and preparation of school health exhibits.

Many organizations sell or lend professionally prepared exhibits for use in schools. The American Medical Association, The Cleveland Health Museum (which sells Suitcase Exhibits for classrooms), several commercial concerns, and a large number of voluntary health agencies are examples of sources for prepared exhibits on health subjects. Exhibits available from these sources include such subjects as certain physiological functions, nutrition, the birth process, various phases of public health, outstanding medical figures and their contributions, and safety problems. Although professionally prepared work may add greatly to the school health exhibit program, it must not be forgotten that exhibit planning and designing and the necessary research accompanying it can constitute an important learning experience for students who prepare an exhibit as a class project.

Exhibits for parents and other visitors. Exhibits are among the many means used to inform parents and other persons as to what students are doing in school. Interpreting the school health program to parents is a most worthwhile activity and one that can be rewarding in terms of both parental cooperation and support. Since parents are likely to take a marked interest in the work of their children, exhibits which have been made by students are likely to attract and thus, perhaps, to instruct the parents on some health of the concepts being given at school.

Some schools make a practice of displaying exhibits and other materials at times when they know that parents will be visiting the school. Meetings of Parent-Teachers Associations and Science Project Night are examples. Exhibits are sometimes prepared for the specific purpose of increasing the parents' health awareness and knowledge with the hope that they will pay closer attention to such things as the eating and resting habits of their children, the importance

Fig. 15. Three-dimensional exhibit in health science. (Courtesy Columbus Public Schools, Columbus, Ohio.)

of a good nutritious breakfast, the use of television, and cleanliness and grooming.

Exhibits in health classes. Exhibits have sometimes been found to be an effective way to introduce units of instruction or even entire courses. When students enter a room, see, and examine new, attractive, meaningful things, their interest tends to be aroused. They are thus introduced to a new subject in a way that involves learning and that encourages more learning.

A recommended procedure is for teachers to collect suitable exhibits when possible from professional and commercial sources as well as from among student projects. The teacher should use these exhibits in introducing new material, in discussing means of educating the public on health subjects, and in planning other exhibits with classes. In the case of planning exhibits, superior, fair, and inferior work may be shown and analyzed for those things which make them good, mediocre, or poor.

It is essential that exhibits be factually correct. Thus it is frequently necessary for students to do considerable study and research concerning many health topics in order that they may present authentic information. The accuracy of the health information conveyed by the exhibit may well constitute a means of appraisal and evaluation of the knowledge of the students involved.

Some principles to keep in mind regarding exhibits are (1) ordinarily they should convey a single message, (2) they should be as simple as possible in order to be quickly understood, (3) they should involve a minimum of reading, and (4) they should be eye-catching in terms of location, color, and lighting. When possible, movement and sound should be included. In other words, not only the exhibit itself but also its meaning should command attention.

Perhaps the most important single principle to keep in mind when preparing an exhibit is that every part of it should contribute to making one very apparent point. A most common error is to attempt to convey too much through a single exhibit, with the result that all points may be obscured even though there may be eye-catching design, color, and motion.

GRAPHS

Statistics, used with caution, provide a valuable means for presenting health science information. These can be organized in the form of a summary chart, as discussed earlier, or they can be organized into one of several kinds of graphs. The nature of the material to be presented usually determines the kind of graph which is most appropriate. Too, graphs are an effective aid to teaching when used to illustrate abstract concepts such as the chemical percentages contained within a particular ingredient, the composition of tobacco, or the changes taking place during a physiological process such as the breakdown of protein through the action of enzymes.

Area graph. Area graphs can be developed in many different forms. Effective for depicting relationships is the wheel or pie graph which provides students with a concept of the relative size of quantities.

The wheel graph has been used very effectively by a dental hygienist in showing the time involved in dental decay. She uses a circle to represent the 24 hours of a full day. Then she discusses decay as a continual process in the presence of between meal feedings, hard and chewy candies, and few or no brushings. Next she shows the limited time that decay is possible with few or no between meal snacks, a regular balanced diet, and efficient oral hygiene shortly after meals.

A second example of the circle graph in health instruction is shown in Fig. 16. These two circle graphs have been used by a junior high teacher in teaching

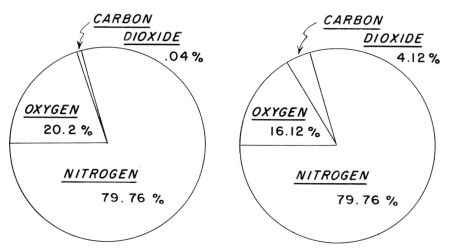

Fig. 16. Composition of inspired and expired air during one respiratory cycle while in the resting stage.

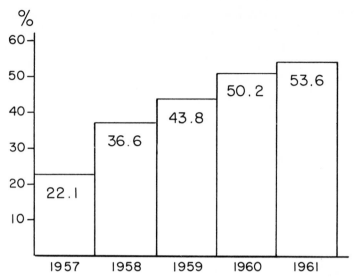

Fig. 17. Chart shows per cent of persons under 60 years of age in the United States who have been inoculated three or more times against poliomyelitis, 1957-1961. (Adapted from Sirken, M. G.: National participation trends, 1955-1961, in the poliomyelitis vaccination program, U. S. Public Health Reports **77:** Aug., 1962.)

Fig. 18. Pictorial graph showing proportion of accidental deaths by age and sex. (Courtesy National Safety Council.)

a unit on the respiratory system to demonstrate visually the composition of air inhaled and exhaled.

Bar graph. The bar graph may also be used to show relationships. It has two added advantages over the circle graph. First, the bar graph is easier to construct since pie-shaped wedges are not always accurate to the degree that they should be, and, second, comparisons are more obvious when the material is organized on a linear perspective. Fig. 17 illustrates a bar graph which was used to accompany a class discussion on the gradual acceptance of poliomyelitis immunization by the public.

Pictorial graph. The type of graph illustrated with pictures combines the graphic and picture ideas. It is effective in showing number concepts and has been used extensively by safety organizations when numbers of people are involved. An example of this, developed by the National Safety Council, is shown in Fig. 18.

MAPS

Many kinds of information are well suited for representation in map form because it offers a spatial and regional relationship that is quite effective. Examples in which maps have been used recently in health education include (1) incidence of communicable diseases in regions of a state or nation, (2) per cent of population residing in areas with fluoridated water, (3) variable agricultural patterns in the country, (4) number and location of doctors and nurses being trained, and (5) multiple accident statistics. Fig. 19 is an example of a map which gives multiple accident statistics.

Although maps are difficult material aids to produce in the classroom, one method may be valuable in this respect. On a stencil 8½ × 11 inches in size the teacher can prepare a map of a state with counties and major towns shown; a second stencil of the United States by states and perhaps major cities could also

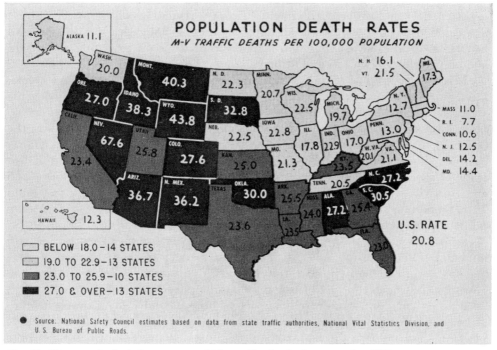

Fig. 19. Map graph depicting motor vehicle traffic deaths by states for 1961.

be cut. When reproduced in quantity these two maps will provide excellent work sheets for a multitude of problems that may develop. Occasionally more extensive study might necessitate a larger, more detailed map. This can be produced by a class committee or may be purchased if funds are available.

MUSEUMS

With the increased interest in science, public and private support for museums has grown in recent years. Certainly health education is in an excellent position to profit from this. The secondary school health teacher may utilize museums in two ways: (1) through a visit as an aspect of health education that takes place beyond the classroom and (2) in developing a health museum within the school.

Museum visits. Because of the fact that increasing numbers of museums have taken an interest in and have prepared exhibits and materials on health subjects, teachers of health should explore the possibility that museums in their locality may have displays dealing with some phase of health and related fields. In some instances, visiting school groups may see models showing the human nervous system in a transparent model, a giant heart with ingenious operative devices, pictures and other displays showing new surgical techniques and the operation of artificial limbs, working models of digestive systems, food exhibits, representations of the embryonic and fetal periods of life, and the birth process.

Class trips should be planned carefully in advance. A psychological readying process should include alerting the students to what is to be seen and providing sufficient insight into the museum offering to assure maximum benefit from the experience. Follow-up activities might involve a review of what was seen and a discussion and study of subjects suggested by the trip. Moreover, visiting natural history, medical, and art museums should stimulate ideas regarding the design and preparation of exhibits and displays.

It is well to keep in mind that most museums are an excellent source of material aids that are useful in health instruction. These can be obtained during the visit for continued study in the classroom or can be obtained by mail upon request. Even though a museum may not list offerings entitled "health" as such, the "science" materials often include information on anatomy, physiology, neurology, medicine, medical history, and other phases of health. An example of this is the Oregon Museum of Science and Industry in Portland. Material aids available in various areas include booklets, records, films, and taped radio programs. Larger museums such as the Cleveland Health Museum and the New York Metropolitan Museum of Natural History rent and sell portable exhibits.

School museums. Many enthusiastic teachers have developed their own health museums. This is possible only when sufficient space is available for both display and storage. In the most ideal situation, health education would be assigned to a regular classroom, thus permitting museum materials to be concentrated.

Exhibits, models, demonstrations, charts, objects, and other suitable materials may be accumulated over a period of time. Health class projects may include planning and building the necessary display space. Planning and setting up the entire museum layout in terms of some central theme can also be a class activity.

In order to round out a complete display, it may sometimes be necessary for students to make new exhibits.

The available space will determine the extensiveness of the school museum display at any given time. However, it is important that the same materials not be left on display for long periods of time. Rather, they should be rotated periodically, preferably in a way to point up some significant phase of health. For example, all elements in a museum display might contribute to a central theme—The World Health Organization and Its Activities. One chart might show the basic structure of this organization. A world map might show the regional offices of the World Health Organization and the location of its major activities. One exhibit might include books, pamphlets, and a supply of different issues of the WHO Newsletters. It is apparent that the several elements in the museum offering could do much to teach the nature and role of the United Nations World Health Organization in the world today.

When museum work of this general kind is done, school classes not involved in the project and perhaps not taking health courses at a particular time may be invited to visit the exhibits. If visitors are invited, mimeographed fliers are useful for providing orientation and commentary on the various displays, and they may be very helpful in subsequent review and discussion.

If materials are to be assembled so that sequences of museum displays may be planned for an entire school year, it is apparent that storage space will be an important consideration. In fact, this constitutes a major limiting factor in many situations in which space and storage facilities are limited. Another factor which sometimes prevents school health museums from playing the role that they might in health education is the common absence of a health education room as such. The old and outmoded procedure, typical of many junior and senior high schools, of scheduling health classes in many different classrooms throughout the school building makes it next to impossible to utilize both demonstrations and exhibits which are so important in health instruction. In this respect attention should be called to the field of science. If junior and senior high school science classes were shifted from one room to another without laboratory facilities, the quality of instruction would likely be very low. Practically the same situation exists in health education. Consequently, health instruction in those schools lacking a health laboratory or at least a health room is usually of a comparably low quality. Unfortunately a majority of junior and senior high schools have not progressed to the point of having a health laboratory or for that matter even a health classroom as such.

The special secondary school health education classroom including allowance for health museums is discussed in Chapter 17.

OBJECTS, SPECIMENS, AND MODELS

Objects are considered "the things themselves," specimens are referred to as "parts of objects," and models are "replicas of objects."* Objects and

---

*Koon, C. M.: School use of visual aids, Office of Education, Washington, D. C., 1938, Bulletin No. 4.

specimens are usually favored over models because they are the real thing under study. In many instances, however, it is not possible to get the real thing such as a heart, lungs, and reproductive system. When objects and specimens are not available, the model may be the next best material aid to teaching.

Attention should be called to the fact that models, and to a lesser extent, prepared specimens are expensive items. Sufficient number and variety may be obtained only by careful long-range planning and purchasing. The health teacher should add a few new items every year so that his teaching does not become dated.

An object, specimen, or model is used in health teaching so that students may have firsthand experience by direct personal contact with these items. In general the more direct the experience, the more meaningful it is to students. This means that in the case of objects, specimens, and models, provision should be made for students to view, hear, touch, taste, or manipulate them, as the case may be. In other words, objects, specimens, and models should be used and not just shown.

PICTURES

Several kinds of pictures are available as material aids. These include photographs, paintings, magazine pictures, advertising brochures, slides, and film strips. Slides and film strips are for projection purposes only, whereas the others may be used with or without a projector. When still pictures are projected, an opaque projector is necessary. Pictures have value because they are easy to obtain, are inexpensive, and may be used many times.

In using pictures in health instruction, teachers should take precautions so that students do not fall victim to false conceptions. One very important consideration is the fact that different students may view a picture in a different light. Although pictures are largely for the purpose of being seen and not read, it may be difficult to keep students from reading certain meanings into a picture. The meaning a picture conveys to a student depends largely on the past experience the student has had with the health or safety idea that the picture is intended to convey. For example, a picture depicting a certain automobile safety practice may have an altogether different meaning for a student who has had a course in driver education than for one who has not.

As in the case of some of the other material aids in health instruction, the teacher should devise standards for critical appraisal and evaluation of pictures. The following list of criteria is suggested as a guide for the selection and use of pictures.

1. Does the picture help in achieving the purpose of the lesson?
2. Does it give a true picture of the health concept to be conveyed?
3. Is the picture technically correct with respect to health concepts?
4. Does the picture have the proper amount of detail?
5. Does the picture stimulate the imagination, thus helping to stimulate thought?

6. Is the size of the picture such that it is large enough to show sufficient details and small enough to be handled and used effectively?
7. Is the picture suited to the age level and abilities of the students?

POSTERS

When used correctly, health posters can be desirable aids to learning in health. The value of posters in health education is directly related to the period of time that they are displayed. If they are displayed for too long a period, it is quite possible that they might become boresome to students to the extent that they will "grow" pencil-drawn beards and moustaches. When this occurs, it is likely that a poster will detract from rather than contribute to learning and retention. An exception to this rule concerns those health posters that are made by students. Student-made posters may remain on display for longer periods of time because students receive a great deal of enjoyment and satisfaction from having their own work displayed.

Posters may be obtained from numerous voluntary and official health agencies at little or no cost. Also, upon request many commercial organizations will distribute health posters to schools free of charge. Posters of this nature that are of greatest value in health instruction are those that attract immediate attention and convey one principle idea related to health.

Teachers often find posters a practical and satisfactory means of introducing a health unit. This is accomplished by displaying numerous posters for the purpose of stimulating the interest of students in the problem of the unit.

STUDY AND ACTIVITY GUIDES

The study and activity guide is a kind of work material, usually in mimeographed form, that is distributed to students when they begin work on a health unit. One of the main purposes of the study and activity guide is to present students with questions and problems that will guide them in the study of the unit.

Study and activity guides may be divided into two broad categories, that is general study guides and special study guides. The general study guide is broader in scope and it is usually a guide for the entire unit. The special study guide is concerned with directions or explanations needed to guide students in performing a certain phase of the unit.

Approximate estimates indicate that about 50% of teachers at the junior and senior high school levels use study and activity guides to some extent. This material ranges from a few copied textbook questions to a well-planned study guide. Lack of use of study guides is generally attributed to (1) mechanical preparation involved, (2) failure of teachers to recognize their value, and (3) confusion as to the time when student-teacher planning takes place.

In the following sample study and activity guide it will be noted that references are not furnished for any of the questions. It is felt that a few direct references should be given to assist students in finding materials. However, they should also have the opportunity to locate material by searching for it themselves.

SAMPLE STUDY AND ACTIVITY GUIDE FOR A
UNIT ON THE PROCESS OF DIGESTION

Questions and problems*

Find the answers to the following. It is recommended that you write in your notebook the materials and findings that may be essential to show the conclusions for each question or problem. Underline all new words that appear in the study guide. Look up the meaning of these words.

1. What is the function of saliva in digestion?
2. What is the function of the gastric juices in digestion?
3. What are carbohydrates?
4. What are proteins?
5. How can one detect the nutrients known as carbohydrates, fats, and proteins?
6. What is the function of the mouth and teeth in the process of digestion?
7. What is the function of the pharnyx and esophagus in the process of digestion?
8. What is the function of the stomach in the process of digestion?
9. What is the function of the small intestine in the process of digestion?
10. What is the function of the large intestine in the process of digestion?
11. Why must food be digested?
12. What is the function of the digestive juices?
13. Are there any foods which are not digestible?
14. What is the peristaltic wave which aids digestion?
15. How long does it take food to digest?
16. Is it necessary to have food in the mouth for the salivary glands to function?
17. What happens when you smell a freshly baked apple pie?
18. What parts of the digestive system are used for the mechanical phase of digestion?
19. What are the factors which influence the chemical phase of digestion?
20. How do the mechanical and chemical digestive changes work together?

Select one of the following activities

1. Keep a record of your diet for one day. List the foods you ate and tell where in the digestive tract the greatest amount of digestion takes place.
2. Go to the school cafeteria and get a copy of the weekly menu from the dietitian. Write down a list of all the foods and tell which organs of the digestive system would do the most work in digesting these foods.
3. Go to one of your local restaurants and procure a menu and follow the above procedure.
4. Follow the above procedure if you bring your lunch to school.
5. Make a collection of pictures of foods advertised in a magazine. Write down where in the digestive tract the greatest amount of digestion of these foods takes place.

*Note: A number of books and textbooks should be available. The teacher should list some of the page references in the books on which the answers to questions can be found.

Optional activities*

Students should obtain the approval of the teacher for optional activities which they wish to select.

1. Visit your physician and find out some of the causes of "indigestion." Report to the class on how these causes might have been eliminated.
2. Write a report on the use of dehydrated foods and digestion.
3. Write a report about how the cooking of food influences digestion.
4. Interview a war veteran about rations. Report to the class on this interview.
5. Report to the class on one of the following topics:
   (a) An apple a day keeps the doctor away.
   (b) You are what you eat.
6. With two or more other members of the class form a panel group to discuss either of the following:
   (a) Is beef easier to digest than pork?
   (b) Which is more important, mechanical or chemical digestion?
7. Draw a cartoon which shows the digestive system as a factory.
8. Write a humorous song or poem which describes the process of digestion.
9. Write a short play in which the characters are the various organs of digestion.
10. Make a poster which indicates the various phases of digestion.

*Some teachers maintain a card file for student use in optional activities. Cards 4 x 6 or 5 x 8 inches giving the title of the activity, key questions, and suggested readings will aid students in pursuing optional activities.

WORKBOOKS

The workbook is of relatively recent origin as a material aid, and it is generally considered an outgrowth of the laboratory manual. Health workbooks are usually one of two types. One may be referred to as the general type which is planned for use without a textbook, or it may accompany any health textbook. The other is known as the specific type, and it is designed to parallel and supplement a particular textbook.

The question often arises as to which of these types of health workbooks is best. Although teachers in general appear to prefer the specific type, each form has its advantages. For example, if the textbook material is valid and up-to-date, the accompanying workbook should be useful, provided that it contains sufficient enrichment and supplementary materials. On the other hand, if the textbook is out of date, until such time as it can be revised, a good general type of health workbook might be provided as an aid to teaching.

The teacher should keep in mind that the health workbook is only one aid to learning, and its use should not preclude other desirable health learning experiences that are not included as workbook activities. In other words, the teacher should not hold the students within the bounds of the material in the workbook. This is to say that the content of the health workbook should be viewed as basic material for class work, and that further student planning should supplement the learning experiences provided by the workbook.

To be of value as an aid to learning, the health workbook should be organized in such a way that the teacher can use it to best advantage in meeting the individual differences of students. A workbook that includes nothing more than a list of drill questions harkens back to mere fact memorization in health and, therefore, cannot be considered a desirable aid to teaching. Workbook activities should be of a problem-solving nature.

If the workbook is such that it makes possible individual adaptation to rate of learning, the teacher should not lose the opportunity for this by insisting that all students go through the workbook material in the same sequence and at the same rate.

EVALUATION OF MATERIAL AIDS

The material aids to teaching in health education are of such great importance that they should be subjected to continuous evaluation. When this is done, means are provided for the improvement of present practices.

Criteria for evaluation of certain particular material aids have been discussed under the appropriate headings in this chapter. However, it seems advisable that there be some general criteria which are common to most of the material aids. The following list of suggested criteria for evaluation is given with this purpose in mind.

1. Does the aid represent a sufficient degree of accuracy?
2. Provided that the aid is accurate in every detail, is it relevant to the particular learning situation?
3. What degree of realism does the aid present?
4. Does the aid have a high degree of comprehensibility?
5. Are the students able to use the aid effectively?
6. Are the students interested in the aid?
7. Do the students display a good attitude toward the aid?
8. What are the reactions of the slow learners to the aid?
9. What are the reactions of the superior students to the aid?

QUESTIONS FOR DISCUSSION

1. What are some of the main purposes of material aids in health education?
2. How can material aids in health instruction be classified?
3. In what ways can cartoons be used satisfactorily in health teaching?
4. What are some advantages of the use of still pictures in health teaching?
5. What is the place of the fill-in map in health teaching?
6. What are the major sources of health exhibits?
7. In what ways can exhibits be used as teaching devices in health education classes?
8. Under what conditions is a health museum feasible in a school?
9. What procedure would you use in evaluating a health workbook?

SUGGESTED CLASS ACTIVITIES

1. Prepare a list of ten material aids to learning and tell where they might be used to advantage in health education.
2. With other members of the class, prepare a class bulletin board for an introduction to a unit on nutrition.
3. Collect some health data on various members of the class. Prepare a chart which interprets the data.
4. Devise a flow chart which shows the functional relationships of an official community health agency.

5. Prepare an original area graph for a specific health topic.
6. Prepare a bar graph for a specific health topic.
7. Prepare a list of exhibit topics which would be suitable for use at (1) the junior high level, (2) the senior high level, and (3) the college level. Of what elements might each exhibit be composed?
8. Draw up a layout for several exhibits, showing charts, models, literature, and other elements to be incorporated. Pay particularly close attention to eye appeal, simplicity, and unity in terms of conveying a single idea or concept.
9. Working as committeees, construct several actual exhibits for presentation to the class.
10. If you are now teaching, evaluate your teaching situation in terms of (1) how exhibits might be utilized, and (2) whether or not a health museum might be feasible.
11. Bring a health poster to class. Use this poster in giving an oral report telling how you would evaluate the poster.
12. Prepare a general study and activity guide for use in a health teaching unit on professional health services.

REFERENCES

1. Adkins, G. H.: Tools for teachers, St. Louis, 1962, Bethany Press.
2. Board of Trustees, Cleveland Health Museum: Making health visible, Jan., 1955.
3. DeBernardis, A. D.: Using instructional materials and resources, Education, 82: Dec., 1961.
4. Department of Audio-Visual Instruction, Instructional Aids Committee: Flat pictures, National Education Association Journal 43: April, 1954.
5. Gebhard, B. H.: How Cleveland Museum educates its public on health matters (reprint), Hospital Management Sept., 1949.
6. Gebhard, B. H., and Doyle, W. G.: Health museums at work, Journal of School Health 28: March, 1958.
7. Gerletti, R. C.: Importance of an educational policy for instructional materials, Audio-visual Instruction 7: May, 1962.
8. Knisley, W. H.: Let's use Presty-cartoons more in junior and senior high school classes, Ohio Schools 40: Dec., 1962.
9. Krugman, H. E.: Education and the new learning devices, National Education Association Journal 51: April, 1962.
10. Museum technique in fundamental education, New York, 1957, UNESCO Publications Dept., Educational Studies and Document no. 17 (United Nations Educational, Scientific, and Cultural Organization).
11. Richmond, H. R.: Make your own teaching aids, Journal of Health, Physical Education, and Recreation 29: March, 1958.
12. Schreiber, R. E.: Non-projected teaching materials, Audio-Visual Guide, 19: Oct., 1952.
13. Shores, L. S.: Instructional materials, New York, 1960, The Ronald Press Co.
14. Thomas, R. M., and Swartout, S. G.: Integrated teaching materials, New York, 1960, Longmans, Green & Co., Inc.
15. Tomlin, G. T.: Three dimensional learning; scale model kits, Texas Outlook 46: Dec., 1962.
16. Wilkins, G. T.: Role of instructional materials, Audiovisual Instruction 7: Dec., 1962.
17. Woelfel, N. F.: How to start a teaching aids program, Nation's Schools 47: Feb., 1951.

Chapter 16

MOTION PICTURES, RADIO, AND TELEVISION

It is difficult to comprehend the vast changes in communication media that have occurred during the past few decades. A person born into the present-day world of motion pictures, radio, and television must accept and grow in an environment drastically different from the more stable, less dynamic environment that existed not many years ago. Some measure of the influence of the communications media is revealed in the sheer number of radio and television stations, both commercial and educational, that are currently licensed to operate. As shown in Table 18, radio stations exceed 4800, whereas there are more than 570 television stations. The number of stations continues to increase yearly. Studies conducted by the National Congress of Parents and Teachers, as well as by other groups, reveal that some children spend more time in viewing television than in attending school. Many families deny themselves medical and dental care and yet find the money to purchase elaborate television sets, often color-adapted. The motion picture industry, which experienced some lean years following the growth of television, seems to be recovering to some extent.

In attempting to reckon with motion pictures, radio, and television, educators have been concerned with at least two basic problems: (1) how to gain access to and use these media of communication so that they might contribute most to the teaching-learning process and (2) how to develop the discriminating abilities of young people so that they will select the superior programs. Both of these general problems are important in health education, and each will be discussed in some detail in this chapter.

For the most part, television and to a lesser extent motion pictures are viewed by the public as entertainment. The beginning of a television program or a film almost automatically engenders a mind-set that presumes pleasure, and unless the subject is inappropriate or the acting very inferior, the observer's attention is usually focused and held.

Table 18. Radio and television stations authorized and on the air in the United States as of October 1, 1962*

Medium	Authorized	On air
Radio		
A.M.	3828	3790
F.M.	1200	1057
Television		
Commercial	584	495
Educational	324†	75

*From 1963 Yearbook issue of Broadcasting, The Business Weekly of Television and Radio, Washington, D. C.
†Number of reserved channels for educational television as established by Federal Communications Commission and thus somewhat different from authorized channels; 75 educational television stations in addition to 324 reserved channels.

The educational value of motion pictures was exploited by the government during World War II in training thousands of troops, and today most business firms rely on film to project the image of their operation that they wish the public to see. In both these instances the controls that operate in the public school education setting are not present. First, the necessary resource of money is not a restricting factor; second, access to the necessary technical assistance for film production has in the past been more readily available to the United States Government and big industry. Both these facts, but especially the latter, have gradually been altered in the last ten years as the larger school systems have established their own audiovisual departments equipped to stage and produce films and educational television programs.

The recent developments in education have made it clear that our problem is not *whether* mass media such as radio, motion pictures, and television should be used in the classroom, but *how* and under what circumstances they should be used. For as we adjust ourselves to the time in which we live, we must grow in ability to handle our problems, and to do this, we must learn more effective and efficient means of bringing information and ideas to students in vivid, realistic, and meaningful ways. Therefore, it is highly important that teachers make use of the many modern devices and media of communication at their disposal.

Most of the state departments of education are engaged in concerted audiovisual activities, and motion picture films constitute a significant part of the total operational budget. An example of the extent of this is one particular state which provides more than 8000 films for distribution. Furthermore, more than a dozen state departments of education are involved to some degree in educational radio and television broadcasting. Partly in anticipation of a need and partly in recognition of an existing need, numerous teacher education institutions now require, or at least highly recommend, that teachers take college courses in audiovisual education in which the mass media play a prominent part.

MOTION PICTURES IN HEALTH EDUCATION

There is little doubt that the motion picture is one of the best media for the presentation of many health problems. The film was perhaps one of the first forms of programed instruction, and studies reveal that it is effective in influencing habits and increasing knowledge.* Health films have been found effective in influencing thought and behavior from the earliest years of a person's life into senescence because they tie words and thought to the emotions and to action and the viewer tends to identify himself with the action of the film. By way of illustration, a film in which a physician teaches women self-examination for breast cancer seems to be talking directly to the individuals in the audience. Also, high school students viewing the film *Human Reproduction* are very likely to identify themselves with one or another of the actors. Obviously, this kind of approach makes for personalized and emotional appeal, as well as for logical appeal.

It is clear from the more than 700 films that are listed in Appendix C that most areas of health subject matter may be supplemented by one or more appropriate films. Before a secondary school teacher selects a specific film, however, questions such as the following should be considered.

1. Does the film make a contribution to learning that other less expensive or more easily accessible aids such as film strips, field trips, or visiting speakers cannot make?
2. Is there a need to show a process in which motion is an important feature.
3. Would a slow motion presentation of a process facilitate comprehension?
4. Are microscopic details or animations desirable for understanding?
5. Would eyewitness observation of some public or other health situation or some corrective action make the health problems under consideration more real?
6. Would a dramatic presentation help to establish desirable concepts upon which good attitudes are built, regarding such subjects as health fads and superstitions, venereal disease, mental health and illness, wise food selection, and cancer?

These and other relevant questions should aid the teacher in determining the contribution a particular film will make to the health subject matter.

Certainly selected films can add greatly to the learning situation. Consequently, they must be considered extremely valuable material aids. Since this is the case, considerable thought should be given to the use of films. The discussion which follows will be concerned with (1) film sources, (2) previewing and scheduling the film, (3) showing the film, and (4) evaluating the film.

Film sources

Although the modern sources of health films are numerous and varied, discussion in this text will be limited largely to centralized sources.

Departments of education. Most schools today have designated a resource person or director of audiovisual aids whose function it is, among other things, to inform teachers as to readily available health films that are provided by state, city, or county education departments. This resource person, frequently the school librarian, is in charge of all of the school's audiovisual information material. The director of audiovisual aids is helpful in locating desirable health films and

---

*Creer, R. P.: Movies that teach health, Today's Health **32**: Oct., 1954.

in providing extensive listings of films available from education and health departments, professional groups, and industrial and commercial organizations. In some states, audiovisual materials including films are concentrated in a special department or bureau at the headquarters of the department of education. In others, a policy of decentralization has been adopted so that audiovisual materials are concentrated at the level of the county department of education or are available through branch libraries in the state. Some large city school systems maintain extensive film libraries for the use of their teachers, and often films need to be scheduled only a few days in advance.

In some states, the state university or an extension division within the state system of higher education has assumed responsibility for acquiring and distributing films and other audiovisual materials; also in some states, private colleges and universities furnish many visual aids to schools. In any event, principals, librarians, or health or general supervisors can usually provide information for teachers concerning the most readily accessible health film sources in the particular education system.

Upon request, established audiovisual centers usually provide a catalog of films contained within their library. In addition, the directors of these centers welcome inquiries about films not included in their current list. When sufficient demand for a specific title appears evident, the film will usually be purchased and made available on a rental basis. If health supervisors are available, they should make every effort to inform teachers concerning suitable films which they may use. In the absence of such assistance, teachers can request the health listings from those responsible for audiovisual aids in the school.

As an added convenience to the resource person and teachers, most established audiovisual departments include a brief description of a film along with its title. Included in this is a general suggestion as to the most appropriate audience, some details as to subject matter coverage, running time, and information regarding whether a film is in black and white or colored and has sound or is silent. Such information simplifies film selection and tends to enhance improvement in the use of educational films.

Departments of health. Local, county, and state health departments are frequently good sources of health films. However, health department films should be carefully evaluated before they are used in the classroom because many are selected for adult and professional groups and may not be well suited for the purpose intended. Descriptive information on each film title can be very helpful in making selections. Another source of guidance is the school nurse. Nurses are usually advised of audiovisual materials available through their health departments, and they can make suggestions to teachers concerning suitable films and can even make the necessary arrangements for obtaining them.

The film catalog of one state department of health contains over 400 titles classified under the following subject index: aging, arthritis, air pollution, alcoholism, cancer, careers in health, civil defense, courtesy, dental health, diabetes, drug addiction, epilepsy, first aid, foot care, general health, general sanitation, growth and development, hearing, heart, infectious diseases, local health services, maternal and child health, mental health, nursing, nutrition, occupational health, poison, safety, vector control, venereal disease, vision, and water pollution and supply. Although perhaps not as extensive, the health departments of the other states provide similar listings upon request. The health teacher who does not explore and make use of the state department as a health film resource would be considered derelict in his duties.

Voluntary agencies and commercial organizations. A great many voluntary health agencies and commercial organizations prepare and distribute audiovisual aids of various kinds, including motion picture films on health subjects. For the most part, films produced by voluntary agencies are excellent, although it should be recognized that the subject matter is often quite narrow due to the fact that their programs are usually oriented to a specific disease entity. In recent years, however, several voluntary organizations have produced films with broad health implications. The catalogs of the National Tuberculosis Association and the American Cancer Society, for example, list excellent films with a more diverse health appeal.

In the past, many films prepared by commercial organizations have been advertising media, with health instruction largely if not entirely incidental. Consequently, most of these films did not qualify as teaching aids. However, at the present time many films from commercial sources are unquestionably of high quality because ranking authorities in various health education areas frequently have been utilized in research and film production. They frequently emphasize desirable health instruction, and advertising is not intruded into the subject matter. In fact, many of the films listed in education and health department offerings have been prepared by commercial groups.

Commercial films are frequently available to teachers by way of local non-school channels. When this is the case, they may be obtained with little or no advance scheduling, whereas films obtained from education and health departments and even voluntary agencies sometimes require three or more weeks advance reservation. In utilizing these local commercial sources the teacher definitely should preview the film in advance to satisfy himself that it meets acceptable educational standards.

Previewing and scheduling films

Teachers should have an opportunity to preview even superior films if they are to make the best use of them. It is also essential that the teachers know just when a given film will be available for use. Both of these things are essential for the best utilization of films as teaching aids. However, in the practical situation it is frequently impossible to preview and schedule properly. Administrators and personnel of audiovisual aids departments should give this problem very careful consideration because the value of films and other audiovisual aids is known to depend to a considerable degree upon whether they are used at the proper time in teaching.

If there is no opportunity to preview films prior to the first time that they are used, the teacher must be guided by descriptive information and by information from other teachers. Once having seen a film, the teacher can henceforth be guided by his own judgment.

If there is doubt as to whether a film will arrive as scheduled, or if it is not possible to adjust the teaching of given material to the date of the arrival of the film, it is usually wise to plan the entire unit without depending upon the film. It is better to have the film added to the unit preparation than to have the unit incompletely or poorly integrated because of its absence.

It has been mentioned previously that the person designated as coordinator or director of audiovisual aids, the librarian or a teacher, takes care to post the dates when films are scheduled to arrive at the school. Guided by this information, all of the teachers who wish to use them can frequently adjust their teaching in such a way that films will fit reasonably well into the unit or lesson. Of course, if the schedules are not reliable, such planning is useless, and administrative action is necessary if audiovisual aids are not to lose a great part of their value.

Showing films

The showing of a film may be regarded as a three-phase sequence consisting of (1) an introductory or orientation phase, (2) the actual showing of the film, and (3) a review and evaluation phase. These phases are discussed here because of the rather universal tendency to regard films as things in themselves, capable of standing alone without aid from the teacher. It must be emphasized that even the best of films need to be supplemented.

In advance of the film showing, the class should be prepared for the subject under consideration in order to realize maximum benefit. As an example, a teacher may wish to include a film on quackery and nostrums when presenting material about community health services and the wise selection of a family physician. In preparation for the film, he may wish to talk about the history of quackery and discuss the characteristics of a culture that gives root to quackery. Also, he may wish to describe the degree of education necessary to qualify as a physician and then discuss the laws that states have established to guard against the practice of medicine by persons who are unqualified. Finally, the new vocabulary in the sound film should be discussed in advance, as well as related terms. In brief, the teacher should try to make certain that the class approaches the film psychologically ready to profit most from it.

When a film is shown, consideration should be given to the physical conditions of the room. It should be properly darkened and ventilated, the screeen should be visible to all, the projector should be properly situated, and the sound should be correctly adjusted. It is usually unwise to require students to take notes during film showings because of the darkened condition of the room and because their concentration may be diverted from the film to the notes. Sometimes, however, it is useful for students to record individual words or phrases for reference in later discussions.

Following the showing, the film should be reviewed and evaluated for the purpose of achieving maximum integration into the objectives of the unit. Occasionally the teacher may administer a brief written quiz in order to determine the effectiveness of the film in teaching and in establishing health concepts on the part of the students. Continuing with the example of quackery in medicine, the teacher might pose the theoretical death of a patient while under the care of a person improperly trained and ask the class to suggest avenues of control to prevent further deaths.

If the film is produced by a company with a commercial or other bias, the teacher may forewarn the class to be on the alert for indications of a slanted approach, perhaps unjustifiably favorable to a product. During the evaluation period, this possibility may be reckoned with, and it may be used as an incentive to further study in order to discover whether certain of the contentions in the film are valid.

It seems apparent that the review and evaluation aspect of film-showing has a threefold value as follows: (1) to recapitulate the contents of the film, (2) to weigh the value of the contents of the film by testing it against other evidence, and (3) to cultivate the discriminative powers of the students to the end that they may be cautious in accepting information presented to them, particularly when it is presented by what may be a prejudiced source.

A brief word of caution is necessary at this point. At no time should motion pictures be allowed to replace the teacher or to reduce his importance in the teaching-learning situation. In fact, motion pictures, as with any material aid, add to the complexity of teaching, and real skills are needed if a maximum of film integration into the over-all health subject is to be achieved.

Evaluating films

Whenever a film is shown, the teacher should analyze its contribution to the outcomes of the unit being studied. Each film, as with any material aid, should contribute to the development or improvement of health habits, attitudes, and knowledge. A film which does not do this is inferior as a material aid.

A basic consideration in the evaluation of a film is whether it materially assists the students in progressing toward the desired learning goals. Of course, technical matters of film making and mechanical matters of visibility, sound, and condition of the film should be taken into account in determining the value of a motion picture.

Following are some questions which should be considered when a health education film is being selected.

1. Is it interesting and appropriate to the age and grade level?
2. Does it convey the desired facts and concepts, and is it likely to contribute to the formation of desirable attitudes?
3. Is it accurate and up to date?
4. Can it be correlated with and integrated into the course of study at the particular grade level?
5. Is the language well suited to the intended audience?
6. Is it likely to be understood by students?
7. Does it meet reasonable standards of technical excellence in terms of good quality pictures, satisfactory sound, and natural acting?
8. Is the film of suitable length?

It is impossible for a teacher to remember both the good and bad qualities of all films. Consequently, it is good procedure to maintain a card file with summarizing information on each film that is used. The form shown on p. 275 can be mimeographed on cards 5 × 7 inches, and whenever a film is previewed, a card for the film can be completed and filed.

FILM PREVIEW CARD

Name of film_____Date previewed_____

Source of film_____

Black and White_____ Color_____ Sound_____ Silent_____ Length in minutes_____

Producer of film_____Publication date_____

Costs: Rental_____Purchase_____

For what groups (community or professional) or grade level do you consider the

film suitable?_____

What theme is stressed by the film?

Front

For what function or purpose could the film be used?

1._____

2._____

The strong points observed in the film:

1._____

2._____

Weaknesses observed in the film:

1 _____

2._____

How do you rate the film?

Outstanding_____ Excellent_____ Good_____ Fair_____ Poor_____

Other comments _____

Back

Silent versus sound motion pictures. Although some teachers feel that silent films are now obsolete, others argue that under certain circumstances they are actually superior to sound films. The two major advantages of silent films are (1) that they cost less and (2) that they involve no spoken words which might be unsuitable for the vocabulary level of a particular group. Although silent films may include a written vocabulary that it not properly graded for a particular group, the teacher may compensate for this by verbalizing and simplifying the reading material when necessary.

Although silent films remain highly useful and effective in education, sound films have certain advantages in some cases, as follows.

1. Sound may be used to enhance the effectiveness of the presentation in ways other than verbalization. For example, a film on the heart may in-

clude amplified heart sounds, thus adding an auditory experience to the visual experience.

2. Sound films do not require reading proficiency and thus are more suitable for groups which may be retarded in reading.
3. Teachers inexperienced in using films, lectures, and oral explanations are probably helped more by sound films.
4. Continuity of the film need not be broken by interruptions of the teacher in explaining titles and elaborate descriptions.
5. Sound films are of special value for inferior students who usually have difficulty handling the more abstract symbols of other forms of communication.

RADIO IN HEALTH EDUCATION

Despite the rise in popularity of other educational media, radio continues to be used extensively as a material aid. Most generally, commercial stations make time available to schools and have assisted in the technical aspects of program production. Also, increasingly, educational radio stations are programing 15 and 30 minute lessons along subject lines that augment the material being covered in the classroom. An example of this in health education is the program *Tune Up In Health,* a series of 15 minute radio broadcasts produced and presented by the Oregon State Department of Education and the Oregon School of the Air, radio station KOAC, Corvallis, Ore. During 1962 and 1963 these were heard once a week at 2:45 p.m. from October through May, and many health classes throughout western Oregon benefitted.

Moreover, as with the Cleveland Public Schools, some school systems have developed such high regard for the educational possibilities of radio that they have purchased their own stations. This permits continual broadcasts throughout the school day and encourages better integration between subject matter and the material aid—in this case, radio. In these situations, schedules of programs are distributed to all teachers so that they may dovetail suitable broadcasts into their teaching plans. In the more successful programs of this type, planning, preparation, and presentation are a joint effort of students, teachers, subject matter specialists, and radio technicians.

Most communities that have made use of radio as a teaching aid have not gone beyond using the facilities of commercial stations. In some cities, regularly scheduled educational programs are beamed into classrooms and auditoriums and on weekends into homes. Thus, radio has helped to bring the world into the classroom and to teach the community something about what is going on in the classroom. Obviously, there are grave difficulties in attempting to meet the unique program needs of many different teachers at any particular time, even in one school system. Difficulties of this kind have been solved in some cases by recording superior local or even national broadcasts and then making them available as needed by individual teachers.

Surveys reveal that radio continues to be used extensively to educate the public on health and safety topics. The American Medical Association has broadcast programs for many years about the history and drama of the medical profession, and the National Safety Council uses radio extensively to develop a safety consciousness on the part of the public. Other educational, medical, and commercial groups have presented innumerable programs dealing with the general fields of health and safety, including some highly informative interviews with health and safety authorities and round table discussions by specialists on various health topics. Major diseases and personal health subjects have been prominent in these presentations. In recent years, radio has been used increasingly to clarify and point up the problems of mental health, effects of smoking on health, air pollution, and water shortage.

As in the case of other mass media, emphasis should be placed upon (1) making radio a teaching aid rather than an end in itself, (2) integrating information of the broadcast into the instructional material under consideration, (3) employing suitable buildup and follow-up activities in order that the fullest value may be derived from the experience, and (4) developing the critical listening ability of the students to the end that they may exercise judgment and caution when listening to claims and possibly biased reports.

The possibilities of television as an audiovisual aid in health education should not blind us to the fact that radio has not been utilized as fully as its value and availability would indicate that it should be. Advocates of educational radio point out its value as a means of stimulating the imagination of students. Opportunities for bringing significant and dramatic health events into the classroom, such as activities of the World Health Organization, medical research, and events in the history of world and national health, can do much to vitalize the teaching of health. Moreover, numerous schools are equipped already to use radio as a teaching aid and need only leadership to develop this possibility more fully.

TELEVISION IN HEALTH EDUCATION

Television is less than twenty years old in the commercial sense and considerably less than this in an educational sense. Tremendous sums of money, hours of research time, and efforts by skilled personnel have been consumed in the study of this most revolutionary material aid. In many teaching situations television dominates to such an extent that it is difficult to distinguish whether it is a teaching method or material aid. Probably it is some of both in all situations in which it is used.

As with motion pictures, television appeals to more than one sense, and because of its appeal as entertainment, it fixes the individual's attention in a manner not evident in the use of radio. Through television, students can become eye witnesses to major events anywhere in the world. For example, Gordon Cooper's twenty-two orbital flight on May 15 and 16, 1963, was followed continually by students in many schools even while they moved from class to class. Also, it lends itself well to the utilization of nearly every other type of material aid and in this sense is more accurately described as a teaching method. Still, major difficulties confront television as an audiovisual aid in schools. A few of the formidable problems which have yet to be overcome are (1) production costs remain high and probably will for some time to come, (2) reception is often

Fig. 20. Eighth grade health education class and receiving teacher. Students view a 20-minute health unit by television which is then used as background material for a traditional class discussion led by the receiving teacher. (Courtesy Columbus Public Schools, Columbus, Ohio.)

poor due to technical or atmospheric conditions, (3) previewing is often impossible, and (4) television schedules do not always coincide with teaching schedules and plans.

Certain basic factors, in addition to its obvious advantages as a medium of communication, account for the rapid and accelerating growth of educational television. For example, the Federal Communications Commission requires that a certain amount of broadcasting time be devoted to educational and other public service programs, and in early 1963 the Commission had set aside 324 channels for noncommercial and educational use. Still another basic consideration is unquestionably the fact that a large segment of the public finds many educational subjects intrinsically interesting when they are skillfully presented. It is noteworthy that the most successful of educational telecasts producers are meticulous in their planning for popular appeal. For example, the science review of one large university is carefully planned in terms of what its producers describe as "time, thought, tempo, theater, title, and talent." This indicates that merely an interesting subject alone is not enough.

Certainly the American public is very much interested in educational television as indicated by the fact that more than 75 educational television stations are in operation. In addition there are more than 90 million Americans within range of educational television programing, and this number will undoubtedly increase steadily in the immediate years to come. Money for financing educational television has been derived from several sources including state legislation appropriations, school budgets, foundations, and private business.

Table 19. Health science television units of study in Columbus, Ohio, eighth grade classes during 1958-1959*

Unit No.	Name of unit of study	Length of unit (days)
	Introduction to course	1
I	Appraising my health	7
II	Seeing and hearing	19
III	Keeping healthy and efficient (nutrition, recreation, rest, and sleep)	20
IV	Making a good impression (skin, hands and fingernails, hair, teeth, voice, posture, and clothes)	17
V	Living with others (making friends, boy-girl relationships, family living, relations with older people, and group relations)	15
VI	Growing up physically (understanding normal human growth and reproduction)	13
VII	Growing up mentally and emotionally (behavior as indication of emotional growth; physiology of emotions)	6
VIII	Diseases and my health (causes of diseases, transmission and recovery, control and prevention)	15
IX	Safe and effective living (safety at school, at home, and in community; emergency care and first aid; care of sick; facing disasters)	19
X	Coping with habit-forming substances (tobacco, alcohol, and narcotics)	9
XI	Columbus, a healthy city (provisions for community health; role of state and federal government in community health)	8
XII	Careers in health science	1
		150

*From Cauffman, J. G.: Problems encountered in teaching health science by television, Journal of School Health **30**: Dec., 1960.

A recent experiment conducted in the Columbus, Ohio, public schools gives some indication of the values of educational television.* During the 1958-1959 school year 150 twenty-minute health science lessons were broadcast by WOSU-TV and were received by 900 eighth grade pupils in twelve junior high schools throughout the city. Each health science class consisted of a twenty-minute television program conducted by a studio teacher plus an additional twenty minutes for discussion led by a classroom instructor. Both phases of the course were closely integrated. A summary of the 150 health lessons is given in Table 19.

Evaluation of each lesson as well as of the total course was continual and included students, teachers, principals, parents, and other professional and lay members of the community. The participating students were asked to record their impressions through the medium of an essay. Analysis of these revealed the following facts.

". . . seemed to associate pleasure with television and indicated that they paid more attention to the lesson in their television class than they did to the lessons in other classes.

*Cauffman, J. G.: Experimenting with direct teaching of health education by television in the Columbus Public Schools, Journal of School Health **30**: Sept., 1960, and Cauffman, J. G.: Problems encountered in teaching health science by television, Journal of School Health **30**: Dec., 1960.

"... claimed that they were able to see things in their television class that it was not possible to see in a nontelevision class.

"... mentioned that instruction by television gave them much needed experience in taking notes.

"... felt that their studio teacher was interesting and convincing and that he possessed a sense of humor.

"... believed that both their studio teacher and their receiving teacher had a thorough knowledge of health and that both played an important part in making the experiment a success.

"... received resource persons with enthusiasm; liked seeing their classmates on television and also enjoyed making personal appearances on television.

"... for the most part, grasped the content of the television classes without difficulty; liked best the following units of instruction: *Safe and Effective Living, Appraising My Health, Diseases and My Health, Coping With Habit-Forming Drugs,* and *Seeing and Hearing.*"*

The seventeen receiving teachers also participated in the assessment by completing an evaluative checklist. In summary this group believed that the time of telecasts, size of receiving class, introduction of telecasts, development of telecasts, summary of telecasts, level of lesson planned for the pupils, number of visual materials, and effectiveness of visual materials were satisfactory. Over half of the receiving teachers thought (1) that there should be four telecasts per week, (2) that the audio was either distinct or clear, (3) that the video was clear, (4) that the pacing was satisfactory, (5) that the length of the telecast was satisfactory, (6) that the amount of time for pupil participation before the telecast should be lengthened, (7) that the amount of time for pupil participation after the telecast was adequate, (8) that the pupil assignment should be made jointly by the studio teacher and the receiving teacher, (9) that health science was more interestingly taught by television, and (10) that more subjects should be taught by television.

The Philadelphia Public School System represents another large metropolitan area which has brought educational television health education into the classroom. Working closely with commercial television stations which provide regular telecasting hours, and technical assistance, and with citizens groups, which, for example, have provided many schools with television sets, this school system has demonstrated a realistic way of utilizing television at this particular point in its development.

Criteria for television use. Apart from considerations of costs and technical matters, health educators have been concerned with how best to utilize television as a material aid or in some cases a teaching method. Following are some suggested objectives of television in health education:

1. To provide an aid to teaching
2. To supplement and broaden the health education program
3. To motivate learning and stimulate interest
4. To inspire teachers to better planning and teaching
5. To enable parents and others to better understand the school health program

---

*From Cauffman, J. G.: Problems encountered in teaching health science by television, Journal of School Health **30:** Dec., 1960.

6. To stimulate changes in student behavior in terms of basic concepts of healthful living

7. To present important aspects of school health in a more effective way

With these objectives in mind it would seem that for health education by television in the school to be effective the televised program should do the following.

1. Have an educational purpose and be educationally sound.
2. Provide continuity, be pertinent, and be a part of units of instruction.
3. Be built upon the health needs and problems of a potential audience.
4. Be a means of growth and development for the individual.
5. Allow the viewer to identify himself with the participants.
6. Extend the health experience of the viewer by stimulating him to think, to act, and to make his own decisions.
7. Present material that is authentic and unbiased and that neither arouses fear nor leads to complacency.
8. Communicate clearly and effectively.
9. Be conducive to the best visual health of the students.
10. Reach reasonable standards of technical excellence in production and photography.
11. Be a good educational investment in terms of time and money.

In conclusion, a word of caution should be voiced. Television instruction should not be permitted to usurp the role of the teacher—yet there are a few "progressive" educators who contend that this is possible. To avoid this attitude, which is becoming more widespread, and because educational television is still in its infancy, a teacher should keep the following important points in mind: (1) television provides a most promising opportunity to vitalize the teaching of health in both the school and the community, (2) television should be used according to the criteria of other teaching aids which, if wisely used, contribute to but do not attempt to replace or reduce the importance of good teaching at all grade levels, (3) as it grows, television will need continuous and deliberate evaluation on the part of individual teachers and professional groups in order to keep its great potential power harnessed to the aims of education, and (4) television will remain one of numerous audiovisual aids and should be used only when it meets educational needs better than other available media.

QUESTIONS FOR DISCUSSION

1. What are some of the usual arguments presented in favor of extensive use of films in health education?
2. What are some shortcomings to be reckoned with in relation to using films in health education?
3. What considerations should guide the teacher when he is deciding whether or not to use a particular film or other audiovisual aid?
4. What are the most commonly available film sources in your locality?
5. Under what conditions can teachers best utilize films provided by commercial groups?
6. What are some criteria of good health teaching films?
7. To what uses might film evaluation forms be put?
8. To what extent is radio used as an educational aid in the communities represented by your particular class?

9. In what ways can radio be used as a means of teaching health?
10. What provisions are made by the federal government to encourage educational television?
11. How is television being used as an educational aid at the present time? As an aid in health education?
12. What are some criteria for television programs for health education in schools?

SUGGESTED CLASS ACTIVITIES

1. Make an analysis and evaluation of all film sources available to the schools. What major sources are not being utilized, if any? Explore additional sources suggested in this chapter and elsewhere.
2. Show a film on health. Evaluate it in terms of its suitability for classroom use.
3. Suggest changes in the evaluation card suggested in this chapter to make it more applicable in assessing the learning that a film may or may not stimulate.
4. Study and discuss ways in which fuller use might be made of radio and television in health education in your community. Explore the possibiilties with commercial radio and television authorities and school administrators.
5. Work up specific plans for improving the discrimination of students in their choice of radio and television programs. Discuss the following problem: How can you teach students to look and listen more critically?

REFERENCES

1. Buehler, R. G.: How to help your teacher use the new media, Nation's Schools, **70:** July, 1962.
2. Granstrom, V. E.: Health education by telephone, Journal of School Health **29:** Jan., 1959.
3. Medaris, J. B.: Communication in the space age, Educational Screen and Audiovisual Guide **40:** July, 1961.
4. Uhl, G. M., and Janison, D. E.: The recorded telephone message as a public health education device, Journal of Public Health **50:** July, 1960.
5. Wittich, W. A., and Schuller, C. F.: Audio-Visual Materials: Their Nature and Use, ed. 3, New York, 1962, Harper & Row, Publishers, Inc.

FILMS

1. Allen, J. M. C.: Need for experiment in training colleges, Times (London) Educational Supplement, June 29, 1962.
2. Allen, R. L.: The use of sex education films in schools, Journal of School Health **24:** April, 1954.
3. Films for a unit on first aid and safety, Journal of School Health **30:** Dec., 1960.
4. Knowlton, J. D., and Hawes, E.: Attitude: helpful predictor of audiovisual usage? AV Communications Review **10:** May, 1962.
5. Leahey, F. J.: Stretching the low film budget, Michigan Education Journal **40:** Dec., 1962.
6. May, M. A., et al.: Learning from films, New Haven, 1958, Yale University Press.
7. McAshan, H. H.: Experimental study of traffic safety films, Journal of Experimental Education **31:** Sept., 1962.
8. The teacher utilizes a motion picture film, film strip, 30 frames, Norman, Okla., University of Oklahoma.
9. Clark, H. F.: Continuing problem of efficiency in education, School Executive **79:** Dec., 1959.
10. Holmes, B. F.: International cooperation in school radio and television. In Bereday, G. Z. F., and Lauwerys, J. A., editors: Yearbook of education, Tarrytown-on-Hudson, 1960, World Book Co.
11. Miller, M. V.: Radio project teaches your class, Journal of Health, Physical Education, and Recreation **23:** Nov., 1952.
12. School broadcasting: a Nigerian experiment, Times (London) Educational Supplement, Nov. 23, 1962.

13. Teaching with radio, United States Office of Education and the Radio Television Manufacturer's Association, Washington, D. C., 1953.

14. Wendt, P. R., and Butts, G. K.: Audiovisual materials: recordings and radio, Review of Education Research **32:** April, 1962.

TELEVISION

1. Barrow, L. C., and Westley, B. H.: Television Effects, Madison, 1958, University of Wisconsin.

2. Bauer, W. W.: Television in health education, Journal of Health, Physical Education, and Recreation **24:** March, 1953.

3. Bretz, R. D., and Ewing, R. H.: Educational-Instructional Television and Closed Circuit TV, Los Angeles, 1959, National Institute of Leadership.

4. How to get more from your best teacher, School Management, **6:** Dec., 1962.

5. Robinson, C. F.: New Horizons for educational television, Journal of Business Education **38:** Dec., 1962.

6. Rock, W. C.: Improving instruction through multi-purpose educational television: a system-wide program, New York State Education **50:** Nov., 1962.

7. Ruhe, D. S.: Medical demonstration will offer rare opportunities, Audiovisual Instruction **7:** Feb., 1962.

8. Rynearson, E. L., and Cochrane, J.: Teachers, television, and teen-agers, Clearing House **37:** Dec., 1962.

9. Story of Shaggy Sherlock, Safety Education **42:** Dec., 1962.

10. Syrocki, B. J., and Wallin, B. S.: Two year study of teaching human biology via television, Science Education **46:** Oct., 1962.

11. Tyler, I. K.: Sharing teaching with television, Education Digest **27:** May, 1962.

12. Westley, B. H., and Jacobson, H. K.: Teacher participation and attitudes toward instructional television, AV Communication Review **10:** Nov., 1962.

13. Young, D. A.: Preparing teachers to use television, Journal of Teacher Education **13:** June, 1962.

Chapter 17

THE HEALTH
EDUCATION CLASSROOM

One of the most urgent needs in secondary school health education is for suitable classroom facilities and conditions. The following descriptions of classroom conditions are quite typical in most schools through the country.

A three-second bell, indicating the end of sixth period, interrupted the student panel which had been debating the pros and cons of fluoridation. The eleventh grade health teacher rose quickly to caution the students to be careful of the band instruments and music stands as they left the room. When the last student had gone, the teacher returned a few chairs to their semicircular position, straightened one or two music stands, and turned off the lights. As he closed the door behind him, he smiled ruefully at the neat lettering across it—Band, Orchestra, and Chorus. He moved down the crowded hallway, nodded to an occasional smiling face, and dodged several open locker doors where students were exchanging books in preparation for the seventh and last period of the day. He strode quickly down the short flight of stairs, turned the corner, and opened a door marked Business and Stenography. The sound of spasmodic clicking greeted him, and he quickly asked his seventh period health class to replace the covers and to please leave the typewriters alone. Another three-second bell signaled the start of the last period of the day. For the teacher it marked his sixth eleventh grade health class and the fourth room in which he had been that day. A silent sigh of relief passed his lips at the thought that the ordeal was once again almost over.

In the junior high school next door the eighth grade health teacher found herself having to talk louder than usual as her last class period for the day commenced. She had been requested by the principal to move her class into the cafeteria, and the vastness of the room and the happy but noisy kitchen crew in the background made communication difficult. The principal had told her that a visiting specialist in Spanish was in the school that period to demonstrate new language teaching methods. A dozen of the advanced Spanish students were needed to assist, and a quiet room was a prerequisite. Since there were no other rooms available in the building, he hoped that she would not mind if hers was preempted this one time. She smiled pleasantly and said of course not, but remembered that a similar request had been made the previous week for another equally valid reason and knew that others would be made in the future as well.

The two situations just described point up a problem that is twofold: (1) many administrators believe health education can be taught in any setting because special facilities are not needed, and (2) they believe that if a classroom is needed for some special but temporary reason and none is immediately available, the health education teacher will not mind moving into the cafeteria, auditorium, or gymnasium "just this once." Previous discussions in this book indicate that health education is increasing in importance, and when it is taught properly with competence and enthusiasm, it warrants a place in the high school curriculum. It is the main purpose of this chapter to show that health education methods and materials can best be developed within a setting that is properly planned, equipped, stable, and respected. Such a setting would be the *health education classroom*.

In surveying the literature, one is struck by the scarcity of material dealing with classroom planning. We spend endless time and write volumes of words concerning teaching methods, improvement of academic standards and professional qualifications, school building architecture, and materials to aid the teaching process. Yet in this last respect, the material aid which is perhaps the most important of all, the classroom itself, is the most disregarded.

WHY HEALTH EDUCATION CLASSROOMS HAVE NOT BEEN PLANNED

Recently there has been a beginning tendency for educators to give some thought to health classroom planning. This trend is shown by a series of published articles dealing with classroom planning.*

There are at least five reasons why health education classrooms have not been planned according to the functions to be performed.

First, school planning in regard to function is a new concept. This is especially true in the area of health science. Not until the early 1930's did the majority of students finish high school. The greater emphasis prior to the era of the New Deal was to provide everyone with an eighth grade education, and consequently elementary school construction received strong emphasis while existing high school structures gradually deteriorated. The depression years of the 1930's and the resulting slump in the birth rate did not signal the need for a change in this negative philosophy of new construction. World War II, however, and the rapid rise in birth rates throughout the 1940's forced communities across the country to reassess their building plans. Thus, throughout the 1950's and now into the 1960's secondary school construction has been on the upswing. Although many of these buildings have been poorly planned, there is serious

---

*Ovard, G. F.: On planning academic classrooms, The American School Board Journal 144: Jan., 1962.

Fig. 21. Junior high school health education class. This is a traditional rectangular classroom—in this instance devoted to full-time health instruction. Note the permanent screen, teacher's demonstration table, and attractive bulletin board. This room also contains a sink with hot and cold water and adequate storage space. It is too small, however, for the number of students being taught, and there is no room for laboratory work, either individually or in groups.

effort in new building construction to meet the demands of exploding educational theory and method. In Chapter 13 a brief insight into what these demands will be for health education in the future was provided.

Second, the typical academic classroom that health education must share with other subjects in the curriculum has a long tradition. The rectangular room which places the teacher between a blackboard and several neat rows of student desks was functional when the lecture-question-answer or recitation method was practically the only teaching approach which most teachers employed. Books were scarce and therefore the teacher had to read directly to the students. Today, by contrast, the health teacher can draw on thousands of free and inexpensive pamphlets to supplement the up-to-date health textbooks available, and the number of films listed in Appendix C is an indication of the visual resources available in this field as well. Although rectangular rooms continue to be built, there is no real reason why they should be unless educators believe them to be functional. If not, educators and architects need to establish better rapport so that needs may be implemented before, and not after, the fact of actual construction.

Third, health education has not really demonstrated that it requires special facilities. For example, although the case for experimentation in the secondary school health education classroom is presented in Chapter 11 and use of this method presumes sufficient student work space, few health education classrooms are so equipped. By contrast, home economics courses usually have a laboratory setting with equipment such as stoves, sinks, and dishes, and industrial education space is equipped with lathes, hand tools, and other necessary equipment. Picture, if you can, a successful educational program for either home economics or industrial education occurring in the traditional rectangular classroom with only one stove or one lathe for a class of thirty students. These two subject areas have developed their own tradition within the school curriculum, and, fortunately, they are not stereotyped, as is health education.

Fourth, school districts have been hard pressed to meet the needs of an expanding population. Many school bond issues have been defeated in recent years by voter reluctance to increase their property tax, the primary source of support for school construction. Consequently, the frills of special classroom planning, admittedly more expensive than the traditional classroom, have not often been realized. The health education classroom, as well as other special classrooms, is a rarity, and this most important aspect of the educational program has been the first to suffer in the name of economy.

Fifth, teachers of health education have failed to demonstrate the need for a more functional environment. Too, many of them silently accept the semi-academic reputation attributed to health instruction by some school administrators and voice no objection when situations occur similar to those mentioned previously. Although it is true that school administrators are gradually accepting health instruction, persons who teach it need to become more articulate, particularly with respect to suitable space. Health education classrooms are likely to appear in new school plans when enthusiastic teachers develop programs that meet the needs of students and when it is realized that health teaching can be more effective in an appropriate setting.

NEED FOR HEALTH EDUCATION CLASSROOMS

The following four reasons point up the need to plan health education classrooms that are more functional than they have been to date.

First, the recent emphasis on physical fitness has placed pressure upon the schools to improve this aspect of education. Health instruction is the cornerstone of this emphasis because its objective is to develop the health practices, attitudes, and knowledge necessary for a lifetime of accomplishment and enjoyment. Most states require secondary health instruction, and the trend is toward an increase in this requirement. It is clear that satisfactory clasroom environment and facilities must be provided if the educational program is to be most successful.

Second, it is a fallacy to believe that economy is achieved when the facilities known to be necessary are omitted and over-all room dimension is reduced in new construction. When a community builds a new school, it will have to live with that school for many years. Educational values should not be compromised in order to appease those who oppose progress. It is wrong to force teachers into classroom situations in which they have no alternative but to lecture. The classroom setting should permit a wide variation in methods of teaching and should allow the inclusion of all available materials. When this is possible, student achievement will be more rapid and will reach a higher level of attainment than under more traditional situations; thus, education will be less expensive per unit of time. Whereas this is the argument supported by persons who favor the more progressive methods as discussed in Chapter 13, it is also true of the traditional methods when the classroom setting is satisfactory.

Third, the expanding field of psychology has revealed many clues to the learning process in recent years. The application of some principles of learning to health education was discussed in Chapter 8. Careful rereading of this material will reveal, however, that a basic assumption has been made. This assumption is that the environment for learning will be ideal or at least satisfactory. Psychologists would expect this to be the case; otherwise, there is at least partial failure of the learning process. Our improved methods and materials have enabled us to apply these principles of learning to the growing body of knowledge we call education. The physical facilities of the classrooom represent a material aid to learning which should contribute to and not detract from the educational activities.

Fourth, the professional preparation for beginning teachers who major or minor in health education today is geared to new methods and the rapidly advancing concepts of the learning process. When the health education student learns how to correctly apply each of the methods or materials cited later in this chapter, he is likely to feel frustrated and dissatisfied if his first position is in a situation which prevents variation. He will know that his students cannot learn as they should, and his teaching potential will be materially reduced. If good teachers see no hope for a change, they soon move or become cynics.

HEALTH EDUCATION ACTIVITIES INFLUENCE FACILITY NEEDS

Industry leaders learned long ago that specialization of function required specialization of facility. Thus, the production of transistors requires an assembly procedure quite different from that for the production of an automobile; a single man with a panel of buttons controls most of the plywood production process, whereas the hand tooling of a comfortable chair, also done by one man, requires a considerably different facility and method. Although success in each of these examples may be defined in the same way, that is unit production at the lowest possible cost, each example represents a decidedly different approach in the accomplishment of this objective. Application of this concept to education in general and to health education in particular needs to be more widespread.

In few other curriculum areas is there opportunity to use as many diversified activities as in secondary school health education. Many of these activities require student planning and participation in small groups, and several activities are often necessary to achieve expected students outcomes. In addition, differences in individual health needs, interests, and abilities also necessitate the utilization of a variety of activities. Thus, as we have seen in earlier chapters, the health education teacher utilizes activities which involve the following methods and materials:

1. Bulletin board activities   3. Charts
2. Cartoons   4. Class discussion

5. Collections	22. Objects and specimens
6. Committee work	23. Panels
7. Debates	24. Pictures
8. Demonstrations	25. Posters
9. Essays	26. Problem-solving
10. Exhibits	27. Programed instruction
11. Experiments	28. Radio
12. Field trips	29. Recordings
13. Flexible scheduling	30. Reports
14. Graphs	31. Slogans
15. Guest speakers	32. Sound film strips
16. Interviews	33. Surveys
17. Lectures	34. Teaching machines
18. Maps	35. Team teaching
19. Models	36. Television
20. Newspaper clippings	37. Tests
21. Notebooks	

While some of these will always be used more regularly than others, each has its place in a well-developed health education curriculum and makes necessary a health education classroom with certain features that are unique to it.

DESIRABLE AREAS WITHIN THE HEALTH EDUCATION CLASSROOM

The health education unit in the secondary school includes many different types of areas and equipment.

Individual student stations. This area is the backbone of the health classroom and when properly furnished permits a wide range of activities. Although many types of student desks are available, the most satisfactory should accomodate two students, should be approximately 2 feet × 4 feet, and should have a smooth, flat, water-resistant surface such as formica. The tables should not be fastened to the floor, so that two or more can be pushed together for laboratory work, committee study, development of displays, and other small group learning activities.

Direct teaching area. This area includes those aspects of the total classroom which contributes to direct health instruction by the teacher as differentiated from small group and individual work. The following facilities will contribute to the efficiency of this area.

1. *Permanent screen.* A permanent screen, always in place, will encourage extensive use of the large array of visual aids now available to the health teacher.

2. *Teacher's storage area.* The storage area should provide sufficient cabinet, drawer, and adjustable shelf space to accomodate the charts, maps, slides, posters, and models that the competent health teacher will collect. If at all possible, the health classroom should be equipped with a 16 mm. projector, slide projector, and overhead projector, in that order of importance.

3. *Chalkboard.* The chalkboard should be of sufficient size to permit considerable teacher and student use. If a small committee room is available, it also

should have a chalkboard. It is recommended that the junior high school health classroom have at least 24 linear feet of chalkboard space, and the senior high school health classroom should have 16 to 20 linear feet.

4. *Models and charts.* There is a continual need for various models and charts in health education. Although they are expensive initially, they are very durable and with proper care can be used for many years. New charts and models need to be purchased on a regular basis so that obsolete and deteriorating items may be replaced. Examination of the two teaching units in this text indicates the extent to which models and charts can be used as teaching aids when available.

Health counseling room. In the modern secondary school the health teacher should be able to schedule one class period a day for health counseling. Consequently, there should be adequate counseling facilities apart from both the school administration offices and the nurse's suite. Since the students will be familiar with the location of the health classroom, it is recommended that the health counseling room adjoin it. Thus, the health teacher will be able to counsel students at times other than the assigned counseling period such as class time when small committees may be working independently.

Small committee room. It is recognized today that students profit greatly when they can work in small peer group committees under the guidance of a superior teacher. An area, a small committee room, adjoining the larger health classroom permits more extensive use of this method. In a school in which flexible scheduling and team teaching are being developed a small committee room is invaluable.

Experiment and demonstration center. Waist-high laboratory tables to accommodate at least four to six students should be provided. It is recommended that four of these be included in the health education classroom. Each should have a sink with hot and cold water and sufficient drawer space for the storage of test tubes, slides, and other materials to be used by the students. One of these tables can be used by the teacher when he is teaching by the experimental and demonstration methods.

Counter and bulletin board display area. Total bulletin board space should exceed chalkboard space, and it should be provided in conjunction with counter space for student displays as well as for displays of commercial and voluntary health agency materials. The policies and procedures regarding this area were discussed in Chapter 15.

Reference area. There should be sufficient linear shelf space to accommodate the health textbooks, reference books, pamphlets, booklets, films, film strips, records, and other permanent classroom materials. This center should be at least 6 to 10 feet long and 10 inches deep and should contain adjustable shelves to a height of 7 feet. Racks for storing periodicals and journals should be contained within this area.

PLANNED HEALTH EDUCATION CLASSROOM

When new secondary school buildings are constructed, teachers, administrators, and architects should give careful consideration to planning for health education facilities.

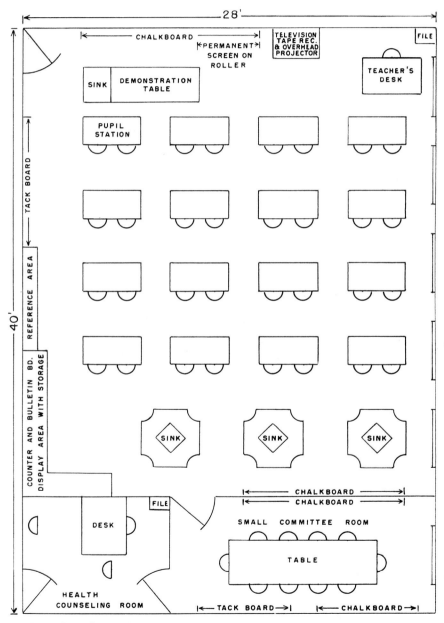

Fig. 22. Floor plan of secondary health education classroom for thirty-two students.

A suggested floor plan for health education facilities is shown in Fig. 22. This floor plan is based on an over-all dimension of 28 × 40 feet and is a rough floor plan for a health education classroom that would incorporate all of the recommendations previously discussed. This is not presented as the only suitable plan, but as one of several that would be far more functional than the traditional classroom which makes little or no allowance for individual, small group, and multiple-group activities.

QUESTIONS FOR DISCUSSION

1. Why have school personnel failed to plan health education classrooms in the past?
2. What is the need to plan health education classrooms in the present?
3. What other areas might be included in the health education classroom in addition to those suggested?
4. Did you receive your high school health instruction in a traditional classroom or in one that was planned specifically for health? What were its advantages and disadvantages?

SUGGESTED CLASS ACTIVITIES

1. Talk with a secondary school administrator concerning his philosophy of planned classroom facilities with special reference to health education.
2. Visit a local secondary school and examine the health education classroom. Suggest changes that would improve its value as a learning center for health.
3. Form several small committees and plan alternative health education facilities incorporating the additional suggestions developed in question 3 above.
4. Discuss the implications of the opening examples given in this chapter. How prevalent do you believe such situations to be?

REFERENCES

1. Kilander, H. F.: School health education: a study of content, methods and materials, New York, 1962, The Macmillan Co.
2. Nimnicht, Glen, and Ovard, G. F.: New approaches to teaching require planned academic facilities, American School Board Journal 145: Sept., 1962.
3. Olsen, L. C.: Planning high school physical science facilities American School Board Journal 144: March, 1962.
4. Participants in National Facilities Conference: Planning facilities for health, physical education, and recreation, Chicago, 1956, The Athletic Institute, Inc.
5. Shapiro, J. W.: How can I decide if a building plan is good? American School Board Journal 144: May, 1962.

Chapter 18

SOURCES OF HEALTH EDUCATION MATERIALS AND INFORMATION

There are perhaps more teaching materials in health and safety education available to teachers from all types of organizations throughout the country than in any other area of the school program. There are literally thousands of international, national, state, and local governmental, educational, voluntary, philanthropic, and commercial organizations that develop, distribute, or make available materials for use in teaching health for all age and grade levels from kindergarten through college. Also, many produce materials for adult health education. Much of the printed material, apart from prepared textbooks, is free or relatively inexpensive. Films (Appendix C) are available at nominal rental fees or else are free for single or multiple showings.

Although health materials of all kinds are readily available, many teachers do not use them as much as they should. The reasons for incomplete use of resources are two: first, many teachers do not plan sufficiently far in advance to order the material that would contribute most to the learning situation, and, second, teachers are frequently unaware of where and how to secure materials. The information in this chapter, as well as in Appendix C, should help the teacher in selecting and procuring health teaching materials.

CRITERIA FOR EVALUATING HEALTH MATERIALS

As with anything, quantity of health materials does not guarantee quality. There is much, both printed matter and visual aids, that should not be used in education for a number of reasons. Much of it is too commercial, factually incorrect, and too immature or advanced for the intended audience. For his own protection and in the educational interests of his students, the health teacher should review all materials before using them as aids in the learning process.

In a review of health and safety material aids, the following criteria should be kept in mind.

1. The material should be scientifically accurate and in accord with the most recent findings pertaining to the health of students.
2. The content should be interesting and challenging and should arouse a desire for further information.
3. The approach should be positive, realistic, and free from emotional bias, and the emphasis should be on desirable health practices.
4. The material should be presented in a clear, specific, and definite manner.
5. Attention should be given to social and emotional health as well as to physical health.
6. The message presented should strive to help the student assume responsibility for his own health in relation to his devolpmental and cultural levels.
7. The content should stimulate the student to apply the knowledge gained to his own health practices.
8. The material should be appropriate for those students for whom it is written.
9. The material should be reappraised and revised at regular intervals; it should be up-to-date.
10. The educational message should be free from undesirable advertising.

TEXTBOOKS

In preparing to teach a health education class, it is logical to give serious consideration to the textbook to be used. When a teacher first arrives in a school system, he will usually have no choice in the health textbook or series selection. Books are likely to be on hand, and he will have to plan his units and daily lessons on the basis of those available.

Regardless of whether the choice of textbook falls to the teacher, he should consider the textbook as a valuable aid to the learning process. If it is a good textbook, there are at least five major advantages for the students who use it.

1. It gives an accurate presentation of essential facts.
2. It presents an orderly and comprehensible arrangement of the material.
3. It furnishes a common core of content for the class.
4. It contains such teaching and learning helps as references, questions, summaries, reviews, exercises, pictures, maps, and diagrams.
5. It saves time.*

There are several textbooks currently available for student use at the junior and senior high school levels. Some of these are part of a series that usually consists of a textbook for each grade from 1 to 8; others stand by themselves as junior or senior high school texts. This difference is indicated in the listing that follows. Only recently copyrighted books are included.

---

*Adapted from Turner, C. E., Sellery, C. M., and Smith, S. L.: School health and health education, St. Louis, 1961, The C. V. Mosby Co.

Junior high school textbooks

Barnard, J. D., Stendler, Celia, and Spock, Benjamin: A search for evidence, New York, 1959, The Macmillan Co. (grade 7 of grades 1 through 8 series)

Barnard, J. D., Stendler, Celia, and Spock, Benjamin: A way to solve problems, New York, 1959, The Macmillan Co. (grade 8 of grades 1 through 8 series)

Bauer, W. W., et al.: Growing and changing, Chicago, 1962, Scott, Foresman & Co. (grade 7 of grades 1 through 8 series)

Bauer, W. W., et al.: Advancing in health, Chicago, 1962, Scott, Foresman & Co. (grade 8 of grades 1 through 8 series)

Bolton, W. W., Foster, J. C., and Nicoll, H. S.: Your health today and tomorrow, Summit, N. J., 1958, Laidlaw Brothers (may be used in grades 9 through 12)

Brownell, C. L., Evans, Ruth, and Hobson, L. B.: About your health, New York, 1959, American Book Co. (grade 7 of grades 1 through 8 series)

Brownell, C. L., Evans, Ruth, and Hobson, L. B.: Building better health, New York, 1959, American Book Co. (grade 8 of grades 1 through 8 series)

Burkard, W. E., Maroney, F. W., and Irwin, L. W.: You and your health, Chicago, 1958, Lyons & Carnahan, Educational Publishers (grade 7 of grades 1 through 8 series)

Burkard, W. E., Maroney, F. W., and Irwin, L. W.: Good health for all, Chicago, 1958, Lyons & Carnahan, Educational Publishers (grade 8 of grades 1 through 8 series)

Byrd, O. E., Jones, Edwina, Landis, P. E., and Morgan, Edna: Improving your health, Summit, N. J., 1960, Laidlaw Brothers (grade 7 of grades 1 through 8 series)

Byrd, O. E., Jones, Edwina, Landis, P. E., and Morgan, Edna: Today's health, Summit, N. J., 1960, Laidlaw Brothers (grade 8 of grades 1 through 8 series)

Cornwell, Oliver, and Irwin, Leslie W.: My health book: grade 7, Chicago, 1963, Lyons & Carnahan, Educational Publishers (grade 7 of grades 3 through 8, workbook series)

Cornwell, Oliver, and Irwin, Leslie W.: My health book: grade 8, Chicago, 1963, Lyons & Carnahan, Educational Publishers (grade 8 of grades 3 through 8, workbook series)

Hallock, G. T., Allen, R. L., and Thomas, Eleanor: Exploring the ways of health, Boston, 1958, Ginn & Co. (grade 7 of grades 1 through 8 series)

Hallock, G. T., Allen, R. L., and Thomas, Eleanor: On our own, Boston, 1959, Ginn & Co. (grade 8 of grades 1 through 8 series)

Jones, E. G.: Living in Safety and health, New York, 1961, J. B. Lippincott Co.

O'Keefe, Pattric, et al.: Junior health horizons, Philadelphia, 1960, The John C. Winston Company, (grade 7 of grades 1 through eight series)

O'Keefe, Pattric, et al.: New wider horizons, Philadelphia, 1960, Holt, Rinehart & Winston, Inc. (grade 8 of grades 1 through 8 series)

Phair, Speirs: Good health today, New York, 1958, Ginn & Co.

Thackston, John, and Newson, William: Protecting our health, Indianapolis, Ind., 1955, The Economy Co., Educational Publishers (grade 7 of grades 1 through 8 series)

Thackston, John, and Newson, William: Keeping our health, Indianapolis, Ind., 1955, The Economy Co., Educational Publishers (grade 8 of grades 1 through 8 series)

Wilcox, Charlotte, Brouilette, Jeanne, Bolton, William, and McCall, Edith: Healthy days, Chicago, 1960, Benefic Press (grade 7 of grades 7 through 8 series)

Wilcox, Charlotte, Brouilette, Jeanne, Bolton, William, and McCall, Edith: Stay healthy, Chicago, 1961, Benefic Press (grade 8 of grades 1 through 8 series)

Williams, Dorothy: Building health, Chicago, 1959, J. B. Lippincott Co. (grades 7 through 9)

Wilson, Charles, and Wilson, Elizabeth: Men, science and health, Indianapolis, Ind., 1961, The Bobbs-Merrill Co., Inc. (grade 7 of grades 1 through 8 series)

Wilson, Charles, and Wilson, Elizabeth: Health, fitness and safety, Indianapolis, Ind., 1961, The Bobbs-Merrill Co., Inc. (grade 8 of grades 1 through 8 series)

Senior high school textbooks

Bolton, W. W., Foster, J. C., and Nicoll, J. S.: Your health today and tomorrow, Summit, N. J., 1958, Laidlaw Brothers.

Diehl, H. S., Laton, A. D., and Vaughn, F. C.: Health and safety for you, New York, 1961, McGraw-Hill Book Co., Inc.

Fishbein, Morris, and Irwin, Leslie W.: First aid training, Chicago, 1961, Lyons & Carnahan, Educational Publishers.

Gallagher, J. R., Goldberger, I. H., and Hallock, G. J.: Health for life, New York, 1961, Ginn & Co.

Lawrence, G. L., Clemenson, J. L., and Burnett, R. W.: Your health and safety, New York, 1963, Harcourt, Brace, & World, Inc.

Leader, Barbara, et al.: Health and safety for high school students, Philadelphia, 1959, John C. Winston Co.

Meredith, Florence L., Irwin, Leslie W., and Staton, Wesley M.: Health and fitness, Boston, 1962, D. C. Heath & Co.

Otto, J. H., Julian, Clyod, and Tether, Edward: Modern health, New York, 1959, Henry Holt & Co.

Rathbone, J. L., Bacon, F. L., and Keene, C. H.: Health in your daily living, Boston, 1958, Houghton Mifflin Co.

Often a teacher is fortunate to participate on a committee whose function it is to recommend a new health textbook or series for a school system or perhaps even for state wide adoption. Service on such a committee demands conscientious effort since many teachers and students must live and work with the decision that is ultimately made.

Evaluation of a textbook or series is difficult at best, and every attempt should be made to make objective judgments. The following textbook evaluation form is based on the content areas suggested in this book. It provides at least some measure of the many factors which need to be considered. When several people make assessments and the scores are averaged, reasonable objectivity is achieved through the use of a scale such as the following.

An Objective Scale for Evaluating Health Textbooks*

Teacher_____   In the blanks following each question, place a number
School_____   from 5 to 0, on this basis:

5 for Excellent	2 for Fair
4 for Very good	1 for Poor
3 for Good	0 for Omitted or Unsatisfactory

Names of series or textbook to be judged _____

I. Content and Organization

1. How satisfactory is the development of information in the areas of:

*Personal
health*

Personal hygiene	_____
Nutrition	_____
Wholesome activity and rest	_____
Choice and use of health services and practices	_____

---

*Adapted from materials developed by the Health Curriculum Committee, Chenango Valley Central Schools, Binghampton, N. Y.

Community health	Prevention and control of disease	
	Health services and agencies	_____

| Mental
health | Personality and character development, Individual
    adjustments to society, and Family living | _____ |
| | Alcohol, other narcotics, and tobacco | _____ |

Safe living	Home safety	_____
	School safety	_____
	Community safety	_____

2. How effectively would this text be in developing good habits and attitudes in the areas of:

Personal health	Personal hygiene	_____
	Nutrition	_____
	Wholesome activity and rest	_____
	Choice and use of health services and practices	_____

| Community
health | Prevention and control of diseases | _____ |
| | Health services and agencies | _____ |

| Mental
health | Personality and character development, Individual
    adjustments to society, and Family living | _____ |
| | Alcohol, other narcotics, and tobacco | _____ |

Safe living	Home safety	_____
	School safety	_____
	Community safety	_____

3. How satisfactory is a balance in time and emphasis maintained among the above areas? _____
4. How satisfactory in quality and quantity is the material on body structure and function? _____
5. How satisfactory is the treatment of subjects sometimes embarrassing to students, such as elimination and pediculosis? _____
6. How clear and well developed is the lesson pattern throughout the book? _____
7. How well can this text be adopted to the needs of the following:
    (a) Educationally retarded student _____
    (b) Slow learner _____
    (c) Gifted student _____
8. How well is the material distributed to prevent overloading of one grade? _____
9. Is the treatment of alcohol, tobacco, and drugs sensible? _____
10. Does the text make provision for correlating health and physical education? _____

II. Teaching and Study Aids

1. How satisfactorily organized for use are the table of contents and the index? _____
2. How satisfactory are provisions for learning the meanings of new words, either through a glossary or explanation in the text? _____
3. How useful are the supplementary activities and study aids? _____
4. How well does the text aid the teacher in arousing interest in each new topic? _____
5. How effectively do the illustrations and diagrams serve as teaching aids rather than as just window dressing? _____
6. Do the illustrations express positive concepts? _____
7. How satisfactory are the chapter questions which are provided in the text? _____
8. How well is the purpose of each activity kept before the student? _____
9. How much will the arrangement of the text aid the teacher in organizing units of work? _____
10. What provision is made for enlisting the aid of the parents in the health program? _____

III. Appropriateness for Grade

1. To what extent is the material which is used within the range of the student's knowledge and experience?   _____
2. To what extent is the treatment of material of definite interest to the students of this grade level?   _____
3. To what extent will the illustrations interest students of this grade?   _____
4. How well will students of this grade understand the ideas and concepts introduced?   _____

IV. Physical Makeup

1. How attractive, modern, and appealing to students is the general appearance of this book?   _____
2. How readable is this book from the viewpoint of print and amount of spacing between words and lines?   _____
3. How well does the format emphasize new ideas and major teaching points?   _____
4. How satisfactory is the quality and shade of paper used in the book?   _____

Total the points you have assigned and record in the space below.
Possible score: 250
Your score: _____

LOCAL SOURCES

Before listing those sources which are more remote, it seems wise to point out that there are often many local sources which will provide an unlimited supply of materials. Use of local sources, when available, provide a great savings in time and often result in a personal contact for the teacher that will return many future dividends.

Telephone directory. *Use Your Yellow Pages* is certainly a good slogan for the health educator. Many of the national organizations listed later in this chapter maintain local offices in the larger cities and counties. A phone call often gets helpful results from local branches of commercial businesses, county and city health offices, and county or city chapters of the many voluntary health organizations.

Public library. The health teacher should have a thorough knowledge of the resources available at his local public library. Included in these would be complete and up-to-date film catalogues, items from which the library will circulate just as it does books. Also, the library should always be used as a technical resource to help the teacher remain abreast of the rapidly accumulating health knowledge. The various indices and abstract journals will prove helpful in this regard.

Organizations and associations. The larger, more well-established health organizations and associations maintain chapters and executive secretaries on the local level. The main responsibility of these individuals, apart from fundraising, is to provide an educational liaison with the public. Consequently, they usually welcome inquires and are cooperative in providing printed matter, films, and other visual material, as well as speakers when requested.

STATE AND NATIONAL SOURCES

Many different state and national organizations provide a variety of teaching aids.

University film libraries. Most state and many private colleges and universities maintain extensive film libraries. They usually provide free catalogues on request, and the film rental costs are ordinarily minimal. Requests from out of state are honored, but should be made three weeks or more in advance of the desired date. Selected centers include the following.

1. Florida State University, Audio-Visual Center, Tallahassee, Fla.
2. Indiana University, Audio-Visual Center, Bloomington, Ind.
3. Michigan State University, Audio-Visual Center, East Lansing, Mich.
4. Pennsylvania State University, Audio-Visual Aids Library, University Park, Pa.
5. University of California Extension, Department of Visual Education, Berkeley, Calif.
6. University of Colorado, Bureau of Audio-Visual Instruction, Boulder, Colo.
7. University of Michigan, Audio-Visual Education Center, Ann Arbor, Mich.
8. University of Missouri, Adult Education and Extension Service, Visual Education Department, Columbia, Mo.
9. University of Wisconsin, Extension Division, Bureau of Audio-Visual Instruction, Madison, Wis.

Regional and national film distributors. There are several regional and national film distributors that handle a large supply of health films. They usually do not produce films but provide the handling and mailing services necessary for reaching as large an audience as possible. Representative among these are the following.

1. Association Films, 347 Madison Avenue, New York 17, N. Y.
2. Ideal Pictures, Inc., 58 East South Water Street, Chicago 1, Ill.
3. Modern Talking Picture Service, 3 East 54th Street, New York 22, N. Y.
4. Sterling Movies, U.S.A., 205 East 43rd Street, New York 17, N. Y.
5. United World Films, Inc., 1445 Park Avenue, New York 29, N. Y.

Business and commercial organizations. Many concerns that sell products for profit have discovered it is good business to develop departments oriented toward health education. This is especially true with those companies whose products have a health appeal.

In the greater number of commercial firms distributing health materials there is a concerted effort to be conservative with their advertising. Consequently, published health materials usually contain only a credit line to the commercial company. Also, several companies will join resources to support an organization that is in the common interest of all. Such an example is the National Safety Council which is partially supported by the major automobile manufacturers and insurance companies and has as one of its objectives the improvement of driver safety.

Some firms produce materials that are poorly written and contain excessive advertising. When any commercial health materials are used, the teacher should first evaluate them against the criteria listed earlier in this chapter.

The following firms produce and distribute health education materials including films. In most cases the name of the firm will indicate the type of material produced. If not, the single word or phrase in parenthesis will indicate its nature. When making a request, the health teacher should specify the grade level for which he wishes the material. Inclusion in this list does not imply uncommitted endorsement for all materials produced.

1. Abbott Laboratories, 14th and Sheridan Road, North Chicago, Ill. (nutrition and drugs)
2. Aetna Life Affiliated Companies, Information and Education Department, 151 Farmington Avenue, Hartford 15, Conn. (health and safety)
3. American Automobile Association, Pennsylvania Avenue at 17th, N. W., Washington 6, D. C.
4. American Can Company, Home Economics Section, 100 Park Avenue, New York 17, N. Y.
5. American Dry Milk Institute, Inc., 221 N. LaSalle Street, Chicago 1, Ill.
6. American Fire Insurance Companies, Engineering Department, 80 Maiden Lane, New York 7, N. Y.
7. American Institute of Baking, Consumer Service Department, 400 East Ontario Street, Chicago 11, Ill.
8. American Meat Institute, 59 E. VanBuren Street, Chicago 5, Ill.
9. American Seating Company, 9th and Broadway, Grand Rapids 2, Mich. (posture)
10. Association for Family Living, 32 W. Randolph, Chicago 1, Ill.
11. Association of American Railroads, School and College Service, Transportation Building, Washington 6, D. C.
12. Association of Casualty and Surety Companies, Accident Prevention Department, 60 John Street, New York 38, N. Y.
13. Athletic Institute, 209 S. State Street, Chicago, Ill.
14. Better Vision Institute, Inc., 630 Fifth Avenue, New York 20, N. Y.
15. Bicycle Institute of America, 122 E. 42nd Street, New York, N. Y.
16. Borden Company, Consumer Services, 350 Madison Avenue, New York 17, N. Y. (nutrition)
17. Carnation Milk Company, Home Service Department, 5045 Wilshire Blvd., Los Angeles 36, Calif.
18. Cereal Institute, Inc., Home Economics Department, 135 S. LaSalle Street, Chicago 3, Ill.
19. Church and Dwight Company, Inc., Health Education Department, 70 Pine Street, New York 5, N. Y. (dental health)
20. Ciba Pharmaceutical Products, Inc., Summit, N. J. (health science)
21. Colgate-Palmolive Company, 300 Park Avenue, New York, N. Y. (skin care and dental health)
22. Dental Digest, Inc., 1005 Liberty Avenue, Pittsburgh 22, Pa.
23. Equitable Life Assurance Society of the United States, Bureau of Public Health, 393 7th Avenue, New York 1, N. Y.
24. Evaporated Milk Association, 228 North LaSalle Street, Chicago 1, Ill. (nutrition)
25. Florida Citrus Commission, Production Department, Lakeland, Fla. (citrus fruits and nutrition)
26. Good Housekeeping Institute, 57th Street and 8th Avenue, New York 19, N. Y. (grooming and child growth)
27. Health Insurance Council, 488 Madison Avenue, New York 22, N. Y.
28. Insurance Institute for Highway Safety, 1710 H Street, N. W., Washington 6, D. C.
29. International Cellucotton Products Company, 919 N. Michigan Avenue, Chicago 11, Ill. (menstrual hygiene)
30. John Hancock Mutual Life Insurance Company, Health Education Services, 200 Berkeley Street, Boston 17, Mass.
31. Johnson and Johnson, Director of Education, New Brunswick, N. J. (safety)
32. Kellogg Company, Home Economics Service, Battle Creek, Mich.
33. Lederle Laboratories, Public Relations Department, Pearl River, N. J. (immunizations and nutrition)
34. Liberty Mutual Insurance Company, 175 Berkeley Street, Boston, Mass.
35. Mental Health Materials Center, 104 East 25th Street, New York 10, N. Y.
36. Metropolitan Life Insurance Company, School Health Bureau, 1 Madison Avenue, New York 10, N. Y.
37. National Dairy Council, 111 N. Canal Street, Chicago 11, Ill.
38. National Foot Health Council, Inc., 321 Union Street, Rockland, Mass.
39. Nutrition Foundation, 99 Park Avenue, New York 16, N. Y.
40. Personal Products Corporation, Education Department, Milltown, N. J. (cleanliness)
41. Pet Milk Company, 1401 Arcade Building, St. Louis 1, Mo.

42. Public Affairs Pamphlets, 22 East 38th Street, New York 16, N. Y. (health science)
43. Remington Arms Company, Inc., Bridgeport 2, Conn. (gun safety)
44. Science Research Associates, 57 West Grand Avenue, Chicago 10, Ill.
45. Smith, Kline and French Laboratories, 1530 Spring Garden Street, Philadelphia 1, Pa.
46. Swift and Company, Union Stock Yards, Chicago 9, Ill.
47. United Fruit Company, Educational Service Department, Pier 3, North River, New York 6, N. Y.
48. Upjohn Company, Trade and Guest Relations Department, Kalamazoo, Mich. (vitamins)

Departments of health and education. It was pointed out in Chapter 2 that there is a close relationship between departments of health and education in regard to the school health program. A primary function of both groups is to provide information, audiovisual aids, and other materials for educational purposes.

Federal government. Various branches of the federal government provide numerous and worthwhile health materials. Most valuable in this regard is the Department of Health, Education, and Welfare and its subbranches, the Office of Education, the Public Health Service, and the Children's Bureau. Each of these branches maintains consultative services in health education.

Other government organizations at the federal level that offer various health education materials are the Library of Congress, the Bureau of Human Nutrition and Home Economics of the Department of Agriculture and the World Health Organization (WHO), a branch of the United Nations.

Voluntary and professional health organizations. A voluntary health organization is a medium which permits people of varied backgrounds to band together in a common interest—usually education about, research in, and defeat of a specific disease entity. Funds are most often raised by individual donations.

A professional health organization is a medium which permits people with the same or similar professional interest to band together in educational fellowship designed to further their individual and collective interests. Funds are most often raised by solicitation of dues from members.

Both these broad categories of health organizations consider education of the public concerning their program and objectives a very important function. Hence, they spend considerable sums of money and have developed highly suitable materials to assist the health education process on all age and grade levels.

The list which follows includes voluntary, professional, and governmental (health and education) organizations. As with the commercial listings, when the organization's name does not indicate the type of material produced, a single word or phrase in parenthesis will indicate its nature. In some instances, as with the governmental organizations, the nature of the materials is so broad that the health teacher should write for a catalogue before making a specific request.

1. Alcoholics Anonymous, P. O. Box 459, New York 17, N. Y.
2. Allergy Foundation of America, 801 Second Avenue, New York 17, N. Y.
3. American Academy of Pediatrics, 1801 Hinman Avenue, Evanston, Ill.
4. American Association for Gifted Children, 15 Gramercy Park, New York 3, N. Y.
5. American Association for Maternal and Infant Health, 116 South Michigan Avenue, Chicago 3, Ill.

6. American Cancer Society, Inc., 521 W. 57th Street, New York 17, N. Y.
7. American Dental Association, 222 East Superior Street, Chicago 11, Ill.
8. American Diabetes Association, 1 East 45th Street, New York 15, N. Y.
9. American Dietetic Association, 620 North Michigan Avenue, Chicago 11, Ill.
10. American Foundation for the Blind, 15 West 16th Street, New York 11, N. Y.
11. American Genetic Association, 1507 M Street, N. W., Washington 5, D. C.
12. American Geriatric Society, 2907 Post Road, Warwick, R. I.
13. American Hearing Society, 919 18th Street, N. W., Washington 6, D. C.
14. American Heart Association, Inc., 44, East 23rd Street, New York 10, N. Y.
15. American Home Economics Association, 1600 20th Street, N. W., Washington 9, D. C.
16. American Hospital Association, 840 N. Lake Shore Drive, Chicago 11, Ill.
17. American Institute of Family Relations, 5287 Sunset Blvd., Los Angeles 27, Calif.
18. American Leprosy Foundation, One Madison Avenue, New York 10, N. Y.
19. American Medical Association, 535 North Dearborn Street, Chicago 10, Ill.
20. American National Red Cross, 17 and D Streets, Washington 13, D. C.
21. American Nurses Association, 10 Columbus Circle, New York 19, N. Y.
22. American Optometric Association, Inc., Department of Public Information, 4030 Chouteau Avenue, St. Louis 10, Mo.
23. American Physical Therapy Association, 1790 Broadway, New York 19, N. Y.
24. American Public Health Association, 1790 Broadway, New York 19, N. Y.
25. American School Health Association, 515 East Main Street, Kent, Ohio.
26. American Social Health Association, 1790 Broadway, New York 19, N. Y.
27. Arthritis and Rheumatism Foundation, 23 West 45th Street, New York 19, N. Y.
28. Association for Aid of Crippled Children, 345 East 46th Street, New York 17, N. Y.
29. Association for Childhood Education International, 1200 15th Street, N. Y., Washington 6, D. C.
30. Association for Family Living, 28 East Jackson Blvd., Chicago 4, Ill.
31. Brain Research Foundation, Inc., 600 South Michigan Avenue, Chicago 5, Ill.
32. Child Study Association of America, 132 E. 74th Street, New York 21, N. Y.
33. Cleveland Health Museum, 8911 Euclid Avenue, Cleveland 6, Ohio.
33a. Common Cold Foundation, Inc., 370 Lexington Avenue, New York 17, N. Y.
34. Health Information Foundation, The University of Chicago, Chicago 37, Ill. (health and medical economics)
35. International Union for Health Education of the Public, American Chapter, 800 Second Avenue, New York 17, N. Y.
36. Leukemia Society, Inc., 27 William Street, New York 5, N. Y.
37. Margaret Sanger Research Bureau, 17 West 16th Street, New York 11, N. Y.
38. Maternity Center Association, 48 East 92nd Street, New York 28, N. Y.
39. Muscular Dystrophy Associations of America, 1790 Broadway, New York 19, N. Y.
40. Myasthenia Gravis Foundation, Inc., 155 East 23rd Street, New York 10, N. Y.
41. Narcotics Education Bureau, 1730 Chicago Avenue, Evanston, Ill.
42. National Academy of Sciences, National Research Council, Washington 25, D. C. (food and nutrition)
43. National Association for Mental Health, Inc., 10 Columbus Circle, New York 19, N. Y.
44. National Association for Retarded Children, 99 University Place, New York 3, N. Y.
45. National Congress of Parents and Teachers, 700 N. Rush Street, Chicago 11, Ill.
46. National Council on Alcoholism, Inc., 2 East 103rd Street, New York 29, N. Y.
47. National Cystic Fibrosis Research Foundation, 1616 Walnut Street, Philadelphia 3, Pa.
48. National Education Association of the United States, 1201 16th St., N. W., Washington 6, D. C. Related subassociations include the following:
    (a) American Association for Health, Physical Education, and Recreation
    (b) American Association of School Administrators
    (c) American Council on Education
    (d) Department of Home Economics
    (e) Educational Policies Commission

(f) International Council for Exceptional Children
(g) National Association for Secondary School Principals
(h) National Commission on Safety Education
(i) National Science Teachers Association
49. National Epilepsy League, Inc., 208 North Wells Street, Chicago 6, Ill.
50. National Foundation, 800 Second Avenue, New York 17, N. Y.
51. National Health Council, 1790 Broadway, New York 19, N. Y.
52. National Hemophilia Foundation, 175 Fifth Avenue, New York 10, N. Y.
53. National Institutes of Health, United States Public Health Service, Bethesda 14, Md.
54. National Kidney Disease Foundation, 143 East 35th Street, New York 16, N. Y.
55. National League for Nursing, 10 Columbus Circle, New York 19, N. Y.
56. National Multiple Sclerosis Society, 257 Fourth Avenue, New York 10, N. Y.
57. National Recreation Association, 8 West 8th Street, New York 11, N. Y.
58. National Rehabilitation Association, 1025 Vermont Avenue, N. W., Washington 5, D. C.
59. National Safety Council, 425 N. Michigan Avenue, Chicago 11, Ill.
60. National Society for Crippled Children and Adults, Inc., 2023 West Ogden Avenue, Chicago 3, Ill.
61. National Society for Medical Research, 920 South Michigan Avenue, Chicago, Ill.
62. National Society for the Prevention of Blindness, Inc., 1790 Broadway, New York 19, N. Y.
63. National Tuberculosis Association, 1790 Broadway, New York 19, N. Y.
64. National Womens Christian Temperance Union, 1730 Chicago Avenue, New York 10, N. Y.
65. Planned Parenthood Federation of America, 501 Madison Avenue, New York, N. Y.
66. Public Health Nursing, 1790 Broadway, New York 19, N. Y.
67. Rehabilitation Center for the Disabled, 28 East 21st Street, New York 10, N. Y.
68. United Cerebral Palsy Associations, Inc., 321 West 44th Street, New York 38, N. Y.
69. United States Department of Health, Education, and Welfare, Washington 25, D. C.
(a) Children's Bureau
(b) Office of Education
(c) Public Health Service
70. World Health Organization, Office of Public Information, 1501 New Hampshire Avenue, N. W., Washington 6, D. C. (international health)
71. Yale Center of Alcohol Studies, Yale University, New Haven, Conn.

PERIODICALS

Health teaching is enhanced greatly when the secondary school teacher makes regular use of the several valuable journals which are available to him. There is contained within these much information about health content and methods and materials that will keep the teacher abreast of changes taking place in both the teaching and medical professions.

The journals of regular value will likely be those which the teacher receives by virtue of a continuing membership with a professional organization. Those beneficial from the informational viewpoint as well as from the professional viewpoint include the following.

1. American Journal of Public Health, American Public Health Association, 1790 Broadway, New York 19, N. Y.
2. Journal of Health, Physical Education, and Recreation, American Association for Health, Physical Education, and Recreation, 1201 16th Street, N. W., Washington 6, D. C.
3. Journal of the National Education Association. National Education Association, 1201 16th Street, N. W., Washington 6, D. C.
4. Journal of School Health, American School Health Association, 515 East Main Street, Kent, Ohio.

5. Safety Education, National Safety Council, 425 North Michigan Avenue, Chicago 11, Ill.
6. Science, American Association for the Advancement of Science, 1515 Massachusetts Avenue, N. W., Washington 6, D. C.
7. Today's Health, American Medical Association, 535 North Dearborn Street, Chicago 10, Ill.

In addition, the school library should subscribe to some or all of the following periodicals.

1. Adult Leadership, Adult Education Association of the United States of America, 743 North Wabash Avenue, Chicago 11, Ill.
2. Child, The, Children's Bureau, Department of Health, Education, and Welfare, Washington 25, D. C.
3. Child Development, Society for Research in Child Development, National Research Council, 1341 Euclid, Champaign, Ill.
4. Childhood Education Association for Childhood Education International, 3615 Wisconsin Avenue, N. W., Washington 16, D. C.
5. Health Bulletin for Teachers, Metropolitan Life Insurance Company, 1 Madison Avenue, New York 10, N. Y.
6. Health Education Journal, Central Council for Health Education, Tavistock House, Tavistock Square, London, W. C. 1, England.
7. International Journal of Health Education, International Union for Health Education of the Public, 3, Rue Viollier, Geneva, Switzerland.
8. Parents Magazine, The Parents Institute, Inc., 52 Vanderbilt Avenue, New York 17, N. Y.
9. P.T.A. Magazine, The, National Congress of Parents and Teachers, 700 North Rush Street, Chicago 11, Ill.
10. Public Health Reports, Public Health Service, U. S. Department of Health, Education, and Welfare, Washington 25, D. C.
11. Social Hygiene News, American Social Health Association, 1790 Broadway, New York 19, N. Y.
12. State health bulletin of any state in the United States.
13. World Health, World Health Organization, Pan American Sanitary Bureau, Regional Office of the World Health Organization, 1501 New Hampshire Avenue, N. W., Washington 6, D. C.

QUESTIONS FOR DISCUSSION

1. Why do commercial companies prepare and distribute health education materials free of charge? Are their materials actually free?
2. Define the nature of a voluntary health organization. Give examples.
3. Define the nature of a professional health organization. Give examples.
4. Why do we not have health textbooks for all senior high school grades as we do for grades 1 through 8?
5. How many of the periodicals listed at the end of this chapter are subscribed to by your college or university library?

SUGGESTED CLASS ACTIVITIES

1. Write to several sources listed in this chapter for samples of health materials. Analyze the content for accuracy and advertising. Rate the pieces you receive. Include all types of organizations in your requests.
2. Use the textbook evaluation scale to assess the available high school textbooks. How do they rate? Work by committees on this as you might if on a textbook selection committee.
3. Discuss the criteria for selecting suitable health education materials. Can you suggest others equally important?
4. Investigate the resources in your local library (not college or university library) to see how much health education material and information is available appropriate to the secondary school level. Do the same for the local high school library.

REFERENCES

1. American Association of School Administrators: Choosing free materials for use in the schools, Washington, D. C., 1955, National Education Association.
2. A-V materials handbook, ed. 2, Bloomington, 1960, Indiana University, Audio-Visual Center.
3. Boydston, D. N. (editor): New teaching aids, Journal of School Health **31:** June, 1961.
4. George Peabody College for Teachers, Division of Surveys and Field Services: Free and inexpensive learning materials, Nashville, published annually, The Division.
5. Graham, M. D.: Your librarian will collect curriculum materials, Instructor **71:** Nov., 1961.
6. LeFevre, J. R., and Boydston, D. N. (editors): Free and inexpensive health instruction materials, Carbondale, Ill., 1959, Southern Illinois University Press.
7. Oregon State Department of Education: Health materials and resources for Oregon teachers, Salem, 1961, The Department.
8. NDEA title III filmstrips, New York, 1961, Text-Film Department, McGraw-Hill Book Co., Inc.
9. Page, J. L.: Films, filmstrips, recordings, Grade teacher **79:** Nov., 1961.
10. Pepe, T. J.: Free and inexpensive educational aids, New York, 1960, Dover Publications, Inc.
11. Phillips, F. K., and Boydston, D. N.: New teaching aids, Journal of School Health **32:** Feb., 1962.
12. Reid, Surley, Carpenter, Anita, and Daugherty, A. R.: Directory of 3,660 16mm. film libraries, United States Department of Health, Education, and Welfare, Washington, D. C., bulletin 1959, no. 4, Superintendent of Documents, United States Government Printing Office.
13. Salisbury, Gordon: Catalog of Free Teaching Aids, P.O. Box 1057, Ventura, Calif. (The author.)
14. Spencer, Mary E.: Health texts . . . contemporary style, Grade Teacher **79:** April, 1960.
15. Wasserman, C. S., and Wasserman, Paul: Health Organizations of the United States and Canada: National, Regional and State, Ithaca, N. Y., 1961, Graduate School of Business and Public Administration, Cornell University.
16. Williams, C. M.: Sources of teaching materials, Columbus, 1958, Bureau of Educational Research and Service, The Ohio State University.

Part V

THE TEACHER IN
HEALTH EDUCATION

Chapter 19

STUDENT TEACHING AND IN-SERVICE EDUCATION IN HEALTH EDUCATION

A truly good teacher never ceases to learn, and each school year, whether the first or the fortieth, should be viewed as a challenging experience. The first of these teaching experiences is usually student teaching.

CHALLENGE OF STUDENT TEACHING

Student teaching is a unique experience. No other activity during undergraduate days is comparable. Among the several ways in which student teaching differs from usual college experiences is that it changes (1) from acquiring to applying knowledge, (2) from association with peers to association with persons of younger ages, (3) from somewhat passive acceptance of college classroom procedures to direct participation in teaching, and (4) from little personal involvement to supreme expression of dependability, originality, and initiative.

Most prospective teachers enter their student teaching assignment unaware of the extreme demands that teaching will place upon them. The inherent confidence of youth and the success of three years in college usually blind the undergraduate education major to the requirements of the teaching profession. Student teaching thus becomes an awakening experience for most prospective teachers which is most valuable to their education. Furthermore, it frequently helps many students make final decisions as to whether they really wish to teach.

Eventual success in health teaching can be more accurately predicted by student teaching than by any other undergraduate requirement. During student teaching even average students may display unusual capacity to communicate with members of the secondary school age group and effectively conduct the day-to-day requirements of health education. By contrast, some with excellent academic records may show only limited ability to educate others. These superior students who learn through student teaching that they cannot teach effectively may wish to change their goals.

RELATIONSHIP OF STUDENT TEACHER TO SUPERVISING TEACHER

In one sense the supervising teacher is the student teacher's first employer. It is the responsibility of the supervising teacher to gradually introduce the student teacher into the process of teaching. The success of the supervising teacher in involving the student in teaching determines to a considerable extent the outlook a student teacher develops toward the teaching profession.

Prior to the student teacher's arrival, the secondary school health teacher should take several preparatory measures. First, it is important to have the high school students understand the role of the student teacher. They must understand that they must follow his directions when he is teaching. They should realize that any discourtesy to the student teacher is a discourtesy to their own teacher. Second, the health teacher should designate certain students or committees to acquaint the student teacher with the physical plant and key personnel of the student body. Third, the supervising teacher should be absolutely clear in his understanding of what the college supervisor wishes the student teacher to derive from his teaching experience. Both the supervising teacher and the college supervisor must work for common goals in this important phase of a college student's education.

Because the student teacher usually satisfies the requirement for practice teaching in a term (10 to 12 weeks) or a semester (15 weeks), he must be provided with a variety of experiences in a short period of time. These would logically fall into teaching and nonteaching experiences in which teaching is defined as the direct application of methods and materials for the purpose of attaining a specified teaching unit outcome.

Teaching experiences. The surpervising health teacher should provide the following teaching experiences for the student teacher.

1. Supervising teacher and student teacher should examine the total health curriculum together.
2. The student teacher should understand clearly where the instruction taking place during his stay in the classroom fits into the total secondary health curriculum.
3. An area of instruction should be assigned to the student teacher. A teaching unit should be developed by the student teacher on the specific area assigned to him.
4. The teaching unit should be reviewed by the supervising teacher and student teacher together.
5. Teaching this unit covering the assigned area should be the responsibility of the student teacher, with the supervising health teacher in attendance most of the time.
6. Daily lesson plans should be formulated by the student teacher and should be discussed in advance with the supervising teacher.
7. The supervising teacher should offer advice whenever it is indicated and criticism whenever it is needed.

8. Both supervising teacher and student teacher should develop a rapport that makes the student teacher eager to do his best and willing to profit from constructive, friendly evaluation.

Nonteaching experiences. In addition to the fundamental teaching experiences, there are many other experiences of a nonteaching nature which should be provided for the student teacher. This is usually the supervising teacher's responsibility. These nonteaching experiences, many of which are quite specific in nature, fall into logical categories. These categories with three or four examples of each are as follows

1. Classroom activities apart from direct teaching
    (a) Preparing bulletin and tack boards
    (b) Preparing examinations, as well as administering and grading them
    (c) Homeroom activities such as attendance and school announcements
2. Extraclass activities
    (a) Advising school clubs, publications, plays, and musical events
    (b) Assisting in the coaching program
    (c) Participating in school assemblies and student council activities
3. Professional activities
    (a) Attending faculty meetings
    (b) Attending state education association meetings
    (c) Participating in local Parent-Teacher Association activities
    (d) Attending local school and public health institutes

RELATIONSHIP OF STUDENT TEACHER TO COLLEGE SUPERVISOR

The role of the college supervisor of student teachers is somewhat different from the secondary school supervising teacher. The college supervisor aids the student teacher in adjusting to the new and different situation of practice teaching and smooths out problems which the student teacher might otherwise find difficult. He serves as liaison between the student teacher and the secondary school supervising teacher and communicates to the latter pertinent information concerning the student teacher. Since he is familiar with many teaching situations, he is able to show the student teacher how his particular school and classroom is similar to and different from the others. This is important since the abilities of secondary school supervising teachers vary greatly in dealing with student teachers.

The college supervisor should visit the student teacher's class several times during the period of practice teaching. His visits should be of sufficient length to observe the teaching situation and to assess the student teacher's progress and counsel with him regularly.

Among the items of direct teaching with which the college supervisor should be concerned are the following.

1. Are routine duties such as attendance and announcements handled quickly and efficiently?
2. Is the review of the previous health class adequate?
3. Does the student teacher present a brief outline of the day's activities so that students will have perspective?

4. Are the parts of the student teacher's procedure such as aims, reviews, method, and content clear and readily understood?
5. Does the student teacher handle controversial health topics in a satisfactory manner?
6. Does the student teacher understand the health needs of his students and does he meet these needs?
7. Is the work summarized?
8. Is the next assignment given clearly and accurately?
9. Does the student teacher have control of the class at all times?

The college supervisor should be equally concerned with many other aspects about the student teacher and his performance. These include such things as appearance, grooming, voice, poise, and general reaction of the students in the class.

The student teacher in health should not lose sight of the fact that his college supervisor's chief interest is to assist him through a successful program of student teaching. Very likely there will be more criticism than praise, but this is usually offered in a constructive form, and if it is accepted in the right way by the student teacher, the desired objectives of practice teaching should be realized.

Learning to teach health science is a task that does not end with the termination of student teaching. The student teacher must recognize that learning continues and must be actively pursued if teaching is to be most successful. A very important responsibility of both the supervising teacher and the college supervisor is to indicate the need for continued professional growth through in-service education.

NEED FOR IN-SERVICE EDUCATION IN HEALTH EDUCATION

The growing importance of health education in the schools is such that many more qualified teachers are needed than are currently available. Furthermore, it is likely to be many years before a sufficient number of teachers are properly prepared in this area. This means that school health education will be dependent, to a certain extent, upon in-service education and training programs for whatever degree of success it is likely to attain.

Even in those teacher-education institutions in which students may specialize in health education it is doubtful that they can be expected to become little more than generalists upon completion of the prescribed education. Consequently, there is a very great need for in-service education programs for teachers who must do advanced study while teaching.

Another thing that clearly shows the need for in-service education in health education is the ever-increasing knowledge related to mental, physical, and emotional health and healthful living. The rapid progress that is constantly being made in research concerned with health places strong emphasis on the need for a continuous appraisal and evaluation and in some cases modification of health concepts. Therefore, teachers of health should be kept abreast of the latest findings concerned with all phases of health and healthful living.

The following list delineates some of the reasons why there is a need for continuous in-service education in health education.

1. The curriculums of many teacher-education institutions are or were inadequate to prepare the teachers.
2. There is usually a loss of knowledge caused by the lapse of time between learning and teaching.
3. Continual scientific developments, changing concepts, facilities, and resources necessitate constant study.
4. The teacher can be helped while in service to make adaptations of health education to meet the immediate, continuing, and shifting needs of communities and students.
5. Teachers as individuals seldom concern themselves with health conditions until faced with specific problems.
6. Teachers with limited training and experience in health education need special help.
7. In-service education helps to improve and maintain mental, physical, and emotional health of teachers, students, and the community, as well as to develop wider understanding and convictions.

SCOPE OF IN-SERVICE EDUCATION IN HEALTH EDUCATION

There is a wide scope of possibilities for in-service education in health education. In fact almost anything that a teacher does might be considered as in-service education provided that he benefits by the experience. Perhaps all in-service education could be placed in one of two categories—that is, in-service education methods whereby provision is made to help the teacher, and in-service education in which the teacher accepts the responsibility for helping himself. In the establishment of an in-service education program, teachers should be encouraged to effect self-improvement in whatever ways seem most desirable.

The following list indicates a few of the possibilities of in-service education for health that have been used with relative degrees of success in practical situations throughout the country.

1. Supervision
2. Workshops
3. School-system in-service courses
4. Advanced study
5. Professional literature
6. Professional associations

SUPERVISION IN HEALTH EDUCATION

One of the most satisfactory ways of improving the health education program is through supervision. This indicates that direct assistance should be given to teachers by persons qualified to render this special service. The specialist in health education may be referred to as a health supervisor, coordinator, consultant, or school health educator. Along with making source materials available to teachers, the health supervisor, through a variety of accepted supervisory techniques, can do much to improve the teacher-student learning situation.

The extent to which specific supervisory techniques are applied for the improvement of the teacher-student learning situation in health depends upon a number of conditions. Factors involving the qualifications of the person in charge of supervision, training and experience of teachers, plan of organization of health education, and school enrollment will govern to a large extent how, when, and where specific supervisory techniques may be successfuly employed. The following discussion of some of the regular supervision techniques suggest ways in which the teachers may benefit from supervision.

Visitation. There seems to be no adequate substitute for visitation, for it is through this technique that the supervisor gets a firsthand understanding of certain problems that may be confronting the teaching. By visiting the classroom and observing the teaching, the supervisor has a very good opportunity to render assistance that may be needed. In addition to visits by the supervisor, other members of the school health education staff may be utilized for visitation. For example, the health supervisor might arrange for visits by the school physician, nurses, or other individuals as resource persons to aid the teacher.

Meetings and conferences. Group meetings with supervisors and health specialists for the purpose of discussing desirable health learning experiences and the availability of health materials are most profitable to teachers.

Individual conferences with the supervisor may be supplemented with conferences between the teacher and other health specialists. In this regard teacher-nurse conferences offer excellent opportunities for the teacher to gain a more extensive knowledge about certain school health problems. Consequently, the teacher can plan accordingly with students in attempting to solve some of these problems.

Bulletins. Notices of new health materials may be channeled to teachers by means of bulletins. Also, information pertaining to health examinations, supplements to curriculum materials, and notices of a routine nature may be transmitted to teachers through this medium.

Demonstrations. Because of the rapidly changing concepts concerning teaching methods in health education, demonstration teaching holds great promise as a supervisory technique. The supervisor or a superior teacher can demonstrate a new health teaching technique or the use of certain types of health education materials. Furthermore, group demonstrations of screening devices such as for hearing and vision may be presented to teachers by the supervisor or health specialist.

HEALTH EDUCATION WORKSHOPS

Since the origin of the modern workshop some two decades ago, this plan for teacher growth and improvement in service has had almost universal acceptance. Some of the desirable characteristics of the workshop in health education are as follows.

1. The workshop is a democratic method of learning in which individual participation in group discussion is encouraged.
2. It provides an opportunity for the individual to work, study, and as-

sociate with professional personnel in the same or related fields and thereby promotes good relations and cooperation.
3. It provides an opportunity to deal with actual and practical school and community health problems.
4. Workshops usually provide a wide range of resources including special health consultants.

Health education workshops may be carried on in a number of ways. Teacher education institutions are making more widespread use of them as time progresses.

State departments of education and health sometimes assume the responsibility for health education workshops, and in many instances they cooperate in lending their assistance to teacher-education institutions in the promotion and conduct of workshops.

Another way in which health education workshops are carried on is through the efforts of various commercial organizations which have a specific interest in some phase of healthful living.

The current interest manifested in school health has stimulated some local communities to establish their own school system workshops in an effort to more definitely meet the needs of local teachers. There are a variety of ways in which school system workshops in health education may be effectively carried on. Some schools make a practice of holding a workshop before the school year starts, whereas others may divide the time for a session at the close of the school year. There are still other school systems that hold short workshop sessions periodically throughout the school year.

Although many different procedures may be used in carrying on local school system workshops in health education, each school is likely to have certain problems that may be manifested in a variety of ways. For this reason it is doubtful that a general recommendation can be made for all schools in the development of local workshop procedures. Such factors as available time, personnel, finances, and local needs materially influence the organization of health education workshops at the local level. The following suggested procedures are submitted as a guide for the development of workshops in health education.
1. Workshops seem to be most effective when the need originates with local teachers under the leadership of the school administrator or the county or community health officer.
2. Flexibility in program planning should prevail so that participants are not made to feel obligated to follow a rigid schedule.
3. Continuity of sessions should be preserved so far as possible.
4. Cooperation of the local board of education and board of health should be obtained with respect to use of facilities and personnel.
5. Personnel of colleges and universities and other agencies in nearby areas should be invited to participate as consultants.

The practice of organizing workshops for the in-service education of teachers has become so widespread in a relatively short time that it may be difficult to identify certain trends and to adequately appraise their full potential. However, there appear to be certain developments in some cases that could place a limitation on the workshop as an in-service education device. In some situations the term *workshop* has been used to refer to a variety of meetings that may not conform to the basic idea underlying the true spirit of the workshop program. For example, when a series of all-day lectures comprises a program, it should not be construed as a workshop. The term *workshop* might be interpreted in a combined literal and figurative sense.

Teachers and others convene to "work" and "shop"—to work with others in the solution of health problems of mutual interest and to shop for new ideas that may be adapted and applied to local situations. A workshop carried out on this basis would appear to hold much promise as a means for eventual improvement of teachers in service who have certain responsibilities in the area of health education.

SCHOOL SYSTEM IN-SERVICE COURSES

In-service education classes in health teaching are useful in helping teachers acquire knowledge in an area in which they may have had little or no previous training. Also, these courses serve the purpose of helping the teacher keep abreast of recent discoveries related to healthful living. Courses in which various kinds of screening devices are demonstrated for teachers have proved useful in assisting teachers in gaining a clearer insight into the use and application of these techniques. These classes may be taught by the person who has major charge of health education in the school system or by a superior teacher who has had training and experience in health education.

There are a number of ways in which in-service classes in health education may be carried on. Sometimes these classes occur during the school day, but generally they are likely to be held in the late afternoon after the school day is completed. In some cases they may take place in the evening or on Saturdays. The time that such classes convene will depend largely upon when the greatest number of interested teachers are available because release time of teachers is a very important problem in conducting classes of this nature.

In order to determine those teachers who are interested in certain kinds of health activities, it is advisable for the health coordinator or supervisor to survey the teaching staff. In this way, the need for such instruction originates with the teacher. When a sufficient number of teachers indicates an interest, a class can be organized on the basis of the information obtained from the survey.

In some instances in which health education in-service classes are taught, the participants are given credit for this work in the way of salary schedule increments. Although this practice appears to be concerned with extrinsic motivation, it seems justifiable in this case. It seems advisable also to give some sort of credit or compensation to those individuals who teach in-service courses, particularly if the courses take place after school hours. If it is a policy of the local school system to allow extra remuneration for extraclass activities, teachers of in-service courses should be considered for this additional compensation.

ADVANCED STUDY

Educators generally agree that education is a continuous process. While the teachers may carry on advanced study in a number of ways, this means of professional growth can perhaps be placed in the two broad categories of university education and independent study.

College and university education. Numerous colleges and universities offer summer courses in an attempt to help meet the needs of school personnel. Also, some colleges and universities offer late afternoon and evening courses as well as off-campus extension service and correspondence courses to serve individuals in adjacent and outlying areas. Teachers in service sometimes criticize such courses as being too theoretical in nature and too far removed from their practical needs. However, it should be kept in mind that the content of any course which is not applicable at least in part to a practical situation is also devoid and lacking in its theoretical approach, or the fault may lie in the implementation of the theory. Blanket criticism of these offerings is not entirely justified when it is considered that the courses must be more or less generalized to meet the many different needs of the class members. Teachers attending such classes should perhaps do so with the idea that only a portion of the course content may be applied to their local situation. The teachers must make application of principles themselves. Furthermore, a greater effort should be made on the part of those persons teaching these courses to bridge the gap between theory and practice. In this regard, the extension type of course can be of considerable value in that it can be geared to the needs of teachers in a specific school. This is particularly true in the case of health education because teachers have an opportunity to study the health problems that exist in their own school and then formulate plans for the use of methods and materials accordingly. An additional feature of the extension course is that it is economical for teachers because they have little or no traveling to do.

Extension courses in health education are sometimes arranged through the cooperation of the person who has major charge of health education in the local school system and the teacher-education institution that is to offer the course. In some cases the local board of education assumes a part of tuition expenses for teachers, although this is not a general practice. However, in some school systems teachers are elevated to a higher salary level when they have completed a specified number of credit hours at an approved institution.

Independent study. Teachers whose attitudes are characterized by high professional standards frequently like to engage in independent study. This may take the form of professional study groups or, in many cases, individual study for professional improvement. The former is practiced in some school systems in which staff members may engage in committee work, particularly for the purpose of the advancement of the health education curriculum. The value of any type of independent study is enhanced when it takes place on a voluntary basis. That is, when the teacher feels the need for self-improvement, perhaps a greater contribution will be made toward the teacher-student learning situation.

PROFESSIONAL LITERATURE

The extent to which the professional literature in health education is consulted will rest largely with individual teachers. It is frequently mentioned by some teachers that they do not have sufficient time to engage in any type of professional reading. However, in view of the fact that there are many changing concepts with regard to physical, mental, and emotional health and healthful living, such reading is considered virtually indispensable to growth in service if a teacher is to maintain a reasonably high professional standard.

A few valuable professional periodicals were suggested near the end of Chapter 18. These will serve as desirable references for teachers in terms of keeping abreast of the most valid and important health concepts. Some of these periodicals the teacher will receive through his professional memberships. Others may be found in the local school library.

In addition, most state departments of health issue a periodic bulletin on health conditions, and frequently by request teachers may be placed on the mailing list if they wish to receive current editions of such materials.

PROFESSIONAL ASSOCIATIONS

Membership in professional associations provides a desirable medium for in-service education. Professional organization membership should instill in the teacher the feeling that he is a competent part of a movement consecrated to the progress of a profession which is dedicated to the service of society.

Two examples of professional associations concerned with school health are the American School Health Association and the American Association for Health, Physical Education, and Recreation. The American School Health Association is devoted to the interests and advancement of persons engaged in school health activities and the service rendered by them. The official organ of this Association, the *Journal of School Health,* is published ten times annually and is distributed to members of the organization. The American School Health Association is Affiliated with the American Public Health Association.

The American Association for Health, Physical Education, and Recreation has a Health Education Division devoted primarily to interests in this area. This Association is divided into six district associations, and each state maintains its own association. The official publication of the national organization is the *Journal of Health, Physical Education, and Recreation.* It is published monthly, September through June, except for bimonthly issues in November and December. There are three types of membership: regular, professional, and student. Regular membership includes subscription to the *Journal* whereas professional members also receive the *Research Quarterly* of the Association. The Association is affiliated with the National Education Association.

In addition to these two national professional associations most states maintain local state teachers' associations, which generally have sections devoted to the specific interest of teachers and other school personnel engaged in school health activities.

When feasible, teachers should be encouraged to attend professional meetings and conventions, especially when such activities are held in a nearby area. Attendance at these meetings enables teachers to learn firsthand about new developments in the field of health. Naturally, it would be next to impossible for every staff member of a school to attend all professional meetings. Consequently, some plan of rotation should perhaps be devised for attending meetings. When provision is made for a limited number of teachers to attend education conferences and conventions, those teachers attending should prepare and report the proceedings to the entire staff.

QUESTIONS FOR DISCUSSION

1. Why is student teaching in health important?
2. What are the main differences between the regular classroom experiences and student teaching?
3. What are some responsibilities of the student teacher apart from actual teaching?
4. Why is it necessary to require thorough planning for student teaching?
5. Why is in-service education necessary in health education?
6. How can bulletins be used for in-service education in health?
7. What is the value of school system in-service courses in health education?
8. What are some of the problems involved in inaugurating a school system in-service course for health education?
9. How would you arrange for a plan of individual independent study to improve yourself as a teacher of health?

SUGGESTED CLASS ACTIVITIES

1. If anyone in the class has done his student teaching, have him report on the experience.
2. Have a panel discuss student teaching experiences from the point of view of the place of student teaching in the education process.
3. Role-play a student teacher-supervising teacher conference.
4. Form a panel discussion group for the purpose of discussing the need for in-service education for health teachers.
5. Write a brief report on the scope of in-service education in health.
6. Prepare an agenda for a one-day workshop in health education for a school with which you are familiar.
7. Prepare a bibliography of references for teachers charged with the responsibility of teaching health in the junior high school and the senior high school.
8. Make a list of five professional journals or magazines, in addition to those listed in this chapter, that might be useful professional reading for health teachers.

REFERENCES

1. Allanson, J. F.: School health preparation of prospective teachers in New Mexico: evaluation of an experiment in cooperation, *Journal of School Health* 29: May, 1959.
2. Association for Supervision and Curriculum Development: New Insights and the Curriculum, 1963 Yearbook, 1201 Sixteenth Street, N.W., Washington 6, D. C.
3. Cushman, W. P.: Institutions offering teaching major curricula in health education at undergraduate and graduate levels, Journal of School Health 31: March, 1961.
4. Drumheller, S. J.: Image of a teacher's college as seen by high school counselors, Journal of Educational Research 56: Jan., 1963.
5. Elliott, R. W.: Team teaching: effective in-service training, American School Board Journal 144: Feb., 1962.
6. Flanders, N. A.: Using interaction analysis in the in-service training of teachers, Journal of Experimental Education 30: June, 1962.
7. Foster, R. A.: (chairman): Report of the Sub-Committee of In-Service Education in the School Health Program, Journal of School Health 30: April, 1960.

8. Fourth Report of the Committee on Professional Preparation in Health Education, Journal of School Health **32:** June, 1962.
9. Grayson, W. H.: Student teaching: increasing responsibility, High Points **44:** June, 1962.
10. Haines, A. C.: Role perception: the student teacher, Association for Student Teaching Yearbook, 1961, Cedar Falls Iowa State Teachers' College.
11. Morton, R. K.: What do students expect of a teacher? Improving College and University Teaching **11:** Winter, 1963.
12. Rugen, M. E.: Teacher preparation in education for health, American Academy of Physical Education, no. 6, 1957-58, Washington, D. C., National Education Association.
13. Smith, S. L.: Relationship to other curriculum areas: role of a health coordinator, National Association of Secondary School Principals' Bulletin **44:** May, 1960.
14. Wiles, Kimball: The Changing Curriculum of the American High School, Englewood Cliffs, N. J., 1963, Prentice-Hall, Inc.

Chapter 20

SCHOOL HEALTH
IN THE EMERGING AGE

In beginning a discussion of this kind, the logical procedure would seem to be an attempt to define what is meant by the emerging age. Considerable space would be necessary in attempting to deal with and discuss all aspects of human endeavor that are involved in the approach of what appears to be an age of great and comparatively rapid change to an extent and scope almost unbelievable a few decades ago. Since the space in this chapter is to be given largely to a consideration of school health and some of the factors likely to influence it in the future, perhaps it is sufficient to say that the emerging age is arriving with rapid advances in scientific research, particularly pertaining to nuclear and space understanding and technology as well as to national, political, religious, educational and moral upheavals. Since all aspects of our lives are likely to be markedly influenced by changes in the emerging age, it seems logical and timely for persons interested in and responsible for school health education to give some time, thought, and consideration to future needs, possible changes and progress in the health sciences.

In consideration of health in the emerging age, naturally strong emphasis must be placed upon trends. Since the dictionary defines *trend* as "to have or take a general course or direction," it seems necessary to add some degree of prediction in order to deal more specifically with both the present and future of the school health program.

It would be rather audacious of anyone, regardless of background, experience, or foresight of a prophet, to predict with any high degree of certainty just what will happen in the future. Nevertheless, in the interest of progress it seems desirable to make predictions on the basis of our knowledge of the past, present trends, and seeming needs for the future. Even though these predictions finally prove groundless, they are likely to have been worthwhile at least to the extent that they help us to prepare for the inevitable changes that will occur.

The following discussion will deal with school health in the emerging age in two stages—first, what we can reasonably expect in the next decade or two and, second, school health on a long range basis which will carry into the next century. It should be understood, however, that events in each stage are likely to overlap at times to a considerable extent.

PRESENT TRENDS IN SCHOOL HEALTH

It seems more logical to attempt to predict what is likely to happen in school health in the very near future including the next decade or two in comparison to longer range developments due to the tendency for present trends to continue at least for some time. Nevertheless, in continuing to follow the more clearly defined present trends and guidelines, we should begin to give thought to and take some action toward a national health policy and program for future generations involving and including school health.

School plant and facilities. We can expect many changes and improvements in the school plant and facilities during the next few decades. Many school plants throughout the country are obsolete and others are rapidly becoming so. Many are both hazardous and unhealthful. Federal aid for school plant construction seems inevitable.

In the construction of new plants and facilities there is likely to be much closer cooperation between architects, school authorities, physicians, public health personnel, safety specialists, engineers, teachers, and parents in developing plans for safe and healthful school plants. The latest scientific knowledge in lighting, heating, acoustics, and ventilation will be applied. There will be improved provisions in new school plants for health service programs and for space and equipment for teaching health. Better housekeeping procedures for health and safety will be evident partly through preservice and in-service training of school custodians pointed directly toward improved health and safety for the school population. Furthermore, more adequate inspection systems are likely to be developed for health and safety in the school plant and facilities.

Health services. There is likely to be increased federal aid to certain parts of the school health service program in the very near future. This holds particularly true for immunization phases of the program. With the coming of more federal aid, there is likely to be greater cooperation among members of the school personnel, health departments, and community groups including parents. This development is likely to take the direction of more effective community and school health councils made up of the usually recommended medical, public health, and educational specialists but with the total membership consisting of approximately three fourths lay citizens and parents. The health and education specialists will probably serve strictly in an advisory capacity. They are not likely to have the authority or power to make final decisions. Along with these developments more meaningful health appraisal procedures and techniques will be developed, with greater emphasis on the physical, mental, and emotional health of the students as well as of employees. The school health services will be more closely related to all school activities, particularly to health instruction.

The trend at the present time indicates much greater emphasis on the psychological aspect of the health service program. Studies of the psychological effects of some health service programs show that because of the way these programs are conducted they may (1) create emotional problems, (2) accentuate existing emotional problems, (3) contribute to physical disorders of a psychosomatic nature, (4) create iatrogenic disorder through some of the methods of screening, observation, and examination, (5) create worries, anxieties, deep-seated fears, and complexes, (6) make students overconcerned and neurotic about their health, and (7) adversely affect the attitudes of students concerning health in general and health services in particular. Therefore, in regard to the psychological aspects of the school health program, beginning with the next decade and carrying on into the distant future, it seems safe to predict the following.

1. Teachers, guidance specialists, social workers, speech and hearing therapists, psychologists, and health personnel in general will better realize that the psychological manifestations and reactions of youth vary greatly according to age and kind of health services provided.
2. There will be better education and training of administrators, teachers, nurses, guidance specialists, social workers, speech and hearing therapists, psychologists, physicians, and other persons involved in order to deal properly with the psychological aspects of health services in all of their ramifications.
3. Psychological problems of youth of a health nature will be discovered and treated earlier than in the past, thus making it possible to assure better mental and emotional health.
4. Careful study will be given to the effects of health services on the attitudes of students.
5. The psychological aspects of health will assume greater importance in the process of appraising the health of the school population.
6. There will be more careful control of immunization programs from the viewpoint of the psychological effects on youth.
7. There will be greater concern for the psychological effects of health services on the part of official and voluntary health organizations that provide for or contribute to the school health service program.
8. Greater emphasis will be placed on the individual needs of students in contrast to the frequent mass production type of health services.
9. There will be better education of parents and community leaders concerning the need for greater emphasis on the psychological phases of health services.
10. Proper attention will be given to the discovery and care of physical disorders of a psychogenic nature.

Health education. As time progresses, there will be greater understanding of how and what motivates children and youth to learn about health and healthful living in a way to guide their actions by their knowledge. Health teaching will be more thoroughly established and accepted at all levels in the school, particularly at the high school level. To bring this about there will be better communications concerning health education among parents, teachers, administrators, and public health personnel, as well as among medical and dental health groups. There is likely to be greater cooperative efforts on the part of school, community, and voluntary health groups in teaching school health. In addition, we can expect the following occurrences:

1. More research in regard to health teaching, particularly in determining health concepts for the various grade levels
2. Determination through research of basic and essential health knowledge
3. Health teaching in the future to have greater depth and breadth
4. Greater and more effective use of school health services as elements of the health teaching program
5. Improved preparation of secondary school teachers of health
6. The development of adequate standards with more time in the curriculum for health teaching
7. Development of plans for continuous curriculum revision in health education
8. Development and improvement of team and programed teaching in health education at the secondary school level.
9. Drastic changes in methods of teaching health in the classroom (In the past we have attempted to teach largely by presenting facts which were often questionable or even misconceptions and then judge their achievement by a true-false test. In terms of the behavior-centered approach to health education, these old methods must give way to a more realistic approach to health teaching.)

LONG-RANGE TRENDS IN THE EMERGING AGE

Discussion has been centered so far largely on the more commonplace developments that we can expect in the first stages of the emerging age. Long-range prediction of changes to come that are likely to have a profound influence on the school health program seem more precarious and difficult to make; yet, on the basis of past experience and present knowledge, there is strong support for one main development upon which future changes are likely to be made. This main or central development involves the behavioral sciences in health. The changes are beginning now, and they are likely to carry on into the next century. The main features of these changes have to do with the growing place and importance of the behavioral sciences in all aspects of medicine and in public and school health.

In looking to the future for a psychological breakthrough in the approach to health, perhaps some consideration should be given to possible changes in the status of medicine, public health, and allied fields as a result of the growth of the behavioral sciences in health. In past years, the emphasis has been placed largely on physical health. Even though more attention has been given to the psychological aspects of health in recent years, the emphasis to this day remains largely on the physical.

Although we have known for a number of years that there is a close relationship between physical and emotional health, comparatively limited use has been made of this knowledge. We have been told this fact, and then we promptly forgot it in our preoccupation with doing more searching case findings on fewer and fewer cases. There is now a better understanding than ever before of the relationship of the emotions to the maintenance of good health. It is now known that the emotional stresses, strains, and tensions of the modern world make it extremely difficult to maintain good physical health. We now know that large numbers of physical disorders are psychogenic in origin, that is, they are basically caused and brought on by the emotions. Also, we have known for some time that illnesses which are physical in origin become highly complicated by the emotions to a point at which recovery may be greatly handicapped and retarded. Perhaps a question should be asked at this point as to the seriousness of this problem. Reports in the medical literature indicate that the physicians' offices of this country are crowded with thousands of people who are ill enough to seek the help of a physician but whose illnesses are emotionally conditioned and often do not involve organic disorder. This area of medicine is referred to as psychosomatic medicine, meaning the presence of somatic symptoms. It has been estimated by medical specialists who work in this area that approximately 50% of the people seeking aid from the general practicing physician have psychologically or emotionally induced illnesses. Some medical specialists have placed the incidence of psychologically and emotionally induced illnesses as high as 75% of all the illness in the entire country. There are many reasons for the steady rise in this kind of disability, and nobody understands all of them. But the tensions, frustrations, and complexities in the tempo of life seem to be the main factors. The major point to be drawn from this is that if the majority of illnessess in the country are due to the emotions, then perhaps too much of our time and effort is being placed on the strictly physical approach to health rather than giving our major time, efforts, and resources to the area in which by far the greatest amount of illness originates.

After giving serious thought to the importance of emotions in illness, it seems fairly safe to predict that beginning in the present decade and continuing into the next century more time and effort will be devoted to dealing with and preventing these major causes and contributing causes of illness. Consequently, the behavioral sciences will come to assume much greater importance in health. The balance of emphasis is already beginning to shift in favor of the psychological component. It seems relatively safe to predict that by the turn of the next century the science of medicine will be one of the principal fields of application of all the basic sciences including a highly important place for the behavioral sciences. Health specialists in both research and practice will have to collaborate closely with many nonmedical scientific experts. The social organization of health services will become very complex and will require the collaboration of medical specialists with many categories of nonmedical personnel.

LEADERSHIP IN HEALTH FOR THE EMERGING AGE

Leadership in health education is likely to prove a decisive factor in the effectiveness of health programs for the future. Since leadership toward desirable changes in the modern world can be either positive or negative, can be progressive or retarding, or can merely fight a rearguard action to maintain the status quo, it seems necessary that every health organization, group, and profession in any way associated with the health field should from time to time reconsider and re-examine its place, objectives, and purposes in the effort to serve best and contribute most to health and human welfare. Perhaps each health group or organization as well as its individual members should consider a set of criteria such as the following pertaining to freedom, sincerity, and ability in providing positive leadership for the emerging age.

1. Is the group, organization or profession free to make rapid and unrestricted changes in its approach to health?
2. Is the group bound by tradition to the point at which progressive leadership is restricted?
3. Is the leadership of the group likely to be biased for economic reasons?
4. Is the group for any reason committed to single emphasis or even overemphasis on the strictly physical approach to health?
5. Is the group so highly organized that its individual members do not have unlimited freedom in providing progressive and positive leadership for the emerging age?
6. Is the group providing proper education and training for its members to assure positive leadership?

Since space is limited, only a few of the groups who are expected to provide leadership for the emerging age will be included in the following discussion. The questions raised concerning each of the groups are not meant to be critical. They should be taken in light of the part all of us will be expected to play in the exciting changes to come in the future. They should be considered with an objective attitude quite apart from any particular bias or position any of us may hold at the moment while giving full thought to the most efficient and effective approach in providing a safer, healthier, and better world for the youth in the future.

If we are to make major changes in emphasis from the physical approach to health to the behavioral science approach, many persons in the health field will need to make major changes in their thinking and approach to the problems of health. At the outset we might ask ourselves a question as to whether we are prepared to make major changes and whether we are completely free to make major changes if we are mentally prepared for them. The situation of the practicing general physician is a good example of possible need for a major change in the approach to health. If, as medical specialists state, from one half to three fourths of the patients of the average general practitioner have physical illnesses that are either caused or highly complicated by the emotions, is it then not logical to expect the physician to place strong emphasis or even major emphasis on the behavioral science approach to health? Can the practicing general physician in the traditional setting properly deal with psychologically induced illnesses? For example, the patient with a psychosomatic illness as the result of emotional factors created by his environment may require hours of his physician's time in helping him to solve his perplexing social and emotional problems. In this case drugs and medicines may be of only immediate or temporary aid. Cure for the patient may lie largely in satisfactorily solving the conditions in his life which are creating a seemingly intolerable emotional situation. The physician may not be able to do more in the end than help his patient learn to live with his problem without experiencing physical illness. Nevertheless, hours upon hours of the physician's time may be required to reach even this compromise point. Can the average physician, with his usual number of patients, give sufficient time to persons with psychologically induced illnesses or would the physician have to reduce the number of his patients in order to give more time to those needing the behavioral science approach to medicine? If physicians reduced the number of their patients in order to better apply the behavioral science approach, would there be enough physicians to care for the entire population? Or should we be thinking in terms of training greater numbers of physicians than ever to deal with the new order of things to come in the emerging age? Also, will the behavioral science approach to health require additional kinds of training to deal properly with the psychological aspects of medical practice?

Public health in the emerging age. Public health groups in the United States exert considerable influence on the school health program. Furthermore, they seem to be willing to increase their influence and in many cases even to consent to take complete control of certain phases of the school health program. Since public health groups have made such great contributions to the health of the people in the United States, it is highly important that they keep their organizations as well as their individual members free to continue their superior services into the future. Consequently, there are certain questions such as the following that might be asked about public health groups concerning their ability to change and help make the greatest contribution to school health.

1. Are public health groups becoming so highly organized that they will have difficulty in adjusting to the new order of things to come?
2. Are public health groups becoming political organizations to raise and control large sums of money?
3. Are the large sums of federal, state, and local taxpayers' money being spent wisely and in the direction of greatest need?
4. Are they trying to control too many facets of health largely as a means of perpetuating their power to direct and control large sums of taxpayers' money?
5. Is the training they are giving in public health schools the right kind of training for the new order of things to come?
6. Are they inclined to give lip service to the importance of the behavioral science approach to health while at the same time continuing to emphasize beyond a reasonable proportion, phases of health and diseases that are largely under control while ignoring the vast numbers of disorders of a psychological nature?
7. Do the public health groups realize that they are no longer in the zealous pioneering stage which was so helpful to the improvement of the health of the population in the past?
8. Are public health administrators trained in schools of public health

properly qualified to deal best with the vast amount of psychologically induced illness?

9. Should the training of the public health administrator be basically that of the psychiatrist who is better able to develop and promote community health programs in the area of the greatest need?

10. Are school health programs sometimes retarded by the efforts of public health groups to gain untimely control of them?

These questions are for the public health people themselves to answer. Perhaps they should be weighed and answered in light of the criteria given previously pertaining to freedom, sincerity, and ability in providing positive leadership for the emerging age.

Voluntary health organizations. Voluntary health organizations have for many years contributed to the school health program. It is likely that they will assist more and more in the next quarter century. Since it is highly important that voluntary health organizations keep themselves free to make the greatest possible contributions to the health of the nation in future years, it seems important that they consider criteria such as the following from time to time.

1. Are the policies and procedures of the voluntary health organization overinfluenced by the sources from and means by which it raises its funds?

2. Is the voluntary health organization overemphasizing the comparative importance of certain physical disorders in order to raise large sums of money?

3. Is the money raised by the voluntary health organization being spent wisely and where it is most needed?

4. Does the voluntary organization often fail to cooperate with other voluntary organizations and with school and community officials?

5. Does the organization tend to perpetuate its own existence regardless of the health needs of the people?

6. Is the organization in a position to change its objectives in view of the developments and trends for the greater application of the behavioral sciences in health?

7. Could the money raised and spent by the organization be more advantageously spent in other areas for the better health welfare of the people?

Voluntary health organizations perhaps should apply the criteria of freedom, sincerity, and ability in providing positive leadership for changes to come in the future.

Health educators. There is within the health field a unique group of professional people known as school and public health educators. This group of health workers has the opportunity and the *potential* power to do more for the health of the people in the emerging age than any other single group in the health field. It should be noted that *potential* power is emphasized, for at the present time it is questionable whether health educators, in their present state and makeup, will be able to make the most important contributions they are capable of.

The health educator should be a leader in the health field dominated only by a desire to bring fresh insight, aid, and comfort to the people through knowledge, to prepare the way for new advances in research, to help the people to understand, accept, and apply the fruits of research, to root out the age old misconception that handicap people in obtaining and and maintaining optimum health, and to provide leadership in the application of the behavioral sciences to health. This last factor could be the greatest single stroke ever applied in raising the level of the health of a vast majority of the population, including the school population.

Since there is some difference in the background and education of public and school health educators, perhaps each group should apply different criteria concerning their approach to the future. The public health educators might consider such questions as the following.

1. Do public health educators have perfect freedom in their approach to health education?
2. Are they dominated by medical and public health groups?
3. Do the voluntary health organizations by which they are often employed set the pattern for and often delimit their approach to public health education?
4. Are they being properly educated to deal with the emerging health problems of the future?
5. Are they qualified on the basis of their present training to give needed assistance to schools in the application of the behavioral sciences to health?
6. Are they considered an inferior group by other areas of public health and as a result do they have a general inferiority feeling as a profession?
7. Is the present practice of educating a public health educator during a short graduate period adequate?
8. Would public health educators be more valuable and helpful to the schools if more of their basic education were in the behavioral sciences?
9. Are public health educators assuming their rightful obligation in conducting research and advancing health education?

It is predicted that within the next quarter of a century the profession of school health educators will be more fully crystallized. Consequently, it it important that they apply criteria such as the following to their profession.

1. Are school health educators properly prepared?
2. Do they have sufficient background in both the physical and biological sciences?
3. Do they have sufficient background in the behavioral sciences?
4. Are there large numbers of unqualified school health educators attempting to teach health?
5. Are there too many part-time, inadequately prepared health specialists in the schools?
6. Does the school health educator leave the students with large numbers of misconceptions about health?

7. Would we be better off without much of the health teaching that is currently being done in the schools?

School nurse. Because school nurses have a strong influence on the school health program and they are likely to have greater influence in the future, it is important that they give searching consideration to their approach to the school health program. School nurses might apply the following criteria to their group.

1. Are school nurses adequately prepared to deal best with all phases of the school health program?
2. Should school nurses have the same status and be on the same salary scale as the teachers?
3. When school nurses have adequate education and equal status with teachers in all respects, including salary, are they in a better position to contribute most to the school health program?
4. Is the practice of public health groups in attempting to supplant school nurses with public health nurses the best for the school health program?
5. Are public health nurses properly oriented or prepared to deal best with the school health program?
6. Do public health nurses have sufficient background to provide leadership in the behavioral science approach to school health education?

Other groups affecting the school health program. Some consideration should be given to other groups that are likely to have a very marked influence on the growth and development of school health in the emerging age. Some of the criteria that might be applied to these groups are as follows:

1. Are school administrators cognizant of the importance of the physical, emotional, and mental health of children?
2. Do school administrators have sufficient education and background in school health?
3. Do school guidance specialists largely ignore health as a factor in the problems of students?
4. Do school guidance specialists and counselors have sufficient understanding and background in health to deal with the problems of students?

It is extremely important that school administrators and guidance personnel be better educated concerning the school health program for the emerging age.

QUESTIONS FOR DISCUSSION

1. What is meant by the emerging age?
2. Why is the emerging age dealt with on both short-term and long-term bases?
3. What is meant by the behavioral sciences?
4. What changes are predicted for the immediate future in each of the following areas:
   (a) School plant and facilities?
   (b) School environment?
   (c) School health services?
   (d) School health education?
5. Why is it extremely important for school administrators to be better educated concerning the school health program for the future?

6. Why should guidance specialists be thoroughly educated particularly in the behavioral science approach to health?
7. Why will it be difficult for health educators to make their greatest contribution to health in their present state and makeup?
8. What do you think will be the major changes in the school health program in the next century?

SUGGESTED CLASS ACTIVITIES

1. Discuss the areas generally included in the behavioral sciences.
2. Place the areas of the behavioral sciences on a broad continuum and rate their importance in the area of health.
3. Discuss the importance of the criteria given on p. 326.
4. Apply the criteria given on p. 326 to each of the following groups and professions:
    (a) Public health
    (b) Voluntary health organizations
    (c) Public health educators
    (d) School health educators

REFERENCES

1. Aldrich, Knight: The physician's public image and his social responsibility in 1985, What's New, no. 220, North Chicago, 1960, Abbott Laboratories.
2. Allinsmith, Wesley, and Goethals, George: The role of the schools in mental health, New York, 1962, Basic Books, Inc., Publishers.
3. Beyrer, Mary: The significance of current trends in school and college health programs, doctoral dissertation, 1959, Ohio State University, Columbus.
4. Brameld, Theodore: Education for the emerging age, New York, 1961, Harper & Brothers.
5. Conant, James: The American high school today, New York, 1959, McGraw-Hill Book Co., Inc.
6. Cromwell, Gertrude: The nurse in the school health program, Philadelphia, 1963, W. B. Saunders Co.
7. Fleming, R. S.: Curriculum for today's boys and girls, Columbus, Ohio, 1963, Charles E. Merrill Books, Inc.
8. Keith, Davis: Human relations at work, New York, 1962, McGraw-Hill Book Co., Inc.
9. Menninger, William: How to help your children, New York, 1959, Sterling Publishing Co.
10. Neil, Helen: Better communications for better health, New York, 1962, Columbia University Press.
11. Parsons, Talcot: The physician in a changing society, What's New, no. 220, North Chicago, 1960, Abbott Laboratories.
12. Seidman, J. M.: Educating for mental health, New York, 1963, Thomas Crowell Publishing Co.

APPENDIXES

Appendix A

RESOURCE AND
TEACHING UNITS

Resource units in the teaching-learning situation have largely replaced the frequently disconnected series of daily lesson plans. This is a marked forward step in teaching since unit development requires good organization and long-range planning. Good resource and teaching units not only conform to the needs and interests of students but also bring order and continuity to the entire teaching program. When they are developed and used properly, the classroom becomes more of a laboratory in which constructive work is done, with the students participating in planning and evaluation instead of a place in which lessons are recited in the old formal way. Also, better student-teacher relationships and learning situations prevail.

ALCOHOL EDUCATION—A RESOURCE UNIT*

The study of beverage alcohol constitutes a very large area with a vast number of smaller areas. There are an almost unlimited number of topics that might be included in a resource unit on alcohol education.

This unit in problem form deals with fundamental facts about alcohol, the effects of alcohol on the individual, and the problems of alcohol and alcoholism. It is a lengthy unit in outline form from which a teacher can develop a condensed teaching unit for a particular class. It depends on the teacher to make final decisions as to the parts of this resource unit to be included in the final teaching unit.

General objectives

1. To present objective, scientific information concerning alcohol, its uses and effects on individuals and society, and the current misunderstandings of the causes of alcoholism.
2. To help the student understand that there is cultural conflict in this area because of different religious, racial, and social backgrounds of people in each community.

---

*Adapted from materials developed by George C. Dimas and Gordon Raney of the Alcohol Studies and Rehabilitation Section, Mental Health Division, Oregon State Board of Control, Portland, Ore.

3. To encourage young people to seek information so that they may determine their own feelings and attitudes about drinking alcoholic beverages.
4. To develop an understanding of the extent to which the use of alcohol as a beverage has produced major problems in social and economic life and in personal relations.
5. To develop in students a sense of responsibility for one's own welfare and that of others in regard to the use of alcohol.
6. To help young people understand that any satisfaction which they could obtain through the use of alcoholic beverages can be obtained by more acceptable means.

Specific objectives*

1. To acquaint the student with the history of alcohol (Problem 1; Activities 4 and 27)
2. To help students gain an understanding of the chemical nature and properties of alcohol, particularly of ethyl alcohol (Problem 2; Activity 14)
3. To help students understand the role of alcohol in industrial uses and in the field of medicine (Problems 2 and 3; Activity 16)
4. To help young people understand why people drink (Problems 4 and 5; Activities 9, 10, and 12)
5. To help the student understand what the body does with alcohol (Problem 6; Activity 13)
6. To help the student understand how alcohol affects the body (Problem 7; Activities 5, and 11)
7. To help students understand the effect of alcohol on nutrition (Problem 8; Activity 14)
8. To help students understand the relation of alcohol to specific diseases (Problem 9; Activity 19)
9. To help students understand the illness of alcoholism and the problem drinker (Problem 10; Activities 6, 15, 22, 23, and 26)

Problems

Problem 1—Introduction to the problem

A. To drink or not to drink that is the question
   1. An urgent problem to the parent of the adolescent
   2. The student must acquire a safe and sane attitude toward alcohol
B. Define the problem
C. Facts and fiction
D. Feelings about alcohol
   1. In primitive and biblical times
      (a) Part it played in life
      (b) Folk stories and myths
   2. In early America
   3. Beginning of the temperance movement
   4. Our stand today
E. What about you?
   1. The basis for one's decision
F. Finding out what you know about alcohol
   1. Interest stimulator

REFERENCES

1. *Facts about alcohol,* pp. 4-15 (McCarthy) (pamphlet)
2. *Alcohol education In Oregon Public Schools,* pp. 33-37 (State of Oregon) (manual)

---

*In the complete resource unit there are twenty-six problems. Problems 1 through 10 are included here. Complete copies of the resource unit may be obtained from the Alcohol Studies and Rehabilitation Section, Mental Health Division, Oregon State Board of Control, Portland 4, Ore.

3. *Alcohol and human affairs,* pp. 1-22 (Spalding-Montague)
4. *Effects of alcoholic drinks, tobacco, sedatives, and narcotics,* pp. 3-48 (Rice-Harger)
5. *Alcohol, culture, and society,* pp. 12-42 (Patrick)
6. *Drinking and intoxication,* pp. 251-263; 369-397 (McCarthy)

Problem 2—The nature and composition of beverage alcohol

A. Define alcohol
B. Composition of ethyl alcohol (ethanol) (C_2H_5OH)
C. Other alcohols
    1. Methyl (methanol) (CH_3OH)
    2. Propyl (propanol) (C_3H_7OH)
    3. Amyl (pentonal) (C_5H_3OH)
D. Common sources of alcohol
E. Methods of production
    1. Fermentation
    2. Brewing
    3. Distillation
F. Depressant-sedative-anesthetic
G. Uses of alcohol
    1. Industrial
    2. Medical
    3. Beverage

REFERENCES

1. *Facts about alcohol,* pp. 17-20 (McCarthy) (pamphlet)
2. *Alcohol education In Oregon Public Schools,* pp. 11-14 (State of Oregon) (manual)
3. *The alcohol problem visualized,* pp. 7-11 (national forum)
4. *Alcohol explored,* pp. 37-45 (Haggard-Jellinek)
5. *Basic information on alcohol,* pp. 21-25 (King)

Problem 3—Alcohol in the field of medicine

A. The use of alcohol as an anesthetic in early times
B. Clinical applications of alcohol
    1. Those related to its physical or chemical properties
        (a) Compounding pharmaceuticals
        (b) Solvent and preserving agent
        (c) Skin cleanser
        (d) Cooling agent
    2. Those based on its pharmacological actions
        (a) Protein-denaturing effect
        (b) Depressing of the central nervous system
        (c) Auxiliary source of energy
        (d) Vasodilating agent
        (e) Relaxing for elderly; suggested by physician

REFERENCES

1. *Manual on alcoholism,* pp. 30-45 (American Medical Association) (pamphlet)
2. *Effects of alcoholic drinks, tobacco, sedatives, and narcotics,* pp. 77-84 (Rice-Harger)
3. *Alcohol explored,* pp. 107-108 (Haggard-Jellinek)
4. *Alcoholism,* pp. 207-218 (Thompson)

Problem 4—Why people drink

A. Psychological reasons
    1. Reduction of anxiety
    2. Gain acceptance

    3. Curiosity
    4. Thrill
    5. Rebellion against authority
    6. Inferiority complex
    7. Imitation
    8. For escape
    9. Something to do
    10. Can not get along without it

B. Physical reasons
    1. Relax—reduces tension
    2. Reduce physical discomfort
    3. Feel effect
    4. Like the taste
    5. Relieves fatigue

C. Cultural influences
    1. Nationality background
    2. Celebrations
    3. Religious background
    4. Economic background
    5. Family customs
    6. Friends influence
    7. Business pressures
    8. Socially acceptable; reflected in
        (a) Advertising
        (b) Movies
        (c) Television
        (d) Publications
        (e) Social patterns

REFERENCES

1. *Facts about alcohol,* pp. 30-35 (McCarthy) (pamphlet)
2. *Alcohol education in Oregon Public Schools,* p. 21 (State of Oregon) (manual)
3. *Basic information on alcohol,* pp. 26-45 (King)
4. *The alcohol problem visualized,* pp. 11-14 (national forum)
5. *Alcohol and human affairs, pp.* 147-153 (Spalding-Montague)
6. *Alcohol and social responsibility,* pp. 104-105 (McCarthy-Douglass)
7. *Alcohol, culture, and society,* pp. 43-78 (Patrick)

Problem 5—Why people refrain from drinking

A. Psychological
    1. To gain acceptance
    2. Pressure not to drink
    3. Fear of result

B. Physical reasons
    1. Harm to body
    2. Bad taste
    3. Effect on nervous system

C. Legal reasons
    1. Age
    2. Laws

D. Economic reasons
    1. Cost
    2. Job pressure

E. Religious reasons
    1. Denominational position
    2. Personal conviction

F. Family stand
G. Moral values

REFERENCES

1. *Basic information on alcohol,* pp. 144-149 (King)
2. *Discussion guide No. 3* (entire pamphlet) (McCarthy)
3. *Alcohol education in Oregon Public Schools,* pp. 3-4; 38-39 (State of Oregon) (manual)
4. *Alcohol and human affairs,* pp. 190-191 (Spalding-Montague)
5. *Understanding and counseling the alcoholic,* pp. 229-245 (Clinebell)
6. *Drinking in college,* pp. 64-66 (Straus-Bacon)

Problem 6—What the body does with alcohol
A. How the body absorbs alcohol
    1. Trace alcohol in the body from ingestion
        (a) Path (stomach, intestines, liver, heart, and brain)
        (b) Dilution
        (c) Absorption (factors that influence)
        (d) Oxidation
        (e) Elimination
B. Significance of alcohol concentration in the blood

REFERENCES

1. *Facts about alcohol,* pp. 20-22 (McCarthy) (pamphlet)
2. *Discussion guide No. 1* (entire pamphlet) (McCarthy)
3. *What the body does with alcohol* (pamphlet No. 4) (Greenberg)
4. *Alcohol education In Oregon Public Schools,* pp. 15-16; 59 (State of Oregon) (manual)
5. *Manual on alcoholism,* pp. 30-35 (American Medical Association) (pamphlet)
6. *Alcohol and human affairs,* pp. 73-79 (Spalding-Montague)
7. *Alcohol explored, pp.* 77-108 (Haggard-Jellinek)
8. *Alcohol, science, and society,* pp. 31-44 (Yale)
9. *Basic information on alcohol,* pp. 55-61; 67-68 (King)

Problem 7—How alcohol affects the human body
A. Alcohol as a depressant
    1. Anesthetic effect
    2. Medical use
B. Effect on the brain and nervous system
C. Effect on the heart (circulatory system)
    1. Circulation
D. Effect on the stomach (digestive system)
E. Effect on the kidneys (excretory system)
F. The effect on the senses
    1. Hearing
    2. Sight
    3. Touch
    4. Smell
    5. Taste
G. Reproductive organs
H. Motor activity

REFERENCES

1. *Facts about alcohol,* pp. 23-26 (McCarthy) (pamphlet)
2. *How alcohol affects the body,* (pamphlet No. 3) (Keller)
3. *Alcohol education in Oregon Public Schools,* pp. 19-20 (State of Oregon) (manual)
4. *Basic information on alcohol,* pp. 73-82 (King)

5. *Alcohol and human affairs,* pp. 82-92 (Spalding-Montague)
6. *Alcohol, science, and society,* pp. 59-83 (Yale)

Problem 8—Alcohol and nutrition

A. Define food
B. Food requirements of the body
    1. Fuel
        (a) Carbohydrates
        (b) Fats
    2. Proteins
    3. Vitamins
        (a) Thiamin
        (b) Niacin
        (c) Riboflavin
        (d) Ascorbic acid
    4. Minerals
        (a) Calcium
        (b) Iron
        (c) Iodine
    5. Bulk
        (a) Cellulose
        (b) Fibrin
    6. Water
C. Lack of vitamins in alcoholic beverages
D. Role of alcoholic beverages in obesity
E. Effects of alcoholic beverages on appetite
F. Nutritional diseases related to excessive alcohol usage
    1. Pellegra
    2. Beriberi
    3. Chronic gastritis
    4. Other diseases

REFERENCES

1. *Facts about alcohol,* pp. 27-28 (McCarthy) (pamphlet)
2. *What the body does with alcohol* (pamphlet No. 4) (Greenberg)
3. *Manual on alcoholism,* pp. 34-35 (American Medical Association) (pamphlet)
4. *Basic information on alcohol,* pp. 69-70 (King)
5. *Alcohol, science, and society,* pp. 73-78 (Yale)
6. *Clinic Reports* (State of Oregon)
7. *Alcoholism,* p. 365 (Thompson)

Problem 9—Diseases and illnesses related to excessive use of alcohol

A. Excessive user often suffers from following
    1. Disturbed nutrition
    2. Poor physical makeup
B. Diseases which appear sometimes in inebriates
    1. Beriberi
    2. Pellagra
    3. Cirrhosis of the liver
    4. Arteriosclerosis
    5. Venereal diseases
    6. Other diseases
C. Psychoses associated with alcoholism
    1. Acute reaction
        (a) Pathological intoxication

(b) Delirium tremens
(c) Acute alcoholic hallucinosis
(d) Korsakoff's psychosis
2. Chronic
(a) General personality disorder
(b) Intellectual and moral decline
(c) Memory and judgment disturbance
D. Alcoholism (refer to problem 10)

REFERENCES
1. *Facts about alcohol,* pp. 26-27 (McCarthy)
2. *Alcohol explored,* pp. 177-269 (Haggard-Jellinek)
3. *Alcohol education,* pp. 38-40 (Hirsh)
4. *Phases of alcohol addiction* (Jellinek) (pamphlet)
5. *Alcohol in moderation and excess,* pp. 130-140 (Waddell-Haag)
6. *Alcohol, culture, and society,* pp. 93-96 (Patrick)
7. *Alcoholism, pp.* 33-35; 528 (Thompson)
8. *Abnormal psychology and modern life,* pp. 398-415 (Coleman)

Problem 10—Alcoholism
A. Definitions
1. Alcoholism
2. Alcoholic
B. Basic statistics
C. Progressive picture of alcoholism in an individual
D. Compare the terms *alcoholic* and *drinker*
E. Social groups in which alcoholics are found
1. All levels
2. Skid row type is not the major group
F. Types of alcoholics
1. Primary type
(a) Neurotic throughout lifetime
(b) Prognosis difficult
2. Secondary type
(a) Appears after many years of drinking
(b) Prognosis good
3. Situational type
(a) Unusual emotional strain
(b) Best prognosis of three
G. Common characteristics of alcoholics
1. Low frustration tolerance
2. Inability to endure anxiety or tension
3. Feelings of isolation
4. Devaluated self-esteem
5. Tendency to act impulsively
6. Repetitive acting out of conflicts
7. Often extreme narcissism
8. Self-punitive behavior
9. Somatic preoccupation
10. Hypochondriasis
H. Basic difference between alcoholics and other problem people

REFERENCES
1. *Facts about alcohol,* pp 40-46 (McCarthy) (pamphlet)
2. *Discussion guide No. 3,* pp. 8-10 (McCarthy)

3. *Alcohol education in Oregon Public Schools* (State of Oregon) (manual)
4. *Primer on alcoholism*, pp. 58-72 (Mann)
5. *Thirteen steps to alcoholism* (Weeks) (pamphlet)
6. *Basic information on alcohol*, pp. 109-113 (King)
7. *Understanding and counseling the alcoholic*, pp. 15-36 (Clinebell)
8. *Neurotic interaction in marriage*, pp. 148-168 (Eisenstein)
9. *Alcoholism, its scope, cause, and treatment* (Fox-Lyon)

Selected references

1. American Medical Association: Manual on alcoholism, Chicago, 1956, The Association.
2. Chafetz, Morris E., and Demone, Harold W., Jr.: Alcoholism and Society, London, 1962, Oxford University Press.
3. Clinebell, Howard J.: Understanding and counseling the alcoholic, Nashville, 1956, Abingdon Press.
4. Coleman, James: Abnormal psychology and modern life, New York, 1956, Scott, Foresman & Co.
5. Eisenstein, Victor W.: Neurotic interaction in marriage, New York, 1956, Basic Books, Inc.
6. Fox, Ruth, and Lyon, Peter: Alcoholism—Its scope, cause and treatment, New York, 1955, Random House, Inc.
7. Greenberg, Leon A.: What the body does with alcohol, Connecticut 1955, Publications Division, Yale Center of Alcohol Studies.
8. Haggard, Howard, W., and Jellinek, E. M.: Alcohol explored, New York, 1942, Doubleday & Co., Inc.
9. Hirsh, Joseph: Alcohol education, New York, 1952, Henry Schuman, Inc., Publishers.
10. Jellinek, E. M.: The disease concept of alcoholism, Connecticut, 1960, Publications Division, Yale Center of Alcohol Studies.
11. Jellinek, E. M.: The phases of alcohol addiction, Quarterly Journal of Studies on Alcohol 13:673-684, 1952.
12. Keller, Mark: How alcohol affects the body, Connecticut, 1955, Publications Division, Yale Center of Alcohol Studies.
13. King, Albion, R.: Basic information on alcohol, Mt. Vernon, Iowa, 1957, Cornell College Press.
14. Mann, Marty: Primer on alcoholism, New York, 1950, Rinehart & Co.
15. McCarthy, Raymond G., and Douglass, Edgar M.: Alcohol and social responsibility, (published jointly with the Yale plan clinic), New York, 1949, The Thomas Y. Crowell Co.
16. McCarthy, Raymond G.: A discussion guide for questions about alcohol, I. The physiological effects of alcohol; II. Community opinions on alcohol problems; III. Individual attitudes toward alcohol, Connecticut, 1956, Publications Division, Yale Center of Alcohol Studies.
17. McCarthy, Raymond G.: Drinking and intoxication, Connecticut, 1959, Publications Division, Yale Center of Alcohol Studies.
18. McCarthy, Raymond G.: Facts about alcohol, Chicago, Ill., 1951, Science Research Associates.
19. Oregon State Department of Education, and Oregon Alcohol Education Committee: Alcohol education in Oregon public schools, Salem, Ore., 1956, State Printer.
20. Patrick, C. H.: Alcohol, culture, and society, Durham, N. C., 1952, Duke University Press.
21. Rice, Thurman, and Harger, Rolla N.: Effects of alcoholic drinks, tobacco, sedatives, and narcotics, Chicago, Ill., 1952, Wheeler Publishing Co.
22. Spalding, Willard B., and Montague, John R.: Alcohol and human affairs, New York, 1949, World Book Company.
23. Thompson, George N., editor: Alcoholism, Springfield, Ill., 1956, Charles C Thomas, Publisher.
24. Wadell, J. A., and Haag, H. B.: Alcohol in moderation and excess, Richmond, Va., 1940, William Byrd Press, Inc.
25. Weeks, Morris K., Jr.: Thirteen steps to alcoholism, New York, 1955, National Council on Alcoholism.

26. Yale University: Alcohol, science, and society, Quarterly Journal of Studies on Alcohol, 1954, vol. 13.

Suggestions for teachers

1. Interest stimulator
2. Follow-up test
3. Individual projects
4. Handouts
5. Question box
6. Single activity affairs
7. Vocabulary list
8. Field trips
9. Bulletin board
10. Guest speakers
11. Student evaluation

Suggested student activities

1. Make a recipe scrapbook of nonalcoholic drinks that could be served (Problem 5).
2. Determine and report how your state exercises control over sale and consumption of alcoholic beverages.
3. Call attention to current newspaper and magazine articles, movies, and radio and television programs.
4. Present a series of thought-provoking statements about alcohol (Problem 1).
5. Illustrate by use of a model, drawing, or diagram the effect of alcohol on the brain and central nervous system (Problem 7).
6. Prepare a chart listing the desirable traits of personality and showing what effect alcohol might have upon each one (Problem 10).
7. Make a scrapbook of new stories, pictures, and original work about alcohol.
8. Consult Emily Post's book on etiquette about how to say No graciously (Problem 5).
9. Make a chart, drawing, or cartoon showing the reasons why people drink (Problem 4).
10. Discuss why people drink; point out why these are not valid reasons for drinking (Problem 7).
11. Make a chart, drawing, or cartoon showing the effects of different amounts of alcohol on the body. (Problem 7).
12. Make a drawing or cartoon depicting the needs which people try to fill through drinking, such as a feeling of security, a feeling of importance, etc. (Problem 6).
13. Make charts, graphs, or posters to show the various aspects of the alcohol problem—examples: accidents, economic phases, and concentration of alcohol in the blood (Problem 6).
14. Make a chart or graph comparing the nutritional value of alcoholic beverages with other foods (Problem 8).
15. Invite well-informed resource people such as representatives from an alcohol education committee to discuss particular phases of the problem (Problem 10).
16. Report the results of surveys to the class by means of dramas, panels, forums, role playing, or committee reports.
17. Determine what recreational activities are available in the community for wholesome relaxation.
18. Make a map of the community, pinpointing wholesome recreational areas.
19. Read leaflets and pamphlets made available by such groups as Alcohol Education Committees, Alcoholics Anonymous, Yale School of Alcohol Studies, and the National Safety Council (Problem 9).
20. Compare the drinking habits of the people of other countries with those of the people in the United States.
21. Determine the attitudes of various religious faiths concerning the use of alcohol (Problem 5).
22. Determine what your community and state are doing about the alcohol problem (Problem 10).
23. Debate the following: Resolved: That alcoholism is a public health problem and should be so recognized by state legislatures by appropriating adequate funds for its treatment (Problem 10).
24. Write an editorial for the school or town newspaper about alcohol problems.

25. Publish a summary of the unit in the school or town newspaper.
26. Plan and present a radio or television script on one or more phases of the alcohol problem (Problem 10).
27. Compare drinking customs of primitive peoples with those of the peoples of modern times (Problem 1).
28. Compare drinking customs of various nationalities.

Interest stimulator*

The following pages contain fifty statements concerned with the use and effects of alcohol which are frequently heard. Some of the statements deal with facts, some reflect opinions, whereas others are attitude statements.

This is not a test, and there is no question of passing or failing. You are asked to consider each of the statements and to indicate your selected answer.

If your selected answer is true, place a T in the space found at the beginning of the statement, indicating you are in *agreement*.

If your selected answer is false, place an F to the left of the statement, indicating *disagreement*.

If you are undecided or uncertain about a statement, use the letter U to indicate *uncertain*.

Examples:

  T 1. There are many different drinking customs as well as attitudes toward drinking.
  F 2. All people who get drunk are alcoholics.
_____ 1. Alcoholism ranks as one of the four major public health problems.
_____ 2. Alcohol intoxication is a symptom of alcoholism.
_____ 3. Most people who drink alcoholic beverages do so moderately.
_____ 4. There are equally as many female alcoholics as male problem drinkers.
_____ 5. The blood alcohol content which will convict a drinking driver in Oregon is 15/100 of 1%.
_____ 6. For young people, the most immediate danger in drinking is intoxication.
_____ 7. The action of alcohol on the nervous system resembles that of ether or other anesthetics.
_____ 8. Alcohol is a stimulant.
_____ 9. Alcohol cures colds.
_____ 10. Having an understanding of personality and its adjustments to environment could have influence in preventing and treating alcoholism.
_____ 11. Cirrhosis of the liver does occur among nondrinkers, but it is more frequent among heavy drinkers.
_____ 12. A. A. is a national automobile organization.
_____ 13. The Eighteenth Amendment established national prohibition.
_____ 14. Alcohol effects the *latest learned* and *most complicated* skills first.
_____ 15. Frequent drunkenness and alcoholism mean the same thing.
_____ 16. Ethyl alcohol is contained in such drinks as beer, wine, and whiskey.
_____ 17. People who drink alcoholic beverages do not make good parents.
_____ 18. Excessive drinking may produce serious physical and mental diseases.
_____ 19. There are scientific devices for measuring the concentration of alcohol in the human body.
_____ 20. An understanding of emotions is important if one is to make a proper adjustment when problems arise.
_____ 21. Alcohol cures feelings of inferiority.

---

*It is not intended that this stimulator necessarily be given in its entirety. Teachers often select those statements most pertinent to their study and reproduce sufficient copies for their students. These statements are often used at the beginning of the unit and again at the end to determine increased knowledge and change of attitude.

_____ 22. Most alcoholics are found on skid row.

_____ 23. The alcohol content of alcoholic beverages produced by fermentation is greater than that of beverages produced by distillation.

_____ 24. *Passing out* and *having a blackout* are one and the same.

_____ 25. Alcoholic beverages are a form of food.

_____ 26. Per capita consumption of alcoholic beverages is higher in the United States than in any other country.

_____ 27. Chronic alcoholics are more susceptible to respiratory diseases, especially pneumonia.

_____ 28. The use of alcoholic beverages violates all religious principles.

_____ 29. Judgment, vision, and reaction time in individual performance are frequently impaired by even small amounts of alcohol.

_____ 30. Physical deterioration observed in heavy drinkers is due to nutritional deficiencies.

_____ 31. The control of the sale of alcoholic beverages is a state responsibility.

_____ 32. When a person feels defeated or frustrated, alcohol is frequently used to help relieve the pressure of the problem.

_____ 33. If you drink undiluted whiskey, it will irritate and inflame the brain.

_____ 34. In college drinking the incidence of drinking increases with each college year.

_____ 35. Beverage alcohol, in the forms in which it is usually taken, requires no digestion.

_____ 36. The presence of food in the stomach slows down the rate of alcohol absorption.

_____ 37. Of the alcohol taken into the body, 80% is oxidized by the liver.

_____ 38. A small amount of alcohol may actually temporarily remove an inhibition and allow expression of a repressed need.

_____ 39. The use of alcohol can be used as a real solution to one's problems.

_____ 40. Half of all persons who drink become alcoholics.

_____ 41. The Al-Anon family groups are composed of alcoholics.

_____ 42. Aspirin mixed with a coca drink produces the same effect of intoxication that ethyl alcohol produces.

_____ 43. Drinking interferes with family life, employment, and community welfare.

_____ 44. The average person with one half of 1% of alcohol in the blood is in critical danger.

_____ 45. One should be critical of alcohol and its effects, but we should develop a positive understanding toward the alcoholic.

_____ 46. Alcohol speeds up a driver's reaction time in the event of an emergency.

_____ 47. Nutritional diseases, such as beriberi and pellagra, are often found among alcoholics.

_____ 48. Alcoholics come from all social classes, professions, and backgrounds.

_____ 49. A person by drinking olive oil or other substance containing butter fat can coat the lining of the stomach and then drink beverage alcohol without becoming intoxicated.

_____ 50. People who have been drinking talk louder, move about more vigorously, and seem very gay because they have been stimulated by ethyl alcohol in the body.

Answers and discussion of interest stimulator

1. True   It is commonly published that alcoholism is called our public health problem number three or four. If a specific number is not denoted in the literature, then it is generally referred to as one of the most serious health problems in our society.

2. False   Anyone who consumes enough beverage alcohol can become intoxicated. Although it is true that the alcoholic does become intoxicated, the same condition can be found in persons who drink excessively or unwisely but have not developed the illness of alcoholism.

3. True   It is estimated that approximately 7% of persons who drink become alcoholics. The majority of users in the United States drink moderately.

4. False   The present ratio of female to male alcoholics is approximately 1:6 or one woman with an alcoholic problem for every six male alcoholics.

5. True   15/100 of 1% is stated in most state laws as the blood alcohol content which places a driver of a motor vehicle in violation of the law, and he is subject to arrest and conviction for driving under the influence. Oregon's law 483.630 (5) (c) also uses 15/100 of 1%.

6. True   The most immediate danger that drinking holds for young people is intoxication. There are risks that are far more dangerous than the physiological harm— that is to say that inhibitions are removed and normal behavior patterns are effected.

7. True   "An anesthetic produces a progressive descending depression of the central nervous system, an action peculiar and characteristic of this group. There may be sedation, analgesia, narcoses, and hypnosis preceding the special feature of anesthesia which means loss of all sensation to pain. To this group belong ether, chloroform, and alcohol." (Discussion Guide No. 1, McCarthy, p. 8)

8. False   Alcohol is a depressant, as indicated in statement No. 7. The illusion of stimulation is created by the removal of inhibitions with the result that the person's behavior is no longer restrained.

9. False   Although some of the symptoms of the cold might be temporarily relieved, alcohol does not cure colds. It has been a common notion of long standing held formerly by some physicians that the best way to combat a cold is to dose heavily with liquor and go to bed. The latter advice is still given by doctors, but serious question has been raised about the liquor dosage.

10. True   Having an insight on how the personality functions and its developmental pattern, with an understanding of its relationship to environment, should generally influence more acceptable behavior patterns with the problems of life. This understanding will help the individual to know himself, to be aware of the conflict between environment and personality, and thus see the necessity for compromise. This will influence acceptable reactions with the problems of life, thus avoiding the use of alcohol as a temporary solution to problem-solving.

11. True   Cirrhosis of the liver does occur among nondrinkers, but it is more frequent among heavy drinkers. The exact connection between alcohol and this disease is not yet clear. But cirrhosis probably goes along with disturbances in diet and metabolism. The liver plays an important part in oxidizing alcohol and is usually permanently damaged when cirrhosis occurs.

12. False   A. A. refers to Alcoholics Anonymous, the fellowship that has brought recovery to many thousands of alcoholics. This organization should not be referred to as the 2 A or AAA but either as A. A. or Alcoholics Anonymous.

13. True   By 1919, thirty-three states had prohibition of some kind. Then Congress passed the Eighteenth Amendment, which forbade the manufacture and sale of all alcoholic beverages throughout the land. This act was in force for 13 years, from 1920 to its repeal in 1933 by the Twenty-First Amendment.

14. True   Whenever anything attacks the brain structures and mental processes, whether a drug or a disease germ, it begins by affecting first those processes or qualities which are the last to be developed or most complicated in the history of mental growth. As it proceeds, the effect appears in the lower and more primitive capacities.

15. False   The alcoholic frequently drinks to excess and becomes drunk. However, occasional periods of excessive drinking or drunkenness in themselves do not necessarily indicate that the person is an alcoholic.

16. True   There are many kinds of alcohol which are used for commercial and industrial purposes. These types—methyl, butyl, and others—are dangerous to drink. Ethyl alcohol, a colorless liquid that evaporates quickly, is the kind that is used in beer, wine, and distilled spirits.

17. False   Many people abstain entirely from alcoholic beverages whereas others drink occasionally in moderation. Abstinence or moderate social drinking would not bar a person from being a good parent.

18. True   Physical and mental diseases related to alcoholism are nearly always related to poor nutrition.

19. True   Blood, saliva, urine, and breath are the body materials used to determine the alcohol-blood concentration. The Alcometer, developed by Greenberg, the Drunkometer, developed by Harger, the Intoximeter, developed by Forrester, the Alcotest, a Grosskopf-Scheibe product, and the Borkenstein Breathalyzer are the measuring instruments.

20. True   A basic understanding of the parts of an emotional experience, the types, and their role in life should influence acceptable adjustment to these experiences. Emotions are not bad or dangerous or undesirable in themselves. Emotions are not at fault when we talk of emotional problems. Rather it is the way we handle our emotions or allow them to handle us that causes difficulty. Emotions are very useful and can be assets to one's personality.

21. False   Alcohol is not a cure for any emotional problem. Feelings of inferiority may temporarily be reduced by the use of alcohol. This is not considered to be a desirable way to overcome such feelings. One must understand his problem to alter it; alcohol usage gives temporary relief, not understanding.

22. False   Experts have estimated that less than 15% of the alcoholics are found on skid row. The majority of alcoholics are people with skills and abilities. They have jobs and families.

23. False   The alcoholic content in a beverage is dependent on the process of manufacture. The alcohol content produced by fermentation is about 4% to 14% alcohol by volume, compared to usually 40% to 50% alcohol by volume in beverages produced by distillation.

24. False   A blackout is a period of amnesia for the events of any part of a drinking episode, without loss of consciousness. Passing out refers to a state of complete incapacity. The person is unconscious.

25. True   Alcohol supplies calories, but only calories—no vitamins, no minerals and no protein. It is a very inadequate food and a very expensive source of calories.

26. False   France has the highest per capita consumption of any country in the world. The United States is fifth after France, Italy, Australia, and Belgium in that order. This does not denote that the alcoholism rate in these countries falls in the same order.

27. True   The real danger in influenza is the onset of pneumonia. Numerous studies of its treatment have shown considerable advantage attaching to the nonalcoholic treatment and to patients who are abstainers. Alcohol in the system seems to lessen the normal resistance to the infection. It must be further said that resistance is decreased because the problem drinker substitutes alcohol for food which does not have the vitamins and minerals the body needs to function properly.

28. False   Some religious groups approve the use of wine in the rituals of the church; others do not. Some churches do not condemn moderate social drinking; others see the use of alcohol in any amount as a sin. All religious groups condemn excessive drinking and drunkenness.

29. True   Alcohol slows the time it takes for the eyes to make an adjustment to any stimulus. Studies and the literature generally agree that judgment, hearing, vision, touch, and reaction time may be impaired by even small amounts of alcohol.

30. True   A serious lack of vitamins can cause deterioration of parts of the nervous system. In heavy drinking, organic diseases are evident, but in most cases they are due to the substitution of the beverage alcohol for food. Due to the extreme dilution of alcohol in the body, there is probably no direct effect on cells, tissues, or organs.

31. True   The Twenty-First Amendment to the Constitution returned the control of al-

coholic beverages to the states. The federal government still exerts some control through taxation and regulation of advertising.

32. <u>True</u>   The use of alcohol is a very poor way to relieve feelings of defeat or frustration. A better method would be to understand the source of the pressure or tension and to seek more acceptable methods to relieve them.

33. <u>False</u>   The alcohol is diluted in the stomach and in the bloodstream, and by the time it reaches the brain it would not be more than a fraction of 1% concentration. Undiluted distilled beverages may cause direct injury to the esophagus and to the lining of the stomach.

34. <u>True</u>   It is true that the incidence of drinking increases with each college year. The latest survey shows an increase from 69% among freshmen to 87% among seniors for males. For women the increase was more marked, from 46% among freshmen to 77% among seniors. Each advancing year increases the probability that experimentation in the adult custom of drinking will be tried.

35. <u>True</u>   Like other foods alcohol is swallowed and soon lands in the stomach. But *unlike* other foods, it is absorbed into the blood immediately, without need for digestion. It affects the body much more quickly than ordinary foods, which have to be digested before they can pass into the blood and body fluids.

36. <u>True</u>   The only relation that food in the stomach has to alcohol that has been ingested is to retard the rate that alcohol is absorbed into the bloodstream.

37. <u>True</u>   Although the exact percentage of alcohol that is oxidized by the liver varies in individuals, and in some cases may be as high as 95%, the average for most persons is approximately 90%.

38. <u>True</u>   When it is understood that alcohol is a depressant and not a stimulant, it then becomes clear that alcohol even in small quantities has a dulling effect upon the brain. Certain areas of the brain when dulled allow the expression of certain repressed needs as the brakes or barriers have now been removed by the alcohol.

39. <u>False</u>   The action of alcohol is always temporary and provides no real solution to any problem. Persons who learn to depend upon alcohol in place of learning how to handle problems on a mature basis quite often find increased problems due to this dependency.

40. <u>False</u>   Based on approximately 70 million persons in the United States who use beverage alcohol, the ratio is estimated to be about one in fourteen who become alcoholics. Current figures list the number of alcoholics as approximately 5 million people.

41. <u>False</u>   The Al-Anon family groups are a fellowship of wives, husbands, relatives, and friends of members of Alcoholics Anonymous and of problem drinkers generally who are banded together to solve the common problems of feelings of insecurity, lack of understanding of the alcoholic, and of the warped personal lives resulting from alcoholism.

42. <u>False</u>   The chief effect of aspirin (acetylsalicylic acid) when mixed with a cola drink (caffeine) is to produce nausea and a sense of dizziness. This does not resemble the effects of intoxication because it provides no behavior alteration such as the depressant action of alcohol on the brain.

43. <u>False</u>   One must remember to qualify the word *drinking* by such descriptive adjectives as *excessive* when describing its relationship to family life, employment, and community welfare. It could be stated, however, that drinking and driving do affect community welfare, and in this regard drinking would be likely to interfere.

44. <u>True</u>   When the percentage of alcohol in the blood reaches one half of 1%, paralysis of the lower centers of the brain, which control the instinctive function of breathing, can occur. In this respect, the presence of alcohol could be considered a very dangerous condition, to the extent of causing death from deep anesthesia.

45. <u>True</u>   Positive understanding of the alcoholic should be encouraged at all times in order to help those persons suffering from alcoholism. Sometimes the attitude to-

ward alcohol itself, which might include certain hostilities, is carried over and attached to the alcoholic, which could prove to be very harmful in any effort that is made to provide treatment.

46. False   The action of alcohol in the human body through its depressant effects retards or slows reaction time and in the event of an emergency could be responsible for a serious accident.

47. True   The diseases of chronic alcoholism are essentially nutritional disturbances. The most common severe deficiency is of the vitamins of the B group. The definite diseases of the chronic alcoholic which come from vitamin deficiencies are no different from the same deficiencies occurring in persons who use no alcohol (beri-beri, pellagra, etc.).

48. True   One of the common mistakes often made is to have the stereotype concept of the alcoholic as being found only on skid row. It is known that the problem of alcoholism is a problem of people and may cover a cross section of humanity.

49. False   While it is true that olive oil and other oily substances will retard absorption of alcohol from the stomach into the bloodstream temporarily, as digestion of the oil takes place, the accumulated alcohol enters the bloodstream, often causing serious results due to the heavy concentration of alcohol that reaches the brain at one time.

50 False   The increased activity and gaiety of the person who has been drinking is not caused by stimulation as alcohol is a depressant. The depressant action of alcohol on the brain removes inhibitions and barriers, thus allowing behavior to no longer be controlled by normal checks.

Vocabulary

absorption The process by which ingested alcohol is readily absorbed (taking up of fluids or other substances by the skin, mucous surfaces, or vessels) from the gastrointestinal tract into the blood stream from whence it is distributed to all parts of the body.

abstinence Refraining completely from drinking any alcoholic beverages.

addiction A strong emotional and/or physiological dependence upon alcohol which has progressed beyond voluntary control.

adequacy Suitability for a particular purpose; the ability to meet the problems of life without the use or need of alcohol.

Al-Anon A fellowship of wives, husbands, relatives, and friends of problem drinkers who are banded together to try to solve the common problems of fear, insecurity, lack of understanding of the alcoholic, and of the warped personal lives resulting from alcoholism.

alcohol (ethyl or ethanol, C_2H_5OH) An alcohol produced by the action of yeast on sugars and starches, a colorless, volatile, inflammable liquid which is the intoxicating principal in fermented and distilled liquors. Other alcohols include methanol, CH_3OH; propanol, C_3H_7OH; and pentonal, C_5H_8OH, used industrially.

alcoholic A person whose behavior or condition complies with the definition of alcoholism.

Alcoholics Anonymous A fellowship of men and women who share their experiences with each other in order that they may solve their common problem and help others to recover from alcoholism.

alcoholic beverage A mixture of ethyl alcohol plus water and congeners.

alcoholism A chronic disease manifested by repeated implicative drinking so as to cause injury to the drinker's health or to his social or economic function.

allergy An extreme sensitivity to certain substances coming to the body from without.

ambivalence Simultaneous existence of contradictory emotional attitudes toward the same person, for example, love and hate.

analgesic A pain-dulling drug.

anesthetic A drug that produces a progressively descending depression of the central nervous system, including a special feature of anesthesia which means loss of all sensation to pain.

anxiety A state of emotional tension characterized by apprehension and fearfulness, with the reason for the stimulus not easily defined.

attitude An idea plus a feeling; the way one feels toward situations.

aversion A strong dislike, as is created by the use of certain drugs in conditioned reflex treatment for the problem drinker.

bender (slang) A spree; a bout.

compulsive drinking An insistent, repetitive, intrusive, and unwanted urge to perform an act of drinking contrary to the person's ordinary conscious wishes or standards.

conditioned reflex A reflex that has come to be aroused by a stimulus that was originally inadequate to arouse it.

depressant Any agent which diminishes the activity of the central nervous system.

dilution To reduce the concentration by an addition of a solvent (for example, adding water to whiskey).

displacement A mechanism by which feelings and attitudes are shifted from a person or situation in which they cannot be expressed to a person or situation in which they can be expressed.

distillation A process or act of driving off vapor from a liquid by heat and condensing the vapor to a liquid.

drug Any chemical compound which may be administered to or used for patients as an aid in diagnosis, treatment, or prevention of disease or other abnormal conditions.

elimination The process by which unburned alcohol is removed from the body by the action of the lungs and kidneys.

emotion Stirred up state of the entire organism composed of a stimulus, a physiological reaction, and a response which can be either pleasant or unpleasant.

emotional problem An acute disturbance of an individual involving feelings, attitudes, and widespread physiological changes.

environment All conditions and events external to an organism that affect its activities.

euphoria Exaggerated temporary feeling of well-being and contentment.

fallacious Deceptive; misleading.

fantasy A mechanism by which one develops a fanciful product of the imagination; daydreaming.

fermentation The chemical change produced in an organic substance, such as sugar, by the action of a living organism, such as yeast; a chemical change in the process of producing wine.

folkway Any way of thinking, feeling, behaving, or achieving an end common to members of a social group; a social habit or culture pattern.

frustration Being defeated or prevented from attaining one's purpose or goal; thwarting of a need or desire.

hangover The immediate pathophysiological or pathopsychological aftereffects of drinking, usually of large amounts, other than the effects of the presence of alcohol.

heredity The sum total of characteristics transmitted from parent to child by the germ plasm.

human needs The psychological, physical, and spiritual requirements of the human organism.

human resource Human source of supply or support.

inhibition Conscious restraint of impulse or desire.

impairment To weaken or lessen one's value, strength, or ability to function.

impulse controlled The first reaction or response to a stimulus that enters one's mind when confronted with a sudden impulsion, but not the external response (internal response—not the outward reaction).

impulse yielded to The actual behavior pattern one follows after the controlled impulsion (external response); should be based on thought before action.

instability The state of being not firm, stable, or fixed.

intangible cost A cost not easily expressed or defined.

intoxication (alcohol) An acute mental disturbance due to large (sometimes small) amounts of alcohol; legal intoxication in Oregon is 15/100 of 1% of alcohol in the blood or more.

mechanism Substitute form of expression or behavior used to gratify a desire or adopted to conceal a person's weaknesses.

mores Fixed customs or folkways considered to have ethical significance.

narcotic An addictive drug that induces relief of pain accompanied by deep sleep or stupor.

neurosis Mild functional personality disorder in which there is no gross personality disorganization and in which the patient does not ordinarily require hospitalization.

nutrition The assimilation and utilization of food for proper bodily growth and development.

oxidation A series of chemical changes beginning in the liver by which the alcohol is finally reduced to carbon dioxide and water.

personality The dynamic response of the individual to his environment; the entire make-up of an individual—what he is, has been, and hopes to be.

personality disorder A term used diagnostically to include a number of types of disturbances of personality integration.

prohibition Legal sanction against the sale, manufacture, or transportation of beverage alcohol.

projection A mechanism in which an individual attributes to others his motives or thoughts or places the blame for his difficulties upon others.

proof The amount of alcohol in any alcoholic liquid; in liquor, the stated proof is twice that of the percentage of alcohol; thus, a 100 proof whiskey is 50% alcohol.

psychosis Severe personality disorder involving loss of contact with reality; hospitalization is ordinarily required.

psychotherapy A process by which an attempt is made to relieve the patient of distressing neurotic symptoms or discordant personality characteristics which interfere with his satisfactory adaptation to a world of people and events.

rationalization A mechanism by which one justifies his behavior by giving good rather than the true reason for the behavior.

reflex action An involuntary response or movement in response to some stimulus.

regression A defense mechanism by which the individual retreats to the use of less mature response in attempting to cope with stress and to maintain the integrity of his ego; living in a pervious period of life.

repression A defense mechanism by which one blocks out memory in order to forget painful happenings.

scapegoat An individual (or group) who bears the blame for the misdeeds or mistakes of others.

sedative A drug which relieves nervous tension and induces calmness; predominant action is quieting.

sensory perception The act of interpreting a stimulus registered in the brain by one or more of the senses.

soporific A sleep-inducing drug.

stimulant A substance which rouses to action; the opposite of sedative.

symptom Any functional evidence of disease or of a patient's condition.

temperance (1) moderation; (2) abstinence.

tensions The condition arising out of the mobilizations of psychobiological resources to meet a threat.

tight Under the influence of alcohol (more so than high).

tolerance The ability to endure without ill effects.

toxic Pertaining to, or of the nature of, poison.

tranquilizer A group of drugs used in the treatment of psychoses, hypertension, and other conditions for their sedative and anxiety-relieving effects.

variable A quantity which has different values under similar conditions related to the use of beverage alcohol.

Audiovisual bibliography*

FILMS

Alcohol and the human body (black and white; 15 min.). Explains basic physiological action of alcohol on the body. Describes the characteristics of alcohol and how it is made. Shows the effect of alcohol on the brain. Traces the course of alcohol through the body. The problem drinker sequence requires considerable discussion and use of other films. Identification of

---

*These materials are available on loan from the Alcohol Studies and Rehabilitation Section, Mental Health Division, Oregon State Board of Control, Portland, Ore. Also, in most states they may be obtained from the state or local program on alcohol.

alcoholism solely with skid row is inaccurate. The implication that treatment is terminated as the patient leaves the hospital requires discusson of the psychological factors also involved in alcoholism. This film is useful when these explanations are included. Teacher's discussion guide is available. (Junior high school; senior high school; adults.)

Alcoholism (black and white; 20 min.). Delineates various treatment approaches and gives special details concerning alcoholic clinics. Emphasizes need for increased treatment facilities, further research, public support, and understanding of alcoholism as an illness. A competent educational film production on this social and civic problem. Teacher's discussion guide is available. (College level; adults.)

Alcoholism—the revolving door (black and white; 30 min.). A review of medicine's answer to alcoholism. Alcoholism is shown as a medical rather than a moral problem, and the futility of jail as a basis of correction is stressed. Presents meetings of Alcoholics Anonymous and group therapy sessions in action. Teacher's discussion guide is available. (College level; adults.)

Alcoholism—to your health (black and white; 25 min.). A film illustrating various phases of treatment used by the Oregon Alcoholism Treatment Clinic. Staff members are shown in the treatment program with a patient. (Senior high school; college level; adults.)

Case 258 (black and white; 30 min.). A highly dramatic episode depicts the problems of an alcoholic in industry and the viewpoints of the personnel director and top management. The personnel manager indicates the relationship between accidents, absenteeism, and alcoholism. The role of Alcoholics Anonymous and the need for industrial alcoholism programs are stressed. (Senior high school; college level; industrial.)

David—profile of a problem drinker (black and white; 30 min.). This film portrays the signposts and behavior symptoms which indicate the progressive nature of the illness of alcoholism and some of the forces which lead to recovery. The importance of early recognition of symptoms is stressed. (College level; adults; industrial.)

For those who drink (black and white; 45 min.). This is an intensive lecture type of film dealing with the physical, psychological, and social aspects of alcohol addiction. An effective use is made of blackboard diagrams. This is an unusually informative film using terminology readily understood by nonprofessional persons. Film should be shown by a well-informed teacher or resource person to carry out discussion. (Senior high school; college level; adults.)

Kid brother (black and white; 27 min.). This film explores some of the hidden emotional forces that lie behind drinking and the social pressures to drink. No position is taken for or against use of alcohol or in relation to parental attitudes toward their adolescent children. Discussion of this film should be prepared for by using the help of resource persons familiar with family relations or alcoholism. It is best to use this film to conclude a discussion about use of alcohol rather than to introduce it. Teacher's discussion guide is available. (Senior high school; college level; adults.)

Newsprofile (black and white; 25 min.). Short sequences depict services available to alcoholics by the Alcoholics Rehabilitation Association, help for families and problem drinkers in the Oregon Alcoholism Treatment Clinic facility, assistance by education consultants to schools in Oregon in alcohol studies, and chemical testing as a means to establish blood alcohol levels related to behavior. The programs of Alcoholics Anonymous and Al-Anon are also presented briefly in this film. (Senior high school; college level; adults.)

None for the road (black and white; 15 min.). Presents situations in which teen-age drinking is legal because of age limit being reduced to age 18 years. The problem of drinking and driving is demonstrated in the laboratory and in a drinking driving episode that involves a group of college students. Attitudes and behavior of a heavy drinker, a moderate drinker, and a nondrinker at a party are depicted. A thoroughly informed teacher, discussion leader, or resource person should develop discussion of this film by students or adults. Teacher's discussion guide is available. (Junior high school; senior high school; adults.)

One day at a time (black and white; 30 min.). Factual presentation of the founding of Alcoholics Anonymous by two men considered by society to be hopeless victims of alcoholism. Alcoholism from both the personal and social viewpoints. This film is suitable also for alcoholics and their families in re-educational programs. (Senior high school; college level; adults.)

Out of orbit (color; 14 min.). This film presents a story about an alcoholic and the conflicts, feelings, and attitudes of his wife and son as the whole family attempts to get help. Community resources that may be used in helping to solve the problem are well explained. (Senior high school; college level; adults.)

Should you drink? (black and white; 30 min.). Social drinking and possible personality factors are presented. Does not condemn drinking but illustrates possible relationship of alcohol and its effect on the individual's personality structure. (College level; adults.)

Teaching teen-agers about alcohol (black and white; 20 min.). Intended specifically for showing to teachers. Several scenes illustrate alcohol education teaching methods successfully applied to the classroom. The film demonstrates that it is possible to do a constructive teaching job without jeopardizing the role of the teacher. (College methods classes; teacher in-service programs.)

The bottle and the throttle (black and white; 10 min.). This film is an enlightening study of the problems of drinking and driving. Using an entirely new approach, the film shatters the age-old myth which says a person must be drunk before his driving ability is materially impaired. This film is directed toward the teen-ager who is confronted with alcohol and its effect upon driving skills. (Junior high school; senior high school; college level.)

To your health (color; 11 min.). An animated cartoon, with narration and music, scientifically and objectively explains the nature of alcohol, the physiological effects, the social and psychological reasons people drink, the historical backgrounds of the use of beverage alcohol, and varying attitudes and beliefs concerning it. Provides an excellent method of introducing many areas suitable for discussion and study. (Junior high school; senior high school; adults.)

What about alcoholism? (black and white; 10 min.). An open-end discussion shows conflicting opinions about alcoholism—its symptoms, causes, and treatment. Designed to stimulate further study, not to give detailed information. Planned leadership is required in use of this film. A teacher's discussion guide is available. (Senior high school; college level; adults.)

What about drinking? (black and white; 10 min.). Young people at informal gathering enter into discussion about drinking. The role of social pressures and church positions and the influence of adult attitudes are explored. This film should effectively stimulate discussion on attitudes toward drinking. This film could form a series with the films *None for the Road,* to correlate the drinking and driving aspects, and *Kid Brother,* to underscore the mental health approach. Teacher's discussion guide is available. (Senior high school; college level; adults.)

FILM STRIPS

Alcohol and you (color; parts 1 and 2). A positive and objective presentation of the use of beverage alcohol, relating it to custom and psychological needs. Part 1 relates to basic facts about alcohol—its chemical properties and use in industry. Drinking customs from a historical point of view are presented. Part 2 relates to the physiological effects of alcohol, why people drink, why they abstain, what an alcoholic is, and how he may be treated. This film strip requires an informed discussion leader since only captions are used. Teacher's discussion guide is available. (Junior high school; senior high school.)

Danger—drinking driver (black and white). This film strip was produced by the Northwestern Traffic Institute for the Women's Christian Temperance Union. Illustrates the effect of alcohol on driving ability and the use of chemical tests to determine the amount of alcohol in the blood. (Junior high school; senior high school; college level.)

Tensions—how to deal with them (black and white). This is a film strip dealing with tension. The strip is divided into three phases. (1) The first phase centers around the understanding of tension. (2) The second phase makes an analogy between a human being and a boiling kettle. (3) The third phase suggests in outline form twelve suggested ways of dealing with tension. This strip can be used in part with the pamphlet *How to Deal With Your Tensions* (National Association for Mental Health, 10 Columbus Circle, New York City 19, N. Y.).

SLIDES

Alcoholism (10 slides; 2 × 2; color). Explanation and discussion about alcoholism supplied in a 33⅓ RPM record. Produced by William Swegan of Texas. (Senior high school; college level; adults.)

What we should know about alcohol (66 slides; 2 × 2; color). These slides scientifically and objectively detail drinking as a well-established custom, describe the nature of alcohol and its physiological effects, analyze why people drink, present alcoholism as a disease, and describe its extent and treatment. The slides may be used in any sequence or number to focus on one particular field. They are designed for discussion group presentation. A teacher's manual may be borrowed and is to be returned with the slides. (Junior high school; senior high school.)

TAPE RECORDINGS

Could this be you?

No. 1. Tape recording of drinking and driving of a young driver stopped at a road block near Chehalis, Wash. Recording made by Sgt. Amens, Washington State Patrol.

No. 2. Tape recording of actual scene at automobile wreck involving a drunk driver near Tacoma, Wash. Per cent of alcohol in the blood of the driver was 0.29 of 1%. Recording made by Sgt. Amens, Washington State Patrol.

TEACHER EVALUATION FORM

Teacher _____ School _____ Grade _____

Subject _____ Number of classes _____ Time allowed for unit _____

1. Was the unit: (1) Too long? _____ (2) Too short? _____ (3) About right? _____
2. Was the consultant service used? Yes _____ No _____ (If yes, answer questions 3 and 4)
3. What part of the consulting service do you feel was of most value to you? _____

_____

_____

4. What part of the consulting service do you feel should be added to or strengthened? _____

_____

5. Which of the following sections of the resource unit were helpful to you:

   (a) General objectives _____   (g) Interest stimulator _____
   (b) Specific objectives _____   (h) Class activity sheet _____
   (c) Special activities _____   (i) Vocabulary list _____
   (d) Problem outline _____   (j) Literature order form _____
   (e) Reference pages _____   (k) Audiovisual form _____
   (f) Selected reference list _____   (l) Student evaluation _____
6. Suggestions for improving the teaching and resource unit _____

_____

7. What specific (by title) materials of the following groups were of most value to you?

   Films   Pamphlets   Books
   (1)_____   (1)_____   (1)_____
   (2)_____   (2)_____   (2)_____
   (3)_____   (3)_____   (3)_____
8. Which of the special activities you employed stimulated the most student participation and interest? _____

_____

9. On the reverse side or on an attached sheet, please enlarge upon any opinions, suggestions, or impressions regarding the alcohol education services which will aid us in future programming. Your complete frankness will be appreciated.

				Student references
		Describe disease cycle which occurs within individual	Chart depicting disease cycle: incubation, prodrome, fastigium, defervescence, convalescence, and defection	1. Film: *How our bodies fight disease:* Encyclopaedia Britannica Films, 8 min.; describes four lines of defense in body for fighting disease; explains cause of disease and work of four lines of defense in combatting it
		Discuss the ways in which disease may be transferred from one person to another		2. Roueché, Berton: Eleven blue men, Berkley Publishing Corp., New York, 1953
	B. Diseases that adolescents are interested in or need to understand	Grow germ cultures from nasal and oral fluid and study with microscope; interested students may wish to pursue this by studying and classifying bacterial types	Petri dishes, agar, slides, cover slips, microscopes, and staining material	3. Film: *Unconditional surrender,* National Foundation, Inc., 15 min.; describes preparation of Salk vaccine in Eli Lilly laboratories and 1955 field trials leading to its successful acceptance by public
Knows mode of transmission for most respiratory infection	1. Respiratory infection (general)	Ask an ear, nose and throat specialist to talk to class on respiratory disease		4. Otto, J. H., Julian, C. J., and Tether, J. E.: Modern health, Holt, Rinehart, & Winston, Inc., New York, 1959, Chaps. 25-28
Practices hygienic habits relating to disease control	a. Why common to this age group	Have a panel of students present information on habits, early treatment, and complications		
	b. Habits related to disease prevention	Discuss common use of drugs and relative ineffectiveness		
Knows common symptoms that precede most respiratory diseases	c. Value of early treatment and care	Take samples of cold tablets and study contents on bottle; discuss costs in relation to contents	Several bottles of cold tablets	
	d. Danger signs of early respiratory infection	Administer short scale on misconceptions regarding disease; prepare one yourself or request permission to use one that has been developed		
	e. Common misconceptions concerning cure and treatment			

Continued on next page.

Teaching unit in community health—prevention and control of disease—cont'd

Grade—eleven—cont'd

Expected outcomes	Content	Methods and devices	Evaluation procedures	Teaching aids	References
Specific—cont'd					*Student references—cont'd*
Knows that tuberculosis can be cured Appreciates the need for continuing community-wide detection program Has a skin test or x-ray once a year	I. *Communicable and non-communicable disease—cont'd* B. Diseases that adolescents are interested in or need to understand—cont'd 　2. Tuberculosis 　　a. Why common to this group 　　b. Importance of maintaining normal health and good nutrition 　　c. Value of early diagnosis and importance of x-ray and skin testing program 　　d. Common misconceptions 　　e. Methods of care and treatment, both past and present 　　f. Latest research in drugs 　　g. Function of the National Tuberculosis Association and local associations in control and eradication of disease	Discuss the meaning of skin tests and importance of x-ray Survey class to determine number who have had such tests within last two years Ask school nurse to demonstrate tuberculin test Ask local bacteriologist, if available, to speak of new drug effects on tubercle bacillus Discuss your state's program for care of patients with tuberculosis Have two students report on program of the National Tuberculosis Association and distribute some of its materials	Recency of skin test and/or x-ray among class members; results should be recorded in health records	Various pamphlets on tuberculosis from local association	5. Film: *Tuberculosis*, Encyclopaedia Britannica Films, 11 min.; shows causes, diagnosis, treatment, and control of tuberculosis; shows Mary, a high school student, who becomes infected by tubercular aunt and enters a tuberculosis home for treatment 6. Film: *The anatomy of a disease*, National Tuberculosis Association, 15 min.; fascinating presentation of how modern medical science is set up to handle a complex disease

Knows cause and mode of transmission of venereal diseases
Practices morally sound habits of dating
	3. Venereal diseases
	  a. Disease causes, nature, and problems
	  b. Importance of treatment
	  c. Related factors: educational, social conditions, and economic hardships
		Study your state and national statistics on incidence of venereal disease with attention to age, socioeconomic status, and geographical location
		Discuss causes, mode of transmission, and general characteristics of venereal diseases
		Have panel of students collect data from health officer, ministers, social welfare workers, and other persons and present before class relative to effective control measures
			Statistics from your state health department
			
			Pamphlets from American Social Hygiene Association
				7. Film: *Invader*, Potomac Film Productions, 37 min.; tells of work of scientists who have developed cure for disease and describes educational campaigns designed to enlighten the public
				8. Film: *Sixteen to twenty-six*, National Film Board of Canada, 18 min.; designed for female audiences
				9. Film: *Very dangerous*, National Film Board of Canada, 18 min.; designed for male audiences

Knows accepted scientific facts regarding cancer
Is secure in personal attitudes toward cancer
Appreciates dangers of cancer quackery to individual and society as a whole
Knows what community has done to organize fight against cancer
	4. Cancer
	  a. Current research facts about disease
	  b. What are misconceptions
	  c. Individual responsibility for early diagnosis, knowledge of danger signals, and self-examination
	  d. Dangers in quack treatment
	  e. Voluntary and official agencies contributing to prevention and treatment
		Ask representative to speak on program of American Cancer Society
		Have two students present scientific summary of cancer research
		Discuss emotional and economic pressures that drive people to cancer quacks
		Discuss development of attitudes on basis of current knowledge that will give strength to individual faced with cancer
			Teacher's kit of materials from American Cancer Society
			
			Sufficient copies of *I Have a Secret Cure* from the American Cancer Society
				10. Film: *From one cell*, American Cancer Society, 15 min.; normal and abnormal cell growth and behavior
				11. Film: *Living insurance*, American Cancer Society, 14 min.; a young family man undergoes a complete physical examination to assure himself he does not have cancer
				12. Film: *Is smoking worth it*, American Cancer Society, 14 min.; describes scientific study of cigarette carcinogens

Continued on next page.

Teaching unit in community health—prevention and control of disease—cont'd

Grade—eleven—cont'd

Expected outcomes	Content	Methods and devices	Evaluation procedures	Teaching aids	References
Specific—cont'd	*I. Communicable and non-communicable disease—cont'd* B. Diseases that adolescents are interested in or need to understand—cont'd				*Student references—cont'd*
Understands known factors that relate to the high incidence of heart disease Knows more common types of heart and circulatory diseases Practices wise habits of exercise and nutrition Appreciates need for regular physical examination	5. Heart and circulatory diseases a. Statistics of the problem b. Types and conditions of heart and circulatory disease c. Current methods of treatment and surgery	Present students mortality and morbidity of heart and circulatory disease Have students prepare short paper on several heart and circulatory diseases Have heart specialist in to talk of heart surgery and heart machine and demonstrate use of artificial heart valves Discuss types of health habits which are important now to prevent problems when older Have nutritionist discuss latest research on eating habits and heart disease Have students develop tables on fat content of various foods	Present short quiz on heart and cancer with emphasis on attitudes and habits	Pamphlets from state or local heart association office Chart of heart machine; if available, artificial heart valves	13. Local heart association will supply listing of current films that are excellent for secondary students
Understands what an allergic reaction is Knows types of allergies and their cause Appreciates fact that many adolescents suffer from allergy more severely than they will as adults Understands importance of treatment Practices control measures if allergy is personal problem	6. Allergies a. Some allergies common to this age group b. Known causes of allergy c. Individual differences d. Important preventive and control measures	Discuss nature of allergy and some common allergens Discuss importance of medical treatment Survey class with individual checklist to ascertain incidence of allergies and number under treatment Resurvey later in school year to determine if more are then under treatment		Pamphlets from Allergy Association of America, American College of Allergy, and American Academy of Allergy	14. Film: *Allergies*, Encyclopaedia Britannica Films, Inc., 12 min.; presents basic facts necessary for fundamental understanding of nature of allergies

Seeks professional advice if necessary		Have students develop statistics on total incidence of allergy Ask nutritionist, physician, and psychiatrist to present a panel on natural history of allergy	Survey and resurvey of persons under treatment will determine practical effect of the teaching Follow-up with parents would be in order	

Understands known causes of acne and why it is common to adolescents
Realizes importance of proper health habits and nutrition
Appreciates the probable effect of glandular and metabolic changes that take place during adolescence
Seeks medical consultation if need is indicated
Understands dangers of self-treatment and slavery to commercial advertisement
	7. Acne
	  a. Physiological factors and individual differences that give rise to condition
	  b. Factors contributing to severity of the condition
	  c. Importance of good health habits
	  d. Dangers of self-treatment
	  e. Reasons for medical assistance
		Describe condition of acne and its causes as medical science currently understands it
		Ask local dermatologist to discuss and answer questions about acne and other skin problems
		Have two students present personal health habits that would improve or aggravate conditions of acne
		Have students investigate ingredients of commercially prepared material sold to correct acne; these might be included in discussion with dermatologist
		Determine the Federal Drug Administration standards, regarding ingredients for skin creams, etc.		

Understands causes of obesity Understands relationship of obesity to other diseases	8. Obesity a. Physiological, psychological, and nutritional causes	Have students chart their weight over time and compare with their recommended weight		Valuable teaching aids in area of obesity may be obtained from Metropolitan Life Insurance Co. and American Medical Association 15. Film: *Obesity*, Encyclopaedia Britannica Films, Inc., 12 min.; dramatizes handicap of obesity to adults and adolescents; calls attention to importance of maintaining proper weight

Continued on next page.

Teaching unit in community health—prevention and control of disease—cont'd

Grade—eleven—cont'd

Expected outcomes	Content	Methods and devices	Evaluation procedures	Teaching aids	References
Specific—cont'd	I. *Communicable and non-communicable disease*—cont'd B. Diseases that adolescents are interested in or need to understand—cont'd 8. Obesity—cont'd				*Student references*—cont'd 16. Film: *Owl and Fred Jones*, Equitable Life Assurance Society, 15 min.; shows habits are what we make them—good or bad—and explains how we can develop habits and make them serve us
Appreciates nonorganic causes of obesity Practices wise habits of weight control	b. Relationship of obesity to many other diseases c. Why obesity is considered a disease	Survey cross section of people for indications of weight problems Have physician talk on disease aspects of obesity Discuss a wise schedule of nutrition and activity and relate emotional outlook; tie in discussion of previous diseases and their relationship			
	II. *Factors in prevention and control* III. *Modern medical care* II and III should be closely integrated within I. This entire unit will cover 15 class periods (no more than 20 if teacher is fortunate to extend it somewhat); therefore, teacher may have to select certain areas or have parts of class working on several diseases simultaneously		An objective examination patterned after the outline seen in Appendix B for eighth grade personal health—wholesome rest and activity should be developed for this unit; students' health records and teacher observation will augment this examination		

Teaching unit in personal health—wholesome activity and rest

Grade—eight

Expected outcomes	Content	Methods and devices	Evaluation procedures	Teaching aids	References
General Appreciates function of body as whole organism Understands functions of body systems Understands interrelationship of all body systems Develops vocabulary related to each system Practices appropriate physical activity	I. Relationship of wholesome activity to development of		Pretest students to determine level of knowledge and specific areas that need special emphasis; one of several commercially prepared tests entirely satisfactory and will indicate relative status of students		1. Film: *Human machine*, Moody Institute of Science, 14 min.; compares body's parts and operations with man-made functions; explains how parts of body function together as independent systems 2. Film: *Your body during adolescence*, McGraw-Hill Book Co., Inc, 10 min.; 18 young people from 13-15 years old are shown to vary widely in size and shape although all are changing from childhood to adulthood
Specific Knows relationship between function and size, shape, structure, and arrangement of bones	A. *Skeletal system* 1. How skeletal system serves as functional element in activity a. Form, shape, and support	Compare function of support with bridge construction and balance and shape of bones as related to this function		Human skeleton	3. Bolton, W. W., et al: Your health today and tomorrow, River Forest, Ill., 1960, Laidlaw, Unit 4
		Compare skeleton of cat, bird, fish, and man in terms of support of flesh and organs and shape and form of animal		Skeleton of cat, bird, and fish	4. Film: *The skeleton*, Encyclopaedia Britannica Films, Inc., 12 min.; illustrates formation growth, development, and function of human skeleton
	b. Protection	Discuss general nature of protective bones in size, shape, and location			5. Williams, D. M.: Building health, Philadelphia, 1956, J. B. Lippincott Co., chap. 7
	c. Mobility—motion and locomotion	Compare forms of locomotion in cat, bird, fish, and man and note differences in skeletal form and joint formation			

Continued on next page.

Teaching unit in personal health—wholesome activity and rest—cont'd

Grade—eight—cont'd

Expected outcomes	Content	Methods and devices	Evaluation procedures	Teaching aids	References

Specific—cont'd
Knows relationship between function and size, shape, structure, and arrangement of bones—cont'd
	I. *Relationship of wholesome activity to development of*—cont'd
	A. *Skeletal system*—cont'd
	  1. How skeletal system serves as functional element in activity—cont'd
	    c. Mobility—motion and locomotion—cont'd
		Examine skeleton and x-ray pictures to note movements possible at joints
		Discuss uniqueness of man's hands and feet
				X-ray pictures of human joints including wrist, hand, ankle, and foot	6. Excellent teacher resources for this entire section of the unit are the following: Villee, Claude A.: Biology, ed. 4, Philadelphia, 1962, W. B. Saunders Co.; The wonderful human machine, Today's Health, Oct., 1959, to May, 1960; Anderson, C. L, and Langton, C. V.: Health principles and practice, ed. 3, St. Louis, 1961, C. V. Mosby Co.

Knows correct relationship of skeletal parts
Practices good posture
	2. How bones are constructed and arranged to constitute effective skeletal system
	  a. Structure
	  b. Joints and connective tissue
		Discuss size and shape of bones to their function
		Obtain leg bone from young calf and compare with similar bone from older cow
		Demonstrate how ligaments hold bones together
		Explain structure of typical joint—membrane, fluid, cartilage, and ligaments
		Show on skeleton arrangement of bones in foot and ankle; point out shape as it relates to function
		Examine lumbar vertebra and illustrate its function
				Leg bones from young calf and cow	

Appreciates good posture in others	3. Why there is a general correct posture for each individual	Use vertical plane test to analyze alignment of ankle, knee, hip, shoulder, and head Have students analyze themselves for head, shoulder, and hip tilt		Sufficient lumbar vertebrae for class members Plumb line	7. Film strip: *Let's stand tall*, 35 frames; from a class discussion of circus parade, students see attractiveness of standing, sitting, and walking tall

Knows arrangement of muscle and joint structure Understands extent and limits of muscular action Realizes contributions of muscular efficiency to man's way of life—his life processes, posture and appearance, work, and recreation Practices those exercises essential in maintaining muscular efficiency	B. *Muscular system* 1. How functions of muscular system influence man's life	Use building blocks to demonstrate skeletal balance and posture deviation Discuss support function of pelvis and influence of pelvic tilt on total body support Discuss common postural deviations Have panel of students demonstrate relationship of postural attitudes and personality Discuss fundamental life process and necessity for muscular action of heart and blood vessels, digestion, respiration, birth, etc. Compare action of muscles with rubber band Experiment: prepare frog muscle in advance and demonstrate muscle contraction under electrical stimulus Use model of joint to demonstrate action of bones and muscles involved Ask orthopedist to discuss relationship of activity to developing skeleton and muscular systems	Oral quiz of class members with emphasis on relationship of activity to skeletal development	Building blocks Frog, necessary electrical equipment Model of joint with ligaments, tendons and muscles attached	8. Film: *Your posture*, Young American Films, 10 min.; discusses importance of posture to appearance and health; demonstrates what good posture is 9. Film: *Posture and exercise*, Encyclopaedia Britannica Films, Inc, 11 min.; description and explanation of muscle activity and physiology of exercise 10. Williams, D. M.: Building health, Philadelphia, 1956, J B Lippincott Co, chap. 7 11. Film: *Muscular system*, United World Films, Inc, 11 min.; explains work of muscles and tendons, using muscles of arm as example 12. Film: *Muscles*, Eastman, 17 min.; presents structure and use of muscles; includes consideration of habits of exercise and posture 13. Bolton, W. W., et al.: Your health, today and tomorrow, River Forest, Ill, 1960, Laidlaw, Unit 4

Continued on next page.

Teaching unit in personal health—wholesome activity and rest—cont'd

Grade—eight—cont'd

Expected outcomes	Content	Methods and devices	Evaluation procedures	Teaching aids	References
Specific—cont'd	I. *Relationship of wholesome activities to development of*—cont'd				
	B. *Muscular system*—cont'd				
	2. The effects of exercise on muscular system	Demonstrate and practice few exercises that will strengthen specific parts of body			
	a. Strength and size	Discuss strength, size, and shape of muscle with respect to masculinity and femininity			
		Have students collect advertisements on body building systems and discuss			
	b. Weight control	Have students bring in articles on reducing exercises and critically evaluate	Observe physical activity and posture of class members during school day		
		Discuss exercise in relation to weight change	10 min. written quiz covering combined areas of skeletal and muscular systems as these are affected by activity	Pamphlets on weight control through exercise from Metropolitan Life Insurance Co., American Association for Health, Physical Education, and Recreation, and other sources	
		List contributions of exercise to wholesome activity and our way of life			
Knows how the circulatory system is organized and constructed to perform its functions	C. *Circulatory system*	Discuss function of bloodstream in relation to digestion and respiration		Wall charts of circulatory, digestion, and respiratory systems	14. Film: *Hemo the magnificent,* Pacific Telephone and Telegraph Co., 59 min.; animated story of blood, its constituents, and main functions
	1. Why circulatory system is essential to life	Ask physician to present information on function of blood in spread of disease			
Understands the effects of environment and habits of living on circulatory functioning	2. How circulatory system is constructed	Use heart model and diagram flow of blood through heart		Model of heart	15. Bolton, W. W., et al.: Your health today and tomorrow, River Forest, Ill., 1960, Laidlaw, p. 88-99
	a. Heart	Have students report on use of electrocardiograph and			

Content	Activities	Materials and aids	References
	Ask physician to demonstrate taking of electrocardiogram		16. Williams, D. M.: Building health, Philadelphia, 1956, J. B. Lippincott Co., chap. 8
	Have student panel report on rheumatic heart disease and other heart disorders	Obtain heart quiz from local heart association and give to class; requires 5-10 min.	17. Film: *Heart—How it works*, McGraw-Hill Book Co., Inc., 11 min.; x-ray photographs of heart in action; diagrams and animation to show parts and function of the sections of heart
b. Pathway of blood flow through arteries, capillaries, and veins	Examine arteries and veins of animal that has been injected with red and blue latex	Animal with circulatory system prepared for visual inspection	18. Film: *Circulation*, United World Film Co., 17 min.; describes systemic and pulmonary circulation; structure and function of heart, lungs, arteries, capillaries, and veins and exchange of CO_2 and O_2 in lungs and body cells
	Compare structure and function of arteries, capillaries, and veins		
	Explain blood pressure and demonstrate a blood pressure measuring device (sphygmomanometer) with a pupil	Sphygmomanometer	19. Film: *Circulatory control*, Eastman, 16 min.; blood pressure; methods of measuring blood pressure; structure and work of vaso-veins; nature's method of vasomotor control
	Discuss function of capillaries to internal nutrition and respiration		
	Diagram pathway of blood through body; include pulmonary and systemic circulation and hepatic portal blood supply		20. Burkard, W. E., et al.: Good health for all, Chicago, 1958, Lyons & Carnahan, p. 253-262
3. How blood performs its functions	Have students read and discuss function and nature of plasma		21. Film: *Open heart operation*, McGraw-Hill Book Co., Inc, 27 min.; film record of open heart surgical operation
a. Plasma	Examine drop of blood under a microscope to see red corpuscles	Microscope(s), slides, cover slips, alcohol, cotton, and skin lances	
b. Formed elements— red corpuscles, white cells, and platelets	Discuss anemia, function of spleen, and significance of iron and hemoglobin	Wall chart showing position of spleen	
	Observe prepared slide of white blood cells under microscope	Prepared slides of white cells	

Wall chart of heart (sufficient student copies may be obtained from American Heart Association)

Continued on next page.

Grade—eight—cont'd

Teaching unit in personal health—wholesome activity and rest—cont'd

Expected outcomes	Content	Methods and devices	Evaluation procedures	Teaching aids	References
Specific—cont'd Understands the effects of environment and habits of living on circulatory functioning—cont'd	I. *Relationship of wholesome activity to development of*—cont'd C. *Circulatory system*—cont'd 3. How blood performs its functions—cont'd b. Formed elements—red corpuscles, white cells and platelets—cont'd	Discuss functions of white cells Have student report on use of differential white cell count and several white cell diseases Examine blood clot under microscope Discuss blood clotting and function of platelets			22. Film: *Body defenses against diseases,* Encyclopaedia Britannica Films, 11 min.; examines three lines of defense against infection: skin and mucous membranes, lymphatic system, and circulatory system
	4. How to maintain efficient circulatory system and blood supply a. Exercise	Have students send for life insurance company pamphlets on exercise; read and discuss Collect magazine articles on relationship of exercise to heart health			
Appreciates need for regular exercise					
Willingly participates in vigorous exercise daily	b. Diet	Study heart-rate-return-to-normal after exercise in different students Discuss nutrients necessary for circulatory efficiency	Observe kind and degree of exercise students take part in	Several stopwatches	
	c. Environment	Discuss effect of temperature, attitude, emotions, and habits of living on circulatory system	Oral quiz of class members with emphasis on relationship of activity to development and maintenance of an efficient circulatory system		
Knows how man's habits and ways of living affect respiratory system	D. *Respiratory system* 1. Why inspired air is essential for life	Introduce this section by briefly reviewing muscular and skeletal systems to show how food is necessary for all cells and relate function of circulatory system in transporting this food		Animated cartoon of glucose molecule being destroyed and energy released in presence of oxygen	

Objectives	Topic	Activities	Materials	References
		show why oxygen is necessary for fuel molecule to be burned Discuss liberation of energy and its use by body for growth, repair, and work		
Knows major parts of respiratory system	2. How air is made available for use by body	Trace passage of air on chart and indicate major parts of respiratory system Use model to show relative position of organs of respiration, digestion, and circulatory systems	Wall chart of respiratory system and model of respiratory system	23. Film: *Mechanisms of breathing*, Encyclopaedia Britannica Films, Inc., 11 min.; human breathing mechanism in operation; exchange of O_2 and CO_2 in lungs and body tissue cells; artificial respiration
		Relate circulatory and respiratory systems by having students record their normal heartbeats and then record heartbeat second time after holding breath to full limit and after breathing into sealed bag for a short time Discuss mouth versus nose breathing and rib versus diaphragm breathing List differences in inhaled and exhaled air	Mannequin to demonstrate mouth-to-mouth resuscitation	24. Film: *Artificial respiration*, United World Films, Inc., 11 min.; back-pressure, arm-lift and back-pressure and hip-lift methods 25. Film: *That they may live*, Sears Roebuck Foundation, 27 min.; techniques of mouth-to-mouth resuscitation 26. Film strip: *Respiration and blood circulation*, DuKane Corp., 24 frames; study of nose, mouth, diaphragm, lungs and bloodstream in respiration; function and working of heart
Understands effect of activity on respiration Appreciates complexity of respiration and important relationship between external and internal respiration	3. How habits and practices influence respiratory system	Compare ways of breathing of vocalist, horn player, distance runners, and swimmers Demonstrate on skeleton position of rib cage in relationship to movements of diaphragm Discuss obstructions to breathing: colds, tonsilitis, tobacco tars, polluted atmosphere, industrial wastes, etc.	Skeleton	27. Film: *How now brown cloud*, Oregon State Board of Health, 30 min.; community air pollution problems, meteorological factors, and need for additional local action 28. Film: *What is TB?* National Tuberculosis Association, 10 min.; what tuberculosis is, how it is contracted, how to find out if you have it, and how to cure it

Continued on next page.

Teaching unit in personal health—wholesome activity and rest—cont'd

Expected outcomes	Content	Methods and devices	Evaluation procedures	Teaching aids	References
Specific—cont'd Appreciates complexity of respiration and important relationship between external and internal respiration —cont'd	I. *Relationship of wholesome activity to development of*—cont'd D. *Respiratory system*—cont'd 3. How habits and practices influence respiratory system—cont'd	Discuss effects of attitude and temperature on respiration Explain function of respiratory center and its regulatory effects Summarize contribution of wholesome activity to efficient function of the respiratory system	Oral quiz of class members with emphasis on relationship of activity to proper function of respiratory system		29. Williams, D. M.: Building health, Philadelphia, 1956, J. B. Lippincott Co., chap. 9
Knows gross structure of excretory system as basis for understanding its function Understands interrelationship of excretory system with the digestive, muscular, respiratory, and circulatory systems	E. *Excretory system* 1. How excretory system is constructed	Review digestive system and discuss functions of kidneys, skin, and lungs in excretion			
Appreciates need for varied exercise and regular diet in maintaining healthy excretory system	2. How body's waste materials are excreted	Use model to describe kidney and related structures Discuss function of colon Have nurse discuss importance of dietary liquids and roughage to proper excretion		Wall chart of excretory system; model of kidneys and related structures	30. Film: *Excretory system*, Coronet Films, 14 min.; explanation of how kidneys and urethral tubes do away with body wastes

Outcomes	Content	Learning activities	Evaluation	Materials	References
		Keep individual student records for week of amount of liquid consumed and discuss with class Have a visiting laboratory technician talk on purposes of urinalysis and its diagnostic possibilities Discuss loss of salt through perspiration and reactions of body to profuse and continued perspiration	Oral quiz of class members on excretory system		31. Anderson, C. L., and Langton, C. V.: Health principles and practice, ed. 3, 1961, C. V. Mosby Co, chap. 5 32. Williams, D. M., Building health, Philadelphia, 1956, J. B. Lippincott Co., chap. 16 33. Shacter, H., et al.: Into your teens, What makes you get tired? Philadelphia, 1956, J. B. Lippincott Co., pp. 222-225
General Interested in balanced program of rest, sleep, relaxation, and recreation Practices sensible habits of rest, sleep, relaxation, and recreation Knows that games and activities must be adjusted to individual differences Adjusts safely to fast tempo of modern living	II. *Need for rest, sleep, relaxation, and recreation*				
Specific Gets at least 9 hours sleep every night Recognizes signs of physical fatigue Knows that continued fatigue reduces physical and mental abilities Knows importance of recreational skills in maintaining physical and mental health	A. Why body needs rest, relaxation and sleep	Have two teams of students debate the resolution: It makes no difference whether I get to bed on time or at late and irregular hours Discuss why body needs rest, relaxation, and sleep; discuss fatigue and effect of toxic waste products on body tissues and brain		Chart depicting sleep cycle	34. Craig, G. S., and Urban, J.: Facing tomorrow with science, New York, 1958, Ginn & Co.
	B. How eighth grade pupil may develop needed skills for activity and recreation	Have each pupil develop plan for his own physical activity and recreation			

Continued on next page.

Teaching unit in personal health—wholesome activity and rest—cont'd   Grade—eight—cont'd

Expected outcomes	Content	Methods and devices	Evaluation procedures	Teaching aids	References
Specific—cont'd	II. *Need for rest, sleep, relaxation, and recreation—cont'd*				
Desires to learn individual and group skills and activities	B. How eighth grade pupil may develop needed skills for activity and recreation—cont'd	Discuss what interesting activities students may do to improve their plan of physical activity			
Participates in recreational activities which have real carryover to adult life values		Develop a list of exercises and related activities which improve function of particular part of body such as the stomach muscles, leg muscles, etc.			35. Film: *Fitness is a family affair*. National Film Board of Canada, 15 min.; suggests family projects and tells how they can create cooperative spirit in community
		Discuss kinds of activities which will carry over into adult years			36. Film: *Leaders for leisure*, Athletic Institute, 21 min.; outlines steps community may follow to train and maintain its recreational leaders
		Have students list social values of physical activities—teamwork, personality development, etc.			
Understands role played by recreation departments to total community life	C. How eighth grade pupil may make use of community resources for recreation	Make survey of all recreational resources in community			
Appreciates program of local recreation department		Have students develop questionnaire to be used by other students in high school and college as well as by adults to find out in what recreations they engage	Develop and administer a written examination over material covered in this unit—Personal health: wholesome activity and rest (appropriate examination over this unit and related to material discussed in chap. 7 in appendix B)		
Participates in local community activities		Interview physical education directors, recreation leaders, and other persons to find out what they consider balanced recreational program for individual			
Encourages others to pursue recreational activities		Discuss need for a carry-on plan into adult life in some kinds of physical recreation			

SUMMARY

The resource unit on alcohol education and the teaching units on community and personal health that have been included in Appendix A indicate the depth and breadth required to make health teaching meaningful at the secondary level. Construction of such units usually requires the pooled education and experience of many people as well as subsequent suggestions for change and revision by teachers who use the units in classroom situations. Even ultimate publication does not demand rigid adherence to a specific unit by all teachers, but, rather, a unit should be viewed as a guide to teaching that can be adjusted to the needs and resources of a particular situation.

A word of caution—freedom to adjust teaching units to a local situation does not endorse the extreme of teaching without a unit. The message of this text is that effective health teaching can be achieved only through careful planning; unit preparation and use must be accepted as vital and integral aspects of planning.

Appendix B

OBJECTIVE EXAMINATION

GRADE—8

SUBJECT—PERSONAL HEALTH-WHOLESOME ACTIVITY AND REST

This 100-point examination is included to fulfill three purposes:

1. It provides examples of the various types of questions that may be used in an objective examination. These types were discussed in Chapter 7.
2. It emphasizes the purpose of the table of specifications discussed at length in Chapter 7 in helping to assure curricular validity for the indicated content area of eighth grade health instruction.
3. It continues and concludes the suggested unit planning concept that has been the thread of Chapters 7 and 9 and the eighth grade teaching unit of Appendix A.

The correct answers to the examination are given on pp. 379 to 380. A few poor items are included. These are noted, and a discussion is included with the answers.

Part I: Wholesome activity

Items 1 to 20 are true-false. If the statement is true, encircle the T. If the statement is false, encircle the F.

T	F	1.	The main support of the skeleton is the spinal column.
T	F	2.	Viewed from the back, the spinal column normally takes the shape of a long slender S.
T	F	3.	Movement at the wrist is typical of most other joints.
T	F	4.	Marrow is the spongy substance found within bones.
T	F	5.	Muscles work only when they contract.
T	F	6.	Muscles are composed of thousands of cells called muscle fibers.
T	F	7.	Individual muscle fibers may contract a small amount or completely, depending upon the degree of nerve impulses.
T	F	8.	Carbohydrates are the chief food used by muscles for quick energy.
T	F	9.	Girls have a slower heart rate on the average than boys.
T	F	10.	The heart contraction is the only muscle action in the body that does not require stimulation by nerves in order to perform work.
T	F	11.	Strenuous activity will not injure a completely normal and healthy heart.
T	F	12.	Tonsillitis, diphtheria, and scarlet fever may temporarily weaken the valves of the heart.

T	F	13.	The sound of speech originates in the diaphragm.
T	F	14.	The average respiration rate is about 72 times per minute in the adolescent.
T	F	15.	Rapid breathing may indicate the presence of infection or the need for rest.
T	F	16.	Mouth breathing indicates either nasal obstruction or a bad habit of breathing.
T	F	17.	The liver serves to eliminate waste materials only when the kidneys fail to perform their work satisfactorily.
T	F	18.	The kidneys are primarily complex filtering machines.
T	F	19.	Irregularities in diet have small effect on the normal function of the liver.
T	F	20.	Large quantities of water are reabsorbed into the body from the large intestine.

Items 21 to 40 include samples of several types of multiple-choice items. Read the directions given for each type carefully before answering the questions.

For items 21 to 24 select the *one best* answer and place the letter of the correct answer on the line beside the number of the question.

_____ 21. The largest and heaviest vertebrae are located in what region of the backbone?
    A. Cervical
    B. Thoracic
    C. Lumbar
    D. Sacral
    E. Coccygeal

_____ 22. In an infant the cranial bones have small spaces between them filled with membrane that are called:
    A. Fontanels
    B. Orifices
    C. Depressions
    D. Cavities
    E. Holes

_____ 23. A newborn baby's bones are composed mostly of:
    A. Bone
    B. Ligament
    C. Cartilage
    D. Muscle
    E. Tendon

_____ 24. What is a necessary component of the diet in order to build strong bones?
    A. Calcium
    B. Vitamin D
    C. Phosphorus
    D. All of the first three
    E. None of the above

Items 25 to 28 refer to the muscular system.

Key for items 25 to 28
    A. M is greater or more significant than N.
    B. N is greater or more significant than M.
    C. There is no significant difference between M and N

	M	N
_____ 25.	Size of muscles of women	Size of muscles of men
_____ 26.	Number of muscles in women	Number of muscles in men
_____ 27.	Size of muscle before training	Size of muscle after training
_____ 28.	Energy requirement of working muscle	Energy requirement of muscle at rest

Items 29 to 32 refer to the circulatory system.

Key for items 29 to 32
A. Statement is correct; reason is correct.
B. Statement is correct; reason is incorrect.
C. Statement is incorrect; reason is correct.
D. Statement is incorrect; reason is incorrect.

_____ 29. Both sides of the heart have the same approximate muscle size because both sides have the same work load to perform.
_____ 30. The heart is unable to rest because a person would probably die if the heart stopped beating for 5 minutes.
_____ 31. Good muscle tonus aids the heart in performing its job because the contraction of muscles moves the blood through the venous system.
_____ 32. Too few red corpuscles will result in anemia because red corpuscles fight infectious diseases.

Items 33 to 36 refer to the respiratory system.

Key for items 33 to 36
A. Epiglottis
B. Alveoli
C. Trachea
D. Glottis
E. Bronchi

_____ 33. Division of windpipe leading to the left and right lungs.
_____ 34. Made of several cartilaginous rings.
_____ 35. Space between the true vocal cords.
_____ 36. Functions as a hinged lid.

Items 37 to 40 refer to the excretory system.

Key for items 37 to 40
A. Liver
B. Kidneys
C. Large intestine
D. Skin

_____ 37. Waste materials acted on by large quantities of bacteria.
_____ 38. Filter for circulatory system.
_____ 39. Vitamin K produced here.
_____ 40. Conversion of protein to urea and carbohydrate.

Items 41 to 60 are matching questions. Select the correct alternative in the right-hand column of the related key and place its letter on the line beside the number of the question.

Key for items 41 to 47

_____ 41. Muscle end that moves on contraction.   A. Tonus
_____ 42. Accumulation of lactic acid.   B. Recovery period
_____ 43. Muscle working opposite to an extensor.   C. Actin
_____ 44. Condition in which all muscles are con-   D. Origin
            tracted slightly.   E. Flexor
_____ 45. Requires myosin to function normally.   F. Refractory period
_____ 46. A sustained muscle contraction.   G. Insertion
_____ 47. Time span following one stimulus when   H. Tetanus
            muscle is unable to respond to any   I. Oxygen debt
            other.   J. Smooth muscle

		Key for items 48 to 54*
_____	48. Red corpuscle	A. Helps the blood to clot
_____	49. Antibody	B. A blood protein
_____	50. Plasma	C. Infection triggers increase in number
_____	51. Prothrombin	D. Contains large quantities of iron
_____	52. Pernicious anemia	E. Found only in women
_____	53. Platelets	F. Related to adequate milk in the diet
_____	54. White blood cell	G. Liquid portion of blood
		H. A hereditary blood disease
		I. Protects against specific disease
		J. Produced in the large intestine

		Key to items 55 to 60
_____	55. Pleura	A. Thin covering sheet over each lung
_____	56. Nare	B. Voice box
_____	57. Pharynx	C. Air enters body through this
_____	58. Diaphragm	D. Digestive and respiratory systems cross here
_____	59. Larynx	E. A flap of tissue acting as a hinge
_____	60. Alveoli	F. Individual air sacs
		G. Sometimes called a bronchiole
		H. Divides the two body cavities

Items 61 to 68† are short answer questions. Most of these items can be answered by a single word; in no case use more than two or three words. Specific information is sought.

Bones that are growing require two important minerals to a greater extent than other necessary materials. What are these two minerals?

61. _____

62. _____

Muscle fatigue is due primarily to an accumulation of what waste product of respiration?

63. _____

Muscles which are attached to and move the bones of the skeleton are of a specific type. What is the name of these muscles?

64. _____

Some people are unfortunate in that their blood will not clot at all or, less serious, clots slowly. What is this condition called?

65. _____

If a foreign protein were introduced into your blood stream by any of several ways what would it be called?

66. _____

If a friend of yours received an electric shock so severe that his breathing stopped, what first aid measure would you exercise immediately?

67. _____

When kidney cells are infected by bacteria, what inclusive term is used to describe the condition?

68. _____

Part II—Sleep, rest, relaxation, and recreation

Numbers 69 to 73 are corrected true-false items. If the statement is true, encircle the T and go on to the next statement. If the statement is false, encircle

---

*The matching set of items 48 to 54 contains an error often made by those constructing test items. What is the error?

†Test items should be written so that no unnecessary clues are included. (What is wrong with item number 64 in this regard?)

the F and then correct the statement so that it reads true. You may change only the word or words that are underlined. Do not correct with a negative word or words; your change must be positive. Determine the intent of the statement; this may provide a lead to acceptable correction.

T   F   69. The fatigue that results from monotonous tasks may be reduced by working steadily without interruption.

T   F   70. Self-control is an important part of avoiding fatigue.

T   F   71. Irregular bedtime tends to interfere with fatigue-relieving sleep.

T   F   72. A hot bath before bedtime will aid relaxation and sleep.

T   F   73. The need for sleep increases with age.*

Numbers 74 to 78 are multiple-choice items. Select the one best answer for each and place its letter on the blank line.

_____ 74. Which of the following may cause chronic fatigue?
    A. Infection
    B. Poor nutrition
    C. Eye strain
    D. Painful feet
    E. All of the first four

_____ 75. Regular moderate exercise will do which of the following for the junior high school student?
    A. Increase the susceptibility to infection
    B. Eliminate the chances of developing a chronic disease.
    C. Increase intelligence.
    D. Develop efficiency of circulation.
    E. Cause the body to use less fuel.

Key for items 76 to 78
    A. Increase (increased)
    B. Decrease (decreased)
    C. Not change (not changed)

During sleep the heart rate is 76._____ in relation to its rate during activity. If you increase your physical activity, you will 77._____ your rate of growth. A busy schedule of daily activities with planned periods of relaxation is a good recipe to assure an 78.†_____ in happiness and accomplishment.

Items 79 and 80 are short answer questions. They may be answered by a single word or no more than two or three words. The information sought is quite specific.

79. The period of deepest sleep occurs when during a normal eight-hour cycle? _____

80. Scientific research indicates that exercise and rest have the following effect on the length of life. _____

The last two questions are short essay, and each is worth 10 points. Before you write, think through an outline of your answer including as many important points as possible. Write in complete sentences and stay on the subject. A good answer need not be lengthy.

---

*Number 73 is not a good item. Why?
†Item number 78 will not prove discriminating, but items of this sort are desirable occasionally. Why?

Question 1: What can you do during the two hours before going to bed to assure a satisfying and relaxed sleep?

Question 2: Recreation is important throughout life. What activities *do you* and *should you* take part in now that will be of value to you in later years?

Key to objective examination

Part I—Wholesome activity
True-false

1.	T	11.	T
2.	F	12.	T
3.	F	13.	F
4.	T	14.	F
5.	T	15.	T
6.	T	16.	T
7.	F	17.	F
8.	T	18.	T
9.	F	19.	F
10.	F	20.	T

Multiple-choice

21.	C	31.	A
22.	A	32.	B
23.	C	33.	E
24.	D	34.	C
25.	B	35.	D
26.	C	36.	A
27.	B	37.	C
28.	A	38.	B
29.	D	39.	C
30.	C	40.	A

Matching

41.	G	51.	B
42.	I	52.	H*
43.	E	53.	A
44.	A	54.	C
45.	C	55.	A
46.	H	56.	C
47.	F	57.	E
48.	D	58.	H
49.	I	59.	B
50.	G	60.	F

Short answer

61.	Calcium, and	65.	Hemophilia
62.	Phosphorus	66.	Antigen
63.	Lactic acid	67.	Artificial respiration
64.	Skeletal†	68.	Nephritis

---

*Item number 52 is a blood disease and is out of place among the other items which all refer to specific blood components. Such errors should be avoided if the test is to be satisfactory.

†In item number 64 the answer is cued in the question.

Part II—Sleep, rest, relaxation, and recreation

Corrected true-false

69. F—The corrected statement should contain the following concept. "The fatigue that results from monotonous tasks may be reduced by <u>a 5 or 10 minute rest period every hour.</u>"
70. T
71. T
72. F—This can be corrected in each of two places. The correction will read either: "A <u>tepid</u> bath before bedtime will <u>aid relaxation and sleep,</u>" or "A <u>hot</u> bath before bedtime will <u>stimulate the circulation and make sleep difficult.</u>"
73. F—This is basically a poor question since the only correction possible is to change *increase* to *decrease;* Thus, "The need for sleep <u>decreases</u> with age." Corrected true-false items should seek more important information <u>than simple</u> recognition and recall.

Multiple-choice

74. E
75. D
76. B
77. C
78. A*

Short answer

79. Middle hours
80. No known effect

Short essay

Two questions worth 10 points each are included here. These would be scored as indicated in the related discussion of Chapter 7.

———

*Item number 78 is important for the concept that it is designed to emphasize. As the sentence is written, only one answer is grammatically correct. Consequently, no student should get it wrong. Even so, a few of these questions are good to include, especially in the junior high where good health concepts are being developed.

Appendix C

FILMS

The following list of films is included to encourage and aid the teacher in using a wide variety of health films.

Over 700 film titles appropriate for high school health education are listed here. Most of these films have been produced within the last ten years. They have been grouped under the appropriate subject matter area as established in Chapter 6 and developed extensively throughout later chapters. The films under each area are listed alphabetically and include the rental source (or film producer) and the running time. Addresses are not included because of the number involved as well as of the local nature of film supply. Any local library will likely be able to provide addresses and advise as to whether there is a local or state office. This is especially true for voluntary agencies. Commercial sources often have a regional distributor that will provide rapid service.

PERSONAL HEALTH

Personal hygiene

1. *About faces,* American Dental Association; 4½ minutes.
2. *Betty sees a bird,* National Society for the Prevention of Blindness; 22 minutes.
3. *Body care and grooming,* McGraw-Hill Book Co., Inc.; 17 minutes.
4. *Care of the feet,* Encyclopaedia Britannica Films; 12 minutes.
5. *Clean look,* Association Films, Inc.; 30 minutes.
6. *Come clean,* American Dental Association; 10 minutes.
7. *Confidence because,* Personal Products Corp.; 15 minutes.
8. *Doctor Carter takes a drive* (dental caries), New York State Health Department; 20 minutes.
9. *Drop in the bucket* (fluoridation), American Dental Association; 13 minutes.
10. *Eyes: their structure and care,* Coronet Films; 11 minutes.
11. *Glaucoma,* National Society for the Prevention of Blindness; 22 minutes.
12. *Good grooming for girls,* Coronet Films; 11 minutes.
13. *Hair care,* International Film Bureau; 14 minutes.
14. *Heredity,* Encyclopaedia Britannica Films, Inc.; 11 minutes.
15. *Heredity and environment,* Coronet Films; 11 minutes
16. *Hold back the night* (glaucoma), National Society for the Prevention of Blindness; 22 minutes.
17. *How do you stand?* Modern Talking Picture Service; 15 minutes.
18. *How to be well-groomed,* Coronet Films; 10 minutes.

381

19. *Improving your posture,* Coronet Films; 11 minutes.
20. *Inside story,* American Dental Association; 10 minutes.
21. *It's wonderful being a girl,* Personal Products Corp.; 20 minutes.
22. *Laurie learns a secret,* American Dental Association; 17 minutes.
23. *Make-up,* International Film Bureau; 11 minutes.
24. *Making the most of your face,* Coronet Films; 11 minutes.
25. *Matter of choice,* American Dental Association; 27½ minutes.
26. *Miss Dunning goes to town* (good grooming), Association Films, Inc.; 27 minutes.
27. *Molly grows up,* Personal products Corp.; 15 minutes.
28. *More than meets the eye,* American Optometric Association; 26 minutes
29. *Notions 'bout motions* (posture and body mechanics), University of Minnesota Audio-Visual Education Service; 18 minutes.
30. *Our feet,* Bray Studios, Inc.; 10 minutes.
31. *Personal health for girls,* Coronet Films; 12 minutes.
32. *Personal hygiene for boys,* Coronet Films; 12 minutes.
33. *Posture,* International Film Bureau, Inc.; 9 minutes.
34. *Posture and exercise,* Encyclopaedia Britannica Films, Inc.; 11 minutes.
35. *Posture and personality,* Social Science Films; 11 minutes.
36. *Putting it straight* (teeth), International Films Bureau, Inc.; 14 minutes.
37. *Something to chew on* (dental hygiene), National Film Board of Canada; 19 minutes.
38. *Target: tooth decay,* University of Oklahoma; 10 minutes.
39. *Teeth: their structure and care,* Coronet Films; 13 minutes.
40. *The case of the missing tooth,* American Dental Society; 3½ minutes.
41. *The eyes and their care,* Encyclopaedia Britannica Films; 11 minutes.
42. *The story of menstruation,* Kimberly-Clark Corp.; 10 minutes.
43. *The teeth,* Encyclopaedia Britannica Films, Inc.; 11 minutes.
44. *The thread of life* (genetics), Bell Telephone Co.; 59 minutes.
45. *The value of a smile* (dental health), Knowledge Builder; 11 minutes.
46. *The walking machine,* American Foot Care Institute, Inc.; 14 minutes.
47. *Wardrobe,* International Film Bureau, Inc.; 14 minutes.
48. *Your body speaks* (posture), Center for Mass Communication; 11 minutes.
49. *Your cleanliness,* Young America Films; 12 minutes.
50. *Your ears and noise,* American Academy of Ophthalmology; 13 minutes.
51. *Your voice,* Encyclopaedia Britannica Films, Inc.; 11 minutes.

Nutrition

1. *Admirals in the making,* Oregon Dairy Council; 13½ minutes.
2. *Babies like to eat,* Social Science Films; 11 minutes.
3. *Balance your diet for health and appearance,* Coronet Films; 11 minutes.
4. *Buying food,* Young America Films; 12 minutes
5. *Consumer education series* (13 films), U. S. Department of Agriculture; 5½-6 minutes.
6. *Diet did it* (effects of nutrition), American Dental Association; 8 minutes.
7. *Facts about figures* (weight gain), Health Education Service; 13½ minutes
8. *Food as children see it,* General Mills; 17 minutes.
9. *Foods and nutrition,* Encyclopaedia Britannica Films, Inc.; 11 minutes.
10. *Food that builds good health,* Coronet Films; 10 minutes.
11. *Foundation foods,* Avis Films; 10 minutes.
12. *Fundamentals of diet,* Encyclopaedia Britannic Films, Inc.; 11 minutes.
13. *Fun in food,* Gateway Productions, Inc.; 9 minutes.
14. *It's all in knowing how* (nutrition), National Dairy Council; 13½ minutes
15. *Losing to win,* Metropolitan Life Insurance; 10 minutes.
16. *Making ends meet* (budgeting), National Dairy Council; 11 minutes.
17. *Man against hunger,* Farm Film Foundation; 14 minutes.
18. *Mystery in the kitchen,* National Film Board of Canada; 23 minutes.
19. *One loaf of bread,* General Mills; 15 minutes.

20. *Over the plate,* Oregon Dairy Council; 17 minutes.
21. *Principles of home canning,* Encyclopaedia Britannica Films, Inc.; 11 minutes.
22. *School lunches for a better world,* Farm Film Foundation; 10 minutes.
23. *Something you didn't eat,* U. S. Department of Agriculture; 10 minutes.
24. *Story of human energy,* Farm Film Foundation; 10 minutes.
25. *Terminal heat formula preparation,* Carnation Co.; 10 minutes.
26. *The best way to eat,* American Medical Association; 26 minutes
27. *The color of health,* American Bakers Association; 11 minutes.
28. *The fat American,* Carousel Films; 51 minutes.
29. *The human body: nutrition and metabolism,* Coronet Films; 13½ minutes.
30. *The owl and Mr. Jones* (diet control), Equitable Life Insurance Society; 15 minutes
31. *The right track* (nutrition), National Live Stock and Meat Boards; 15 minutes.
32. *The school that learned to eat,* Southern Educational Film Production Service; 22 minutes.
33. *The three squares* (canning) U. S. Department of Agriculture; 13½ minutes.
34. *Understanding vitamins,* Encyclopaedia Britannica Films, Inc.; 14 minutes.
35. *Visit with Betty Crocker,* General Mills; 15 minutes.
36. *Weight reduction through diet,* Association Films, Inc.; 20 minutes.
37. *Whenever you eat,* National Dairy Council; 12 minutes.
38. *Why won't Tommy eat?* Sterling Educational Films; 17 minutes.
39. *Your daily bread,* American Bakers Association; 12½ minutes.
40. *Your food,* Young America Films; 18 minutes.

Wholesome rest and activity

1. *About the human body,* Churchill Films; 15 minutes.
2. *Attitudes and health,* Coronet Films; 11 minutes.
3. *As boys grow,* E. C. Brown Trust; 15 minutes.
4. *Boy to man,* Churchill Films; 16 minutes.
5. *Circulation and the human body,* Churchill Films; 10 minutes.
6. *Circulation of the blood,* United World Films, Inc.; 16 minutes
7. *Control of body temperature,* Encyclopaedia Britannica Films, Inc.; 11 minutes.
8. *Dental health education in review,* American Dental Association; 6½ minutes.
9. *Digestion of foods,* Encyclopaedia Britannica Films, Inc.; 10 minutes.
10. *Elimination,* United World Films, Inc.; 13 minutes.
11. *Endocrine glands—how they affect you,* McGraw-Hill Book Co., Inc.; 15 minutes.
12. *Exercise and health,* Coronet Films; 11 minutes.
13. *Exercise for happy living,* Encyclopaedia Britannica Films, Inc.; 11 minutes.
14. *From generation to generation,* McGraw-Hill Book Co., Inc.; 32 minutes.
15. *From one cell,* American Cancer Society; 15 minutes
16. *Functions of the body,* United World Films, Inc.; 15 minutes.
17. *Functions of the nervous system,* Knowledge Builders; 11 minutes.
18. *Fundamentals of the nervous system,* Encyclopaedia Britannica Films, Inc.; 16 minutes.
19. *Gateways to the mind,* Bell Telephone Co.; 59 minutes.
20. *Guard your heart,* Bray Studios, Inc.; 30 minutes.
21. *Healthy lungs,* Oregon Tuberculosis and Health Association; 10 minutes.
22. *Heart and circulation,* Encyclopaedia Britannica Films, Inc.; 11 minutes.
23. *Heart—how it works,* McGraw-Hill Book Co., Inc.; 10 minutes.
24. *Hemo the magnificent* (blood), Bell Telephone Co.; 59 minutes.
25. *Hold back the night* (glaucoma), National Society for the Prevention of Blindness; 22 minutes.
26. *How the ear functions,* Knowledge Builders; 11 minutes.
27. *How the respiratory system functions,* Knowledge Builders; 11 minutes.
28. *How to avoid muscle strains,* Bray Studios, Inc.; 17 minutes.
29. *Human body—circulatory system,* American Heart Association; 14 minutes.
30. *Human growth,* E. C. Brown Trust; 20 minutes.
31. *Human reproduction,* McGraw-Hill Book Co., Inc.; 21 minutes.

32. *Johnny's new world*, National Society for the Prevention of Blindness; 13 minutes.
33. *Kidneys, ureters, and bladder*, Bray Studios, Inc.; 10 minutes.
34. *Life before birth*, Carousel Films, Inc.; 26 minutes.
35. *Life of a healthy child*, Knowledge Builders; 12 minutes.
36. *Life's higher goals* (fitness), Calvin Productions, Inc.; 29 minutes.
37. *Man is a universe* (human brain and nervous system), National Film Board of Canada; 12 minutes.
38. *Mechanisms of breathing*, Encyclopaedia Britannica Films, Inc.; 11 minutes.
39. *Muscular system*, United World Films, Inc.; 11 minutes.
40. *Over the plate* (fitness), National Dairy Council; 17 minutes.
41. *Physical aspects of puberty*, McGraw-Hill Book Co., Inc.; 19 minutes.
42. *Protoplasm—beginnings of life*, Bray Studios, Inc.; 10 minutes.
43. *Reproduction among mammals*, Encyclopaedia Britannica Films, Inc.; 11 minutes.
44. *Respiration*, United World Films, Inc.; 12 minutes.
45. *Response to the challenge* (fitness), Calvin Productions, Inc.; 30 minutes.
46. *Rest and health*, Coronet Films; 10 minutes.
47. *Road to health and happiness*, Knowledge Builders; 12 minutes.
48. *Secrets of the heart*, American Heart Association; 29 minutes.
49. *Shake hands with your feet*, Ohio College of Chiropody; 13 minutes.
50. *Spinal column*, Encyclopaedia Britannica Films, Inc.; 11 minutes.
51. *Story of menstruation*, International Cellucotton Products Co.; 10 minutes.
52. *Strokes*, American Heart Association; 7 minutes.
53. *Structure and function of bones*, Knowledge Builders; 11 minutes.
54. *The color of health* (fitness) American Bakers Association; 11 minutes.
55. *The doctor examines your heart*, Bray Studios, Inc.; 10 minutes.
56. *The ears and hearing*, Encyclopaedia Britannica Films, Inc.; 11 minutes.
57. *The foot and its problems*, American Podiatry Association; 20 minutes.
58. *The glass wall*, American Hearing Society; 28 minutes.
59. *The human body*, Institute of International Affairs; 9 minutes.
60. *The human body: digestive system*, Coronet Films; $13\frac{1}{2}$ minutes.
61. *The human body: excretory system*, Coronet Films; $13\frac{1}{2}$ minutes.
62. *The human body: muscular system*, Coronet Films; $13\frac{1}{2}$ minutes.
63. *The human body: nervous system*, Coronet Films; $13\frac{1}{2}$ minutes.
64. *The human body: reproductive system*, Coronet Films; $13\frac{1}{2}$ minutes.
65. *The human body: respiratory system*, Coronet Films; $13\frac{1}{2}$ minutes.
66. *The human brain*, Encyclopaedia Britannica Films, Inc.; 11 minutes.
67. *The human hair*, Bray Studios, Inc.; 10 minutes.
68. *The human skeleton*, United World Films, Inc.; 10 minutes.
69. *The human skin*, Bray Studios, Inc.; 10 minutes.
70. *The human throat*, Bray Studios, Inc.; 10 minutes.
71. *The magic pathway*, Better Vision Institute, Inc.; 21 minutes.
72. *The nose*, Encyclopaedia Britannica Films, Inc.; 11 minutes.
73. *The nose, throat, and ears*, McGraw-Hill Book Co., Inc.; 10 minutes.
74. *The skeleton*, Encyclopaedia Britannica Films, Inc.; 12 minutes.
75. *The time of our lives* (fitness) National Dairy Council; 13 minutes.
76. *The work of the kidneys*, Encyclopaedia Britannica Films, Inc.; 11 minutes.
77. *Wonder engine of the body*, American Medical Association; 11 minutes.
78. *Work of the blood*, Encyclopaedia Britannica Films, Inc.; 13 minutes.
79. *Your body during adolescence*, McGraw-Hill Book Co., Inc.; 10 minutes.
80. *Your ears*, Young America Films; 10 minutes.
81. *Your eyes*, Young America Films; 10 minutes.

Choice and use of health services

1. *American doctor* (osteopathy), American Osteopathic Association; 29 minutes.
2. *Another light* (small town hospital), Baily Films, Inc.; 25 minutes.

3. *At our house* (multiple screening), Center for Mass Communication; 9 minutes.
4. *Career in the profession of dentistry*, American Dental Association; 32 minutes.
5. *Career: medical technologist*, American Cancer Society; 24 minutes.
6. *Choosing a doctor*, McGraw-Hill Book Co., Inc.; 16 minutes.
7. *Citizens participate*, Young America Films; 26 minutes.
8. *Consumer protection*, Coronet Films; 10 minutes.
9. *Doctor in industry*, General Motors Corp.; 60 minutes.
10. *Living insurance* (periodical examination), American Cancer Society; 14 minutes.
11. *Modern surgery*, March of Time–McGraw-Hill Book Co., Inc.; 18 minutes.
12. *Mr. Williams wakes up*, North Carolina Board of Health; 28 minutes.
13. *New day in dentistry*, American Dental Association; 13½ minutes.
14. *Pattern of a profession*, American Dental Association; 28 and 51 minute versions.
15. *Quacks and nostrums*, McGraw-Hill Book Co., Inc.; 19 minutes.
16. *Special request films*, American Cancer Society; 25 minutes.
17. *Student nurse*, International Film Bureau; 30 minutes.
18. *The doctor*, United World Films, Inc.; 14 minutes.
19. *The medicine man* (food faddists and quacks), American Medical Association; 28 minutes.
20. *The misery merchants* (arthritis quackery), Institute of Visual Communication, Inc.; 29 minutes.
21. *The winged foot*, American Podiatry Association; 13½ minutes.
22. *To keep them well*, Sam Orleans and Associates, Inc.; 15 minutes.
23. *Within your hands*, American Physical Therapy Association; 17½ minutes.

COMMUNITY HEALTH
Prevention and control of disease

1. *A voice is heard* (ear operation), McGraw-Hill Book Co., Inc.; 26 minutes.
2. *A way in the wilderness* (pellagra), teaching Films Custodians, Inc.; 11 minutes.
3. *Allergies*, Encyclopaedia Britannica Films, Inc.; 12 minutes.
4. *Antibiotics*, Encyclopaedia Britannica Films, Inc.; 14 minutes.
5. *Are you positive?* National Tuberculosis Association; 13½ minutes.
6. *Arteriosclerosis*, American Heart Association; 14 minutes.
7. *Bacteria—friend and foe*, Encyclopaedia Britannica Films, Inc.; 11 minutes.
8. *Be your age* (heart trouble), Metropolitan Life Insurance Co.; 11 minutes.
9. *Billion dollar malady—the common cold*, Bray Studios, Inc.; 15 minutes.
10. *Birthright* (congenital syphilis), Center of Mass Communication; 45 minutes.
11. *Body defenses against disease*, Encyclopaedia Britannica Films, Inc.; 11 minutes.
12. *Body fights bacteria*, McGraw-Hill Book Co., Inc.; 17 minutes.
13. *Cancer*, Encyclopaedia Britannica Films, Inc.; 12 minutes.
14. *Challenge: science against cancer*, International Film Bureau, Inc.; 33 minutes.
15. *Choose to live* (cancer), Castle Films; 11 minutes.
16. *Cloud in the sky*, Oregon Tuberculosis and Health Association; 18 minutes.
17. *Common cold*, Encyclopaedia Britannica Films, Inc.; 11 minutes.
18. *Common heart disorders and their causes*, McGraw-Hill Book Co., Inc.; 17 minutes
19. *Confessions of a cold*, Medical Motion Pictures; 13 minutes.
20. *Confidential file: Epilepsy*, Epilepsy League of Oregon, Inc.; 22 minutes.
21. *Coronary heart disease*, American Heart Association; 5 minutes.
22. *Crusade*, American Cancer Society; 11 minutes.
23. *Defense against invasion*, Oregon Tuberculosis and Health Association; 16 minutes.
24. *Diabetes and you, too!* International Film Bureau, Inc.; 21 minutes.
25. *Diabetics unknown*, Public Affairs Committee; 30 minutes.
26. *Fair chance*, Oregon Tuberculosis and Health Association; 14½ minutes.
27. *Feeling all right* (syphilis), Center for Mass Communication; Columbia University, 30 minutes.
28. *From one cell*, American Cancer Society; 12 minutes.

29. *Goodbye, Mr. Germ,* Oregon Tuberculosis and Health Association; 14 minutes.
30. *Guard your heart,* American Heart Association; 27 minutes.
31. *Healing of M'Vondo,* American Leprosy Missions, Inc.; 32 minutes.
32. *Heart disease—its major causes,* Encyclopaedia Britannica Films, Inc.; 11 minutes.
33. *Heart to heart,* Oregon Heart Association; 15 minutes.
34. *Helping hands for Julie,* Oregon Tuberculosis and Health Association; 28 minutes.
35. *High blood pressure,* American Heart Association; 7 minutes.
36. *How to catch a cold,* Kimberly-Clark Corp.; 10 minutes.
37. *Hunt for a cancer killer,* McGraw-Hill Book Co., Inc.; 27 minutes.
38. *Immunization,* Encyclopaedia Britannica Films, Inc.; 11 minutes.
39. *Infectious diseases and man-made defenses,* Coronet Films; 11 minutes.
40. *Inside Magoo,* American Cancer Society, Oregon Division; 7 minutes.
41. *Interim report* (poliomyelitis epidemic to Salk), National Foundation, Inc.; 15 minutes.
42. *Lease on life,* Oregon Tuberculosis and Health Association; 20 minutes.
43. *Let my people live,* Oregon Tuberculosis and Health Association; 15 minutes.
44. *Lifted hands* (leprosy), American Leprosy Missions, Inc.; 20 minutes.
45. *Living insurance,* American Cancer Society, Oregon Division; 14 minutes.
46. *Loretta* (birth defects), The National Foundation, Oregon State Office; 28 minutes.
47. *Louis Pasteur: man of science,* Sterling Films, Inc.; 30 minutes.
48. *Man against microbe,* Metropolitan Life Insurance Co.; 10 minutes.
49. *Man alive,* American Cancer Society; 12 minutes.
50. *Merry-go-round,* Oregon Tuberculosis and Health Association; 25 minutes.
51. *Message to women* (venereal disease), U. S. Public Health Service; 20 minutes.
52. *Micro-organisms: harmful effects,* Indiana University; 15 minutes.
53. *Modern medicine looks at the heart,* American Heart Association; 27 minutes.
54. *New frontiers of the brain,* McGraw-Hill Book Co., Inc.; 27 minutes.
55. *On our own* (rehabilitation), The National Foundation; 14 minutes.
56. *On prescription only* (modern miracle drugs), National Film Board of Canada; 30 minutes.
57. *Our job to know* (venereal disease), American Social Health Association; 10 minutes.
58. *Pneumonia,* Encyclopaedia Britannica Films, Inc.; 10 minutes.
59. *Poisons, pests, and people,* National Film Board of Canada, Part I and Part II; 30 minutes each.
60. *Problem of diagnosis,* American Heart Association; 30 minutes.
61. *Question of birth defects,* National Foundation, Inc.; 23 minutes.
62. *Rabies,* McGraw-Hill Book Co., Inc.; 15 minutes.
63. *Rabies in your community,* National Film Board of Canada; 18 minutes.
64. *Report on cancer,* International Film Bureau; 23 minutes.
65. *Round trip* (rheumatic fever), Oregon Heart Association; 14 minutes.
66. *Sappy homiens,* American Cancer Society, Oregon Division; 7 minutes.
67. *Sixteen to twenty-six* (syphilis), National Film Board of Canada; 18 minutes.
68. *Smallpox,* Brandon Films, Inc.; 9 minutes.
69. *Sniffles and sneezes,* McGraw-Hill Book Co., Inc.; 10 minutes.
70. *Social-sex attitudes in adolescence,* McGraw-Hill Book Co., Inc.; 22 minutes.
71. *Story of Dr. Jenner,* Teaching Film Custodians, Inc.; 10 minutes.
72. *Striking back against rabies,* U. S. Public Health Service; 12 minutes.
73. *TB—why does it strike?* Oregon Tuberculosis and Health Association; 22 minutes.
74. *TB—why it strikes,* McGraw-Hill Book Co., Inc.; 26 minutes.
75. *The anatomy of a disease,* Oregon Tuberculosis and Health Association; 14$\frac{1}{2}$ minutes.
76. *The atom and medicine,* Encyclopaedia Britannica Films, Inc.; 12 minutes.
77. *The barbed wire fence* (leprosy) American Leprosy Missions, Inc.; 27 minutes.
78. *The body fights back,* McGraw-Hill Book Co., Inc.; 10 minutes.
79. *The challenge,* The National Foundation; 15 minutes.
80. *The concept,* The National Foundation; 15 minutes.
81. *The discovery of insulin,* International Film Bureau, Inc.; 19 minutes.

82. *The epidemiology of influenza*, U. S. Public Health Service; 13 minutes.
83. *The fight: science against cancer*, International Film Bureau; 21 minutes.
84. *The human cell and the cytotechnologist*, American Cancer Society; 22½ minutes
85. *The innocent party* (venereal disease), Communicable Disease Center, Atlanta; 17 minutes.
86. *The inside story*, Oregon Tuberculosis and Health Association; 14 minutes.
87. *The invader* (venereal disease), Communicable Disease Center; Atlanta, 29 minutes.
88. *The ion knife* (treatment of cancer), Smith, Kline and French Laboratories; 30 minutes.
89. *The other city*, American Cancer Society; 11½ minutes.
90. *The other half of the team*, Muscular Dystrophy Associations of America; 15 minutes.
91. *The quest* (insulin for diabetes), International Film Bureau; 37 minutes.
92. *The Scouler case* (cancer), National Film Board of Canada; 13 minutes.
93. *The story of Louis Pasteur*, Hydrophia Sequence, Teaching Film Custodians, Inc.; 17 minutes.
94. *The traitor within*, American Cancer Society; 10½ minutes.
95. *The warning shadow*, American Cancer Society; 17 minutes.
96. *They live again* (discovery of insulin), Teaching Film Custodians, Inc.; 11 minutes.
97. *This is TB*, Oregon Tuberculosis and Health Association; 11 minutes.
98. *Time out*, National Tuberculosis Association; 25 minutes.
99. *To have dominion*, Muscular Dystrophy Associations of America; 15 minutes.
100. *Tracking the sleeping death* (sleeping sickness), Teaching Films Custodians, Inc.; 10 minutes.
101. *Trail to health*, Oregon Tuberculosis and Health Association; 20 minutes.
102. *Triumph without drums* (passage of Federal Food, Drug, and Cosmetic Act), Teaching Films Custodians, Inc.; 10 minutes.
103. *Tuberculosis*, Encyclopaedia Britannica Films, Inc.; 11 minutes.
104. *Two lives*, Oregon Tuberculosis and Health Association; 15 minutes.
105. *Unconditional surrender* (Salk vaccine), The National Foundation; 15 minutes.
106. *Unsuspected*, Oregon Tuberculosis and Health Association; 15 minutes.
107. *Winged scourge*, Oregon Tuberculosis and Health Association; 20 minutes.
108. *Within man's power*, Oregon Tuberculosis and Health Association; 29 minutes
109. *World of microbes*, Oregon Tuberculosis and Health Association; 30 minutes.
110. *Yellow Jack*, Teaching Film Custodians, Inc.; 29 minutes.
111. *You, time, and cancer*, American Cancer Society; 16 minutes.

Community health services and agencies

1. *Aftermath* (international services), American Red Cross; 14½ minutes
2. *Anatomy of a hospital*, McGraw-Hill Book Co., Inc.; 54 minutes.
3. *And on to the sea* (stream pollution), KOIN-TV, Portland, Oregon, 20 minutes.
4. *Basic sanitation—community fly control*, McGeary-Smith Laboratories; 10 minutes.
5. *Behind the menu* (restaurant sanitation), National Film Board of Canada; 10 minutes.
6. *Capital story* (industrial hygiene), Castle Films; 20 minutes.
7. *Careers in recreation*, Association Films; 27 minutes.
8. *City water supply*, Encyclopaedia Britannica Films, Inc.; 11 minutes.
9. *Clean waters*, General Electric Co.; 21 minutes.
10. *Colorado cares* (migrant problem), Colorado State Department of Health; 28 minutes.
11. *Community health and you*, McGraw-Hill Book Co., Inc.; 10 minutes
12. *Community health in action*, Sam Orleans and Associates; 22½ minutes.
13. *Community health is up to you*, McGraw-Hill Book Co., Inc.; 18 minutes.
14. *Contamination of water supplies by back siphonage*, University of Minnesota Audio-Visual Education Service; 20 minutes.
15. *Decent burial* (sanitary Land fill), Caterpillar Tractor Co.; 12½ minutes.
16. *Defending the city's health*, Encyclopaedia Britannica Films, Inc.; 11 minutes.
17. *Decision* (community hospital), Blue Cross Association; 30 minutes.
18. *Dialogue with life* (modern medical practice), Health Insurance Institute; 26 minutes.

19. *Do unto others* (rehabilitation), National Foundation, Inc.; 14 minutes.
20. *Engineering your health,* U. S. Public Health Service; 14 minutes.
21. *Environmental sanitation,* Institute of International American Affairs; 10 minutes.
22. *Every part of town* (disaster service), American Red Cross; 14½ minutes.
23. *Fluoridation,* American Dental Association; 5 minutes.
24. *For the nation's health,* U. S. Public Health Service; 16 minutes.
25. *For us the living* (governmental health service), Visual Training Institute; 20 minutes.
26. *Friend in blue* (public health nursing), University of Minnesota Audio-Visual Education Service; 30 minutes.
27. *George Washington's river,* U. S. Public Health Service; 28 minutes.
28. *Get rid of rats,* National Film Board of Canada; 10 minutes.
29. *Health careers,* National Health Council; 15 minutes.
30. *Health in our community,* Encyclopaedia Britannica Films, Inc.; 13 minutes.
31. *Join the health team,* Lane County, Oregon, Medical Society; 10 minutes.
32. *Journey into medicine,* Castle Films; 39 minutes.
33. *Leaders for leisure,* Association Films; 21 minutes.
34. *Nancy Edwards—Public Health Nurse,* Health Education Service; 20 minutes.
35. *One thousand dollars for recreation* (community recreation program), Association Films; 12 minutes.
36. *People to people* (United States nutrition survey teams), U. S. Public Health Service; 25 minutes.
37. *Project Hope* (S. S. Hope), Modern Talking Picture Service; 27 minutes.
38. *Pure water and public health,* Modern Talking Picture Service; 28 minutes.
39. *Quality and people* (drug Preparation), Eli Lilly & Co.; 25 minutes.
40. *Report to the nation* (heart research), U. S. Public Health Service; 29 minutes.
41. *Safe TB nursing,* Oregon Tuberculosis and Health Association; 20 minutes.
42. *School health in action,* Sam Orleans Film Productions, Inc.; 25 minutes.
43. *So much for so little,* U. S. Public Health Service; 11 minutes.
44. *The fluoridation story,* U. S. Public Health Service; 3 minutes.
45. *The greatest good* (drugs development), The Upjohn Co.; 27 minutes.
46. *The National Institutes of Health,* U. S. Public Health Service; 24 minutes.
47. *The view from the mountain* (dietetic internship), American Dietetic Association; 20 minutes.
48. *Town and country recreation,* Association Films; 20 minutes.
49. *Truth about fluoridation,* American Dental Association; 12 minutes.
50. *Water for the community,* Coronet Films; 11 minutes.
51. *Water for the west,* U. S. Department of Agriculture; 25 minutes.
52. *You and research,* National Foundation, Inc.; 30 minutes.

MENTAL HEALTH
Personality and character development

1. *Act your age,* Coronet Films; 13½ minutes.
2. *Age of turmoil,* McGraw-Hill Book Co., Inc.; 20 minutes.
3. *Are you popular?* Coronet Films; 11 minutes.
4. *Are you ready for marriage?* Coronet Films; 16 minutes.
5. *As others see us* (manners), Social Science Films; 11 minutes.
6. *Beginning to date,* Encyclopaedia Britannica Films, Inc.; 12 minutes.
7. *Being different,* National Film Board of Canada; 11 minutes.
8. *Belonging to the group,* Encyclopaedia Britannica Films, Inc.; 16 minutes.
9. *Benefits of looking ahead,* Coronet Films; 11 minutes.
10. *Better use of leisure time,* Coronet Films; 11 minutes.
11. *Beyond the shadows* (mental retardation), Colorado State Department of Health; 26 minutes.
12. *Billy and Beethoven* (individual development), National Foundation, Inc.; 14 minutes.
13. *Breakdown,* McGraw-Hill Book Co., Inc.; 41 minutes.

14. *By Jupiter!* (courtesy), Wilding Productions; 27 minutes
15. *Cheating,* Young America Films; 12 minutes.
16. *Child behind the wall,* Smith, Kline and French Laboratories; 30 minutes.
17. *Children's emotions,* McGraw-Hill Book Co., Inc.; 22 minutes.
18. *Choosing your marriage partner,* Coronet Films; 13½ minutes.
19. *College: your challenge,* Coronet Films; 11 minutes.
20. *Date etiquette,* Coronet Films; 11 minutes.
21. *Dating: do's and don'ts,* Coronet Films; 13½ minutes.
22. *Discovery* (social responsibility), American Red Cross; 22 minutes.
23. *Farewell to childhood,* International Film Bureau, Inc.; 23 minutes.
24. *Going steady?* Coronet Films; 11 minutes.
25. *Good sportsmanship,* Coronet Films; 11 minutes.
26. *Gossip,* Sid Davis Productions; 10 minutes.
27. *Habit patterns,* McGraw-Hill Book Co., Inc.; 15 minutes.
28. *He acts his age* (child's development), McGraw-Hill Book Co., Inc.; 15 minutes.
29. *Heritage* (rights of man), McGraw-Hill Book Co., Inc.; 10 minutes.
30. *High school prom* (etiquette), Coronet Films; 16 minutes.
31. *High school: your challenge,* Coronet Films; 13½ minutes.
32. *Honest truth,* McGraw-Hill Book Co., Inc.; 5 minutes.
33. *How do you know it's love?* Coronet Films; 13 minutes.
34. *How much affection?* McGraw-Hill Book Co., Inc.; 20 minutes.
35. *How to say No* (moral maturity), Coronet Films; 11 minutes.
36. *How to succeed in school,* Young America Films; 11 minutes.
37. *Improve your personality,* Coronet Films; 11 minutes.
38. *Is this love?* McGraw-Hill Book Co., Inc.; 14 minutes.
39. *Learning to study,* Encyclopaedia Britannica Films, Inc.; 14 minutes.
40. *Majority vote,* McGraw-Hill Book Co., Inc.; 7 minutes.
41. *Make your own decisions,* Coronet Films; 11 minutes.
42. *Making a decision,* McGraw-Hill Book Co., Inc.; 7 minutes.
43. *Making friends,* Encyclopaedia Britannica Films, Inc.; 11 minutes.
44. *Making life adjustments,* McGraw-Hill Book Co., Inc.; 20 minutes.
45. *Man alive* (psychology of fear), American Cancer Society; 12 minutes.
46. *Mind your manners,* Coronet Films; 11 minutes.
47. *Mr. Finley's feelings,* Metropolitan Life Insurance Co.; 10 minutes.
48. *Other peoples' property,* Young America Films; 11 minutes.
49. *Overcoming fear,* Coronet Films; 13½ minutes.
50. *Overcoming worry,* Coronet Films; 11 minutes.
51. *Personality and emotions,* Encyclopaedia Britannica Films, Inc.; 13 minutes.
52. *Planning for success,* Coronet Films; 11 minutes.
53. *Responsibility,* Young America Films; 14 minutes.
54. *Right or wrong* (making moral decisions), Coronet Films; 11 minutes.
55. *School activities and you,* Coronet Films; 11 minutes.
56. *School spirit and sportsmanship,* Coronet Films; 11 minutes.
57. *Self-conscious guy,* Coronet Films; 11 minutes.
58. *Shy guy,* Coronet Films; 13½ minutes.
59. *Snap out of it* (overcoming disappointments), Coronet Films; 13½ minutes.
60. *Social courtesy,* Coronet Films; 11 minutes.
61. *The baby-sitter,* Young America Films; 15 minutes.
62. *The bully,* Young America Films; 11 minutes.
63. *The good loser,* Young America Films; 14 minutes.
64. *The gossip,* Young America Films; 14 minutes.
65. *The other fellow's feelings,* Young America Films; 11 minutes.
66. *The procrastinator,* Young America Films; 12 minutes.
67. *The show-off,* Young America Films; 12 minutes.
68. *The snob,* Young America Films; 14 minutes.

69. *The teens* (behavior of teen-agers), McGraw-Hill Book Co., Inc.; 27 minutes.
70. *The troublemaker,* McGraw-Hill Book Co., Inc.; 13 minutes.
71. *There was a door* (treatment of mentally retarded), Contemporary Films, Inc.; 30 minutes.
72. *Toward emotional maturity,* McGraw-Hill Book Co., Inc.; 11 minutes.
73. *Understanding aggression,* Contemporary Films, Inc.; 23 minutes.
74. *Understanding your emotions,* Coronet Films; 13½ minutes.
75. *Understanding your ideals,* Coronet Films; 13½ minutes.
76. *What is conscience?* Coronet Films; 13½ minutes.
77. *When should I marry?* McGraw-Hill Book Co., Inc.; 19 minutes.
78. *Wind up a winner* (sportsmanship), Ideal Pictures; 19 minutes.

Alcohol, other narcotics, and tobacco

1. *Alcohol and the human body,* Encyclopaedia Britannica Films, Inc.; 15 minutes.
2. *Alcohol and tobacco* (what they do to our bodies), Coronet Films; 11 minutes.
3. *Alcohol is dynamite,* Sid Davis Productions; 10 minutes.
4. *Alcoholism,* Encyclopaedia Britannica Films, Inc.; 22 minutes.
5. *Alcoholism: the revolving door,* Smith, Kline and French Laboratories; 30 minutes.
6. *Any boy—U. S. A.* (alcohol), National W.C.T.U.; 24 minutes.
7. *Behind the skyscrapers* (alcohol), National W.C.T.U.; 27 minutes.
8. *Brain is the reason* (alcohol), National W.C.T.U.; 30 minutes.
9. *Drug addiction,* Encyclopaedia Britannica Films, Inc.; 21 minutes.
10. *Drunk driving,* National W.C.T.U.; 20 minutes.
11. *Family affair* (alcohol), National W.C.T.U.; 13 minutes.
12. *Friendly enemy* (alcohol), National W.C.T.U.; 25 minutes.
13. *H—A story of a teen-age drug addict,* Young America Films; 20 minutes.
14. *Kid brother* (alcohol), Mental Health Film Board; 27 mintues.
15. *Liquor lore,* National W.C.T.U.; 22 minutes.
16. *Monkey on the back* (drug addiction), McGraw-Hill Book Co., Inc.; 30 minutes.
17. *None for the road,* Young America Films; 15 minutes.
18. *No smoking,* Sid Davis Productions; 10 minutes.
19. *One day at a time* (alcoholics anonymous), E. I. DuPont Nemours and Co.; 30 minutes.
20. *Out of orbit,* Michigan State Board on Alcoholism; 14 minutes.
21. *Profile of a problem drinker,* McGraw-Hill Book Co., Inc.; 30 minutes.
22. *Public enemy number 1* (alcohol), National W.C.T.U.; 23 minutes.
23. *Seduction of the innocent* (drug addiction), Sid Davis Productions; 10 minutes.
24. *Should you drink?* McGraw-Hill Book Co., Inc.; 30 minutes.
25. *Terrible truth* (drug addiction), Sid Davis Productions; 10 minutes.
26. *The addicted* (Parts I and II), Prudential Insurance Co. of America; 30 minutes, each.
27. *The bottle and the throttle,* Sid Davis Productions; 10 minutes.
28. *Theobald faces and facts* (alcohol), National W.C.T.U.; 13½ minutes.
29. *Tobacco and the human body,* Encyclopaedia Britannica Films, Inc.; 15 minutes.
30. *To your health* (alcohol), Center for Mass Communication, Columbia University; 10 minutes.
31. *What about alcohol?* National W.C.T.U.; 12 minutes.
32. *What about alcoholism?* McGraw-Hill Book Co., Inc.; 11 minutes.
33. *What about drinking?* Young America Films; 10 minutes.

Individual adjustment to society

1. *A day in the night of Jonathan Mole* (racial prejudice), McGraw-Hill Book Co., Inc.; 33 minutes.
2. *Age 13* (mental hygiene), Sid Davis Productions; 27 minutes.
3. *After prison what?* National Film Board of Canada; 12 minutes.
4. *Back into the sun* (mental illness), National Film Board of Canada; 27 minutes.
5. *Bitter welcome* (discharged mental patient), Mental Health Film Board; 26 minutes.

6. *Borderline* (mental health), McGraw-Hill Book Co., Inc.; 30 minutes.
7. *Boundary lines* (prejudice), McGraw-Hill Book Co., Inc.; 10 minutes.
8. *Boy with a knife* (delinquency), International Film Bureau; 24 minutes.
9. *Children of the city,* British Information Services; 30 minutes.
10. *Clinical types of mental deficiency,* University of Minnesota Audio-Visual Education Service; 33 minutes.
11. *Developing friendships,* Coronet Films; 10 minutes.
12. *Dr. Pinel unchains the insane,* McGraw-Hill Book Co., Inc.; 27 minutes.
13. *Emotional health,* McGraw-Hill Book Co., Inc.; 20 minutes.
14. *Emotional maturity,* McGraw-Hill Book Co., Inc.; 20 minutes.
15. *Eternal children* (retarded children), International Film Bureau; 30 minutes.
16. *Everybody's prejudiced,* McGraw-Hill Book Co., Inc.; 22 minutes.
17. *Facing reality,* McGraw-Hill Book Co., Inc.; 12 minutes.
18. *Feelings of depression,* McGraw-Hill Book Co., Inc.; 32 minutes.
19. *From ten to twelve,* McGraw-Hill Book Co., Inc.; 26 minutes.
20. *Gang boy* (juvenile delinquency), Sid Davis Productions; 27 minutes.
21. *Head of the house* (emotional problems of young boy), U. S. Public Health Service; 40 minutes.
22. *High wall* (intolerance), McGraw-Hill Book Co., Inc.; 32 minutes.
23. *How much affection?* McGraw-Hill Book Co., Inc.; 20 minutes.
24. *Howard* (problems of adolescence), International Film Bureau; 30 minutes.
25. *In this dark world* (adjusting to blindness), International Film Bureau; 30 minutes.
26. *Jerry joins up,* Agra Films; 22 minutes.
27. *Joe and Roxy* (problems of adolescence), International Film Bureau; 30 minutes.
28. *Life with Grandpa* (problems of old age), McGraw-Hill Book Co., Inc.; 17 minutes.
29. *Mental health,* Encyclopaedia Britannica Films, Inc.; 12 minutes.
30. *Moment of decision* (stealing), Sid Davis Productions; 10 minutes.
31. *Name unknown* (sex crime prevention), Sid Davis Productions; 10 minutes.
32. *Night children* (neglected children), National Film Board of Canada; 27 minutes.
33. *On our own* (rehabilitation), National Foundation, Inc.; 14 minutes.
34. *Out of true* (education for mental treatment), Contemporary Films, Inc.; 38 minutes.
35. *Over-dependency,* McGraw-Hill Book Co., Inc.; 32 minutes.
36. *Picture in your mind* (racial prejudice), McGraw-Hill Book Co., Inc.; 16 minutes.
37. *Shyness,* McGraw-Hill Book Co., Inc.; 23 minutes.
38. *Social acceptability,* McGraw-Hill Book Co., Inc.; 20 minutes.
39. *Stigma* (mental health), International Film Bureau; 20 minutes.
40. *Stress,* McGraw-Hill Book Co., Inc.; 11 minutes.
41. *The cage* (emotional strain), McGraw-Hill Book Co., Inc.; 30 minutes.
42. *The dropout* (from high school), Contemporary Films, Inc.; 29 minutes.
43. *The feeling of hostility,* McGraw-Hill Book Co., Inc.; 33 minutes.
44. *The feeling of rejection,* McGraw-Hill Book Co., Inc.; 21 minutes.
45. *The gifted ones* (gifted children), International Film Bureau; 22 minutes.
46. *The golden age* (geriatrics), McGraw-Hill Book Co., Inc.; 30 minutes.
47. *The hickory stick* (discipline), Contemporary Films, Inc.; 28 minutes.
48. *The longer trail,* National Film Board of Canada; 30 minutes.
49. *The outsider,* McGraw-Hill Book Co., Inc.; 13 minutes.
50. *The quiet one* (juvenile delinquency), Contemporary Films, Inc.; 70 minutes.
51. *The return,* American Physical Therapy Association; 38 or 28 minutes.
52. *The yellow leaf* (geriatrics), McGraw-Hill Book Co., Inc.; 30 minutes.
53. *To live again* (rehabilitation and adjustment), Modern Talking Picture Service; 29 minutes.
54. *To serve the mind,* McGraw-Hill Book Co., Inc.; 25 minutes.
55. *Understanding others,* McGraw-Hill Book Co., Inc.; 12 minutes.
56. *Vandalism,* Sid Davis Productions; 10 minutes.
57. *Wayne University* (juvenile delinquency), McGraw-Hill Book Co., Inc.; 27 minutes.

58. *What about juvenile delinquency?* Young America Films; 12 minutes.
59. *What about prejudice?* Young America Films; 12 minutes.
60. *What's on your mind?* (mental health), National Film Board of Canada; 11 minutes.
61. *Who is Sylvia?* (problems of adolescence), International Film Bureau; 30 minutes.

Family living

1. *A date with your family,* Encyclopaedia Britannica Films, Inc.; 11 minutes.
2. *Bathing time for baby,* Association Films, Inc.; 13 minutes.
3. *Biography of the unborn,* Encyclopaedia Britannica Films, Inc.; 16 minutes.
4. *Care of the newborn baby,* Castle Films; 31 minutes.
5. *Child care and development,* McGraw-Hill Book Co., Inc.; 17 minutes.
6. *Choosing for happiness* (marriage), McGraw-Hill Book Co., Inc.; 14 minutes.
7. *Doctor Spock,* McGraw-Hill Book Co., Inc.; 26 minutes.
8. *Early marriage,* E. C. Brown Trust; 26 minutes.
9. *Fair chance* (planned parenthood), Parthenon Pictures; 14½ minutes.
10. *Family circles,* National Film Board of Canada; 31 minutes.
11. *Family life,* Coronet Films; 11 minutes.
12. *Friendship begins at home,* Coronet Films; 16 minutes.
13. *Getting along with parents,* Encyclopaedia Britannica Films, Inc.; 15 minutes.
14. *Heredity and family environment,* McGraw-Hill Book Co., Inc.; 9 minutes.
15. *Human heredity,* E. C. Brown Trust; 20 minutes.
16. *In search of home* (child adoption), National Film Board of Canada; 11 minutes.
17. *In the beginning* (reproduction), U. S. Department of Agriculture; 17 minutes.
18. *It takes all kinds* (marriage), McGraw-Hill Book Co., Inc.; 20 minutes.
19. *Marriage is a partnership,* Coronet Films; 16 minutes.
20. *Marriage today,* McGraw-Hill Book Co., Inc.; 22 minutes.
21. *Know your baby,* Sterling Educational Films; 11 minutes.
22. *Palmour Strut* (family mental health), Center for Mass Communication, Columbia University; 27 minutes.
23. *Parents are people, too,* McGraw-Hill Book Co., Inc.; 15 minutes.
24. *The lengthening span* (geriatrics), Smith, Kline and French Laboratories; 30 minutes.
25. *This charming couple,* McGraw-Hill Book Co., Inc.; 19 minutes.
26. *Thread of life* (heredity), Farm Film Foundation; 58 minutes.
27. *Who should decide?* (parental influence), Coronet Films; 11 minutes.
28. *Who's boss?* McGraw-Hill Book Co., Inc.; 16 minutes.
29. *You and your parents,* Coronet Films; 13½ minutes.

SAFE LIVING

Home

1. *Are you safe at home?* United World Films, Inc.; 16 minutes.
2. *Case of the cluttered corner,* National Safety Council; 15 minutes.
3. *Doorway to death,* Aetna Life Insurance Co.; 13 minutes.
4. *Giant step,* Creative Arts; 12 minutes.
5. *Home homicide,* Center for Mass Communication, Columbia University; 8 minutes.
6. *Home safety and health departments,* U. S. Public Health Service; 15 minutes.
7. *House in the middle,* Oregon Civil Defense Agency; 12 minutes.
8. *How to have an accident in the home,* Walt Disney Productions; 8 minutes.
9. *Kitchen safety,* Young America Films; 13 minutes.
10. *Let's be safe at home,* Portafilms; 10 minutes.
11. *Mrs. Hazard's house,* Prudential Life Insurance Co.; 13 minutes.
12. *One day's poison,* National Film Board of Canada; 30 minutes.
13. *Safe living at home,* Coronet Films; 11 minutes.
14. *Safety in the home,* Encyclopaedia Britannica Films, Inc.; 11 minutes.
15. *Stop them before they start* (fire), Aetna Life Insurance Co.; 14½ minutes.
16. *Take time to live,* National Safety Council; 12 minutes.

17. *You can take it with you,* National Safety Council; 15 minutes.
18. *Your health at home,* Coronet Films; 11 minutes.

School

1. *A safe shop,* Young America Films; 11 minutes.
2. *Civil defense in schools,* Oregon State Civil Defense Administration; 28 minutes.
3. *Metal shop safety,* Young America Films; 18 minutes.
4. *Safe living at school,* Coronet Films; 11 minutes.
5. *Working safely in the shop,* Coronet Films; 11 minutes.
6. *Your health at school,* Coronet Films; 11 minutes.

Community

1. *A day in court* (traffic court), Rarig Motion Picture Co.; 30 minutes.
2. *A is for atom,* General Electric Co.; 15 minutes.
3. *Accidents don't just happen,* U. S. Public Health Service; 14 minutes.
4. *Aim for safety,* Aetna Casualty and Surety Co.; 15 minutes.
5. *An accident happens to Sam,* National Safety Council; 15 minutes.
6. *Anatomy of an accident,* Bell Telephone Co.; 26½ minutes.
7. *Anyone at all!* Encyclopaedia Britannica Films, Inc.; 22 minutes.
8. *Artificial respiration* (Parts I and II), United World Films, Inc.; 30 minutes.
9. *Bicycle safety,* Young America Films; 10 minutes.
10. *Cycling safety today,* Institute of Visual Communication, Inc.; 20 minutes.
11. *Blasting cap: danger,* Institute of Makers of Explosives; 15 minutes.
12. *Charlie's haunt* (safety), Bell Telephone Co.; 28 minutes.
13. *Checking for injuries,* American Red Cross; 16 minutes.
14. *Civil defense emergency hospital,* Oregon Civil Defense Agency; 14 minutes.
15. *Cornell University* (auto safety), McGraw-Hill Book Co., Inc.; 27 minutes.
16. *Crisis* (hurricane), Federal Civil Defense Administration; 14 minutes
17. *Danger is your companion,* American Red Cross; 16 minutes.
18. *Defensive driving,* U. S. Department of Agriculture; 13 minutes.
19. *Disaster and you,* American Red Cross; 27 minutes.
20. *Do it with E's,* U. S. Department of Agriculture; 23 minutes.
21. *Don't be a sitting duck* (safe driving), National Safety Council; 10 minutes.
22. *Don't skid yourself,* Aetna Life Insurance Co.; 13 minutes.
23. *Down at the office,* National Safety Council; 10 minutes.
24. *Drive defensively,* Encyclopaedia Britannica Films, Inc.; 11 minutes.
25. *Driving tips* (2 films), Sid Davis Productions; 10 minutes each.
26. *Driving without tears,* National Film Board of Canada; 11 minutes.
27. *Easy on the eyes,* National Safety Council; 20 minutes.
28. *Every single minute* (civil Defense), Bornmann Productions; 20 minutes.
29. *Everywhere all the time,* National Safety Council; 23 minutes.
30. *Facts about fallout,* Office of Civil and Defense Mobilization; 12 minutes.
31. *Fallout—when and where to protect yourself,* Oregon Civil Defense Agency; 14 minutes.
32. *Falls are no fun,* National Safety Council; 10 minutes.
33. *Fatal meeting* (driving), Charles Cahill and Associates; 14 minutes.
34. *50,000 lives* (mouth-to-mouth resuscitation), Johnson and Johnson; 13½ minutes
35. *Fire in town,* International Film Bureau, Inc.; 26 minutes.
36. *First aid for air crew,* National Film Board of Canada; 28 minutes.
37. *First aid:* Fundamentals, Coronet Films; 11 minutes.
38. *First aid on the spot,* Encyclopaedia Britannica Films, Inc.; 10 minutes.
39. *Flagged for action* (traffic safety), National Film Board of Canada; 30 minutes.
40. *Flash of darkness* (first aid), Consolidated Film Industry; 28 minutes.
41. *Food for thought* (civil defense food rations), Oregon Civil Defense Agency; 14 minutes.
42. *For experts only* (safe driving), National Safety Council; 10 minutes.
43. *Freeway driving,* International Film Bureau; 11 minutes.

44. *Fun 'n fathoms* (scuba), Aetna Life Insurance Co.; 27 minutes.
45. *Gentleman Jekyll and Driver Hyde,* National Film Board of Canada; 9 minutes.
46. *Give a man a car he can drive,* Department of Motor Vehicles; 14 minutes.
47. *Go to blazes!* Bureau of Communication Research, Inc.; 30 minutes.
48. *H bomb,* Office of Civil and Defense Mobilization; 20 minutes.
49. *Help wanted* (first aid), Johnson and Johnson; 22 minutes.
50. *Highway pioneers,* Sid Davis Productions; 10 minutes.
51. *Hook, line, and safety,* Aetna Casualty and Surety Co.; 17 minutes.
52. *How do you drive?* National Film Board of Canada; 26 minutes.
53. *How to call the fire department,* Bureau of Communication Research, Inc.; 5 minutes.
54. *How to follow safely* (traffic safety), National Safety Council; 10 minutes.
55. *How to pass safely* (traffic safety), National Safety Council; 10 minutes.
56. *I'm no fool having fun,* Walt Disney Productions; 8 minutes.
57. *In case of accident,* National Safety Council; 10 minutes.
58. *In case of fire,* Encyclopaedia Britannica Films, Inc.; 20 minutes.
59. *Interrupted morning* (seat belts), Creative Arts; 40 minutes.
60. *In your defense,* Western Electric Co.; 24½ minutes.
61. *Look alive* (jaywalking), Creative Arts; 15 minutes.
62. *Look who's driving,* Aetna Life Insurance Co.; 8 minutes.
63. *Missing witness* (driver education), Sid Davis Productions; 10 minutes.
64. *Motor mania,* Department of Motor Vehicles; 12 minutes.
65. *New family in town,* Oregon Civil Defense Agency; 11 minutes.
66. *Ninety-day flash* (safe driving), National Safety Council; 10 minutes.
67. *No time to lose,* Oregon Civil Defense Agency; 28 minutes.
68. *No time to spare* (artificial respiration), International Film Bureau, Inc.; 12 minutes.
69. *Objective: survival,* Federal Civil Defense Administration; 29 minutes.
70. *Outboard outings,* Aetna Life Insurance Co.; 19 minutes.
71. *Paddle a safe canoe,* Aetna Life Insurance Co.; 13½ minutes.
72. *Penetrating wounds of the abdomen* (first aid), United World Films, Inc.; 12 minutes.
73. *People afloat,* American Red Cross; 14½ minutes.
74. *Preventable or not?* (traffic accidents), National Safety Council; 10 minutes.
75. *Protection factor 100,* Federal Civil Defense Administration; 13 minutes.
76. *Rescue breathing,* American Film Producers; 25 minutes.
77. *Rescue party* (civil defense), National Film Board of Canada; 29 minutes.
78. *Respiratory protection,* Castle Films; 13 minutes.
79. *Rural community defense,* Office of Civil and Defense Mobilization; 14 minutes.
80. *Safe drinking water from small water supplies,* University of Minnesota Audio-Visual Education Service; 10 minutes.
81. *Safe driving: advanced skills and problems,* Coronet Films; 11 minutes.
82. *Safe driving: car maintenance and care,* Coronet Films; 11 minutes.
83. *Safe driving: fundamental skills,* Coronet Films; 11 minutes.
84. *Safe driving: streets and highways,* Coronet Films; 11 minutes.
85. *Safe driving: techniques of the skilled driver,* Coronet Films; 11 minutes
86. *Safe driving: the defensive driver,* Coronet Films; 11 minutes.
87. *Safe on two wheels,* Aetna Life Insurance Co.; 11 minutes.
88. *Safety or slaughter,* International Film Bureau, Inc.; 14 minutes.
89. *Seconds for survival,* Bell Telephone Co.; 27½ minutes.
90. *Shooting safety,* Institute of Makers of Explosives; 30 minutes.
91. *Skill is your business* (safe driving), National Safety Council; 10 minutes.
92. *Ski tips,* Aetna Casualty and Surety Co.; 22 minutes.
93. *Stay right, stay safe* (safe driving), National Safety Council; 10 minutes.
94. *Stop them before they start* (fire and explosion hazards), Aetna Casualty and Surety Co.; 15 minutes.
95. *Sucking wounds of the chest,* United World Films, Inc.; 14 minutes.
96. *Suddenly, upon the waters* (boating safety), Modern Talking Picture Service; 28 minutes.

97. *Take a look at the odds* (safe driving), National Safety Council; 10 minutes.
98. *Teach them how* (driving), Aetna Life Insurance Co.; 21½ minutes.
99. *10 long minutes,* National Safety Council; 13 minutes.
100. *That they may live* (artificial respiration), U. S. Public Health Service; 19 minutes.
101. *The ABC of baby sitting,* Sid Davis Productions; 10 minutes.
102. *The champ becomes deaf and blind* (safe-driving), National Safety Council; 10 minutes.
103. *The cool hot-rod,* Sid Davis Productions; 27 minutes.
104. *The day called X,* Oregon Civil Defense Agency; 30 minutes.
105. *The perfect crime* (highway safety), Caterpillar Tractor Co.; 20½ minutes.
106. *The price of fire,* Contemporary Films, Inc.; 23 minutes.
107. *Then it happened* (forest fire), U. S. Department of Agriculture; 10 minutes.
108. *To see ourselves* (driving), Aetna Life Insurance Co.; 14½ minutes.
109. *Traffic with the devil,* Association Films, Inc.; 20 minutes.
110. *Two-operator method of artificial respiration,* Office of Audio-Visual Instruction; 20 minutes.
111. *Vacation safety,* National Safety Council; 12 minutes.
112. *Watch your handicap* (safe driving), National Safety Council; 10 minutes.
113. *Water safety,* McGraw-Hill Book Co., Inc.; 12 minutes.
114. *What made Sammy speed?* Sid Davis Productions; 10 minutes.
115. *What right of way?* National Safety Council; 10 minutes.
116. *What's your driver Eye-Q?* Aetna Life Insurance Co.; 13 minutes.
117. *Wheel sense,* Association Films, Inc.; 20 minutes.
118. *Winter driving,* National Safety Council; 23 minutes.
119. *You and your driving,* Modern Talking Picture Service; 14 minutes.
120. *Your civil defense,* Office of Civil and Defense Mobilization; 13 minutes.
121. *Your health in the community,* Coronet Films; 11 minutes.

INDEX